Custom Edition for Mohawk Valley Community College

Exploring
Human Anatomy & Physiology
in the Laboratory

Salvatore Drogo • William Perrotti

PEARSON
Custom Publishing

Cover Art: Courtesy of Scala/Art Resource, NY.

Copyright © 2005, 2004 by Pearson Custom Publishing
All rights reserved.

Permission in writing must be obtained from the publisher before any part of this work may be reproduced or transmitted any form or by any means, electronic or mechanical, including photocopying and recording, or by any information storage retrieval system.

All trademarks, service marks, registered trademarks, and registered service marks are the property of their respective owne and are used herein for identification purposes only.

Printed in the United States of America

10 9 8 7 6 5 4 3 2 1

ISBN 0-536-97198-6

2005100010

KK/NR

Please visit our web site at *www.pearsoncustom.com*

PEARSON CUSTOM PUBLISHING
75 Arlington Street, Suite 300, Boston, MA 02116
A Pearson Education Company

Table of Contents

Part 1: Exercises in Gross Anatomy 1
    Overview of the Laboratory Experience: General Philosophy, Policies 3
    Anatomy Lab Artwork 11
    Lab Worksheet 1: Language of Anatomy 13
- A-1   Introduction to Dissection and Gross Anatomy: Guided Exploration of the Cat 27
- A-2   Human Cadaver Exploration 47
- A-3   Gross Anatomy of the Digestive System 61
- A-4   Human Skeletal System 75
- A-5   A Representative Bony Articulation: The Knee 93
- A-6   Muscles of the Trunk and Shoulder 97
- A-7   Student Musculoskeletal Presentations 113
- A-8   Gross Anatomy of the Human Endocrine System 119
- A-9   Gross Anatomy of the Human Reproductive System 125
- A-10 Gross Anatomy of the Central Nervous System - 1 The Brain 139
- A-11 Gross Anatomy of the Central Nervous System -2 The Spinal Cord .. 159
- A-12 Gross Anatomy of the Peripheral
  Nervous System 1: The Cranial Floor and the Cranial Nerves 165
- A-13 Gross Anatomy of the Peripheral Nervous System 2: Peripheral Nerves 175
- A-14 Special Sensory Structures: The Eye and the Ear 179
- A-15 Gross Anatomy of the Heart 189
- A-16 Gross Anatomy of Systemic Circulation 199
- A-17 Gross Anatomy of the Respiratory System 213
- A-18 Gross Anatomy of the Urinary System 221

Part 2: Exercises in Histology 225
- H-1   An Introduction to Tissues 227
- H-2   Histology of the Integument 245
- H-3   Histology of the Digestive System 253
- H-4   Histology of the Endocrine System 265
- H-5   Histology of the Reproductive System 273
- H-6   Histology of Nerves and Blood Vessels 285
- H-7   Histology of the Respiratory System 291
- H-8   Histology of the Excretory System 297

Part 3: Exercises in Human Physiology 301
- P-1   Skeletal Muscle Physiology-1: The Frog Gastrocnemius 303
- P-2   Electromyography 313
- P-3   Physiology of the Nervous System:
  Audition, Cutaneous Sensation, Sensory Adaptation, Vision 329
- P-4   Biopotentials: The ECU and EEG 345
- P-5   Physiology of Systemic Circulation:
  Capillary Microcirculation & Cardiac Physiology 369
- P-6   Respiratory Physiology-1: Spirometry 375
- P-7   Respiratory Physiology-2: Respirometry 389
- P-8   Physiology of Systemic Circulation: Part 3
  Measurement of Blood Pressure, Heart Rate and (Breathing Rate) 397
- P-9   Physiology of Systemic Circulation:

Part 4 Finger Plethysmography: Pulse Pressure Monitoring **401**
P-10 Graded Aerobic Exercise   413
P-11 A Study of Blood   423

Appendix A: Exploring A&P CD Directions   435

Preface to Students and Faculty
Third edition

In this third iteration of our lab manual, we have undertaken several major modifications from the previous two editions. The first of these is a major change of format. Previously we employed a design that allowed students to read directions on one page of an open book and record their observations on the facing page. It seemed to us an innovative design that suited our exploratory approach perfectly. Instead, over the course of the past four years we have come to realize that this design was not successful because the tendency of the majority of students was to fold the book back on itself in a way that defeated our "facing page" approach. In this edition we have reverted to a more traditional approach in which questions are posed and spaces to record an answer follow immediately. We hope this will focus students more clearly on the tasks at hand and help them to remain engaged in the specifics of the questions being posed and the details and nuances of the exercise.

A second modification is the incorporation of a whole new section dealing with histology. The new histology exercises utilize the same exploration and discovery approach we have been utilizing in the gross anatomy exercises. The study of histology deals first with an introduction to tissues. Following this, the focus then shifts to the major organ systems. To support the study of microscopic anatomy, we have for the first time included a compact disc with the manual which includes, among other things, all the images necessary to complete the new histology exercises. In addition, the CD includes two videos. One presents and clarifies policies and procedures relating to the cadaver facility and the use of human specimens. The other demonstrates techniques that are part of our new electromyography exercise.

A third major change centers on our approach to the physiology exercises. Previously most of the physiology exercises had been conducted as demonstrations with the instructor or a single student volunteer serving as the subject and the rest of the class acting as observers. In this new edition, muscle physiology, biopotentials (EEGs and ECGs), and the measurement of pulse pressure by finger plethysmography have been rewritten so that students working in small groups actually perform the experiments independently after having made predictions about expected outcomes. The sensory physiology has been revised considerably, eliminating a number of exercises that over the years have proved of questionable usefulness. What remains should provide students with a crisper experience in cutaneous and special sensation.

We have also decided to incorporate diagrams in the manual for the first time. Some of these illustrations are labeled anatomical drawings from the Burgess Atlas collection. These serve as references for students as they progress through the various anatomy exercises. Others are simple original drawings intended to help clarify elements of technique. To accomplish these latter drawings, we enlisted the talents of two members of our Art Department, Christi Harrington and Jedediah Kimball. They created the original line drawings that we hope will successfully clarify directions that students have apparently not been understanding from our textual directions alone. If students have an easier time completing the anatomy and physiology exercises than previously, we hope that will translate into improved performance on their quizzes as well.

As we look back on this revision, what began as a series of limited changes has evolved into a much bigger project than initially anticipated. We think that we have improved the manual to a significant degree. What remains is for the next two years of students to verify (or refute) our assumption.

> Salvatore Drogo
> William Perrotti
> May 2005

Acknowledgements

Many thanks are in order. Thanks go first to Ellen Nichols, Secretary to the Life Science Department, for her willing assistance in all things. Thanks also go to Robert Jubenville, Head of the Life Science Department, for his encouragement and for his support of our efforts in so many ways over so many years. Thanks are also in order for former Vice President for Instruction John Bolton because of his early and enthusiastic support of the proposed move to a cadaver-based laboratory experience and for his continued enthusiastic support. Thanks go also to Sharon Zohne, Public Information Department, for her photographic contributions to the book covers and for her willingness to lend her expertise whenever we were in need. This year special thanks are due Christi Harrington and Jedediah Kimball for lending their artistic talents to the new procedural illustrations that appear for the first time in this edition. They are a real step forward for the manual and should greatly benefit the students who will be using it.

We must also thank the College for its commitment to quality in science education, for its support of our involvement in HAPS, and for the development and construction of the cadaver facility. Likewise, we must thank our elected county representatives who supported the concept of cadaver study when first proposed and who continue to provide the support needed to maintain our facility and keep our program of human anatomy study flourishing on campus. Our colleague in the Life Science Department, Don Kelly, has from day one been a willing participant in this approach to lab and has offered many thoughtful suggestions that we have incorporated into this manual. We must also thank our many friends and colleagues in HAPS for their critical evaluation of many of our ideas. For her patience and support we must thank our editor, Lori Bittker. Most importantly, special thanks go to our students who every semester in so many ways show us when we are on the right track and when we need to return to the drawing board. One student in particular stands out from the rest. Aaron Glass provided invaluable assistance in the development of the electromyography exercise and contributed very significantly to the preparation of the compact disc which is included with this manual.

Lastly, we especially thank Linda and Mona for their patience, love, encouragement, and support during all the time that went into this project. We appreciate this more than we can ever express.

PART 1

Exercises in Gross Anatomy

Overview of the Laboratory Experience:
General Philosophy, Policies
Human Anatomy and Physiology 1 & 2 (BI 106-107)

Typically, courses in human anatomy and physiology offered at most colleges include a laboratory experience totaling 2-3 hours per week. Generally these labs use either cats or fetal pigs as the primary study/dissection specimens, complemented by selected non-human organs. Here at MVCC, students begin their two semesters of study in BI106-107 (Human Anatomy and Physiology 1 and 2) with a dissection exercise focused on the cat. Very quickly however, they move from this experience to the study of actual prosected (already dissected) human cadavers. This cadaver study is in turn complemented by the availability of a number of selected non-human organs (for dissection and/or study) and further enriched by a number of preserved human organs/structures, a sizeable collection of human skeletal material, and numerous radiographic images. Throughout the two semesters of study and in addition to other lab activities, students will manipulate and explore the prosected specimens and perform supervised dissections on selected non-human specimens.

Human Anatomy Lab: This facility is a restricted access laboratory dedicated to the single purpose of allowing the study of human cadavers. It comprises approximately 1000 square feet to accommodate three or four cadavers for study and a large walk-in cooler to store up to four cadavers at any one time. The facility is kept cool (~64° F) and is well ventilated with a non-recirculating downdraft system. Regular air quality assays are performed in the lab to insure that the environment is conducive to healthful study. In addition, there are three adjustable overhead surgical light available for use over the cadaver stations. Except when in use, the facility is locked. The cadavers are kept on covered tables which may be individually locked and stored in a walk-in cooler which is kept locked.

Life Science Department Cadaver Access Policy:

1. Since the cadavers are departmental resources intended primarily to support instruction in Human Anatomy & Physiology 1 and 2 (BI 106 and 107), and Human Dissection (BI210), the utilization by and needs of these courses shall have priority over all other needs and utilization.

2. Any member of the department may use the cadavers for personal study, or, with department head approval, can incorporate a limited cadaver experience into an existing departmental course with a human focus.

3. Any member of the department who will be using the cadavers for study or teaching must receive orientation from the designated member of the anatomy and physiology faculty and must abide by the rules which are followed in Human Anatomy & Physiology 1 and 2.

4. Exposure to human cadavers for interested colleagues and adult family members of the Life Science Department is limited to occasional lectures given by the Anatomy & Physiology faculty on anatomy and pathology using the human specimens.

5. Exposure to human cadavers for members of the college community at large will be limited to an annual presentation during Summer Institute given by the Anatomy & Physiology faculty on anatomy and pathology using the human specimens.

6. Any other viewing of the cadavers or presentation which involves their utilization must first be approved by the Director of the MVCC Non-Transplant Human Anatomic Tissue Bank (Life Science Department Head).

Lab Access: Access to the lab during any semester is limited to the faculty and students enrolled in BI106, BI107, or any of the cadaver dissection modules (BI211, BI212, or BI213) and to the head, other faculty, and technical assistants of the Life Science Department. Students in BI106, BI107, or BI211-213 are allowed to work in the lab only under the direct supervision of one of the A&P faculty. Times when such access is possible will be determined and posted outside the lab early in the semester. With the exception of Life Science faculty, technical assistants, and enrolled students, no visits to the lab are allowed when BI106, BI107, or BI210 labs are in session.

Safety and Health

Most of the specimens we use in Anatomy & Physiology lab have been fixed with a formaldehyde-based solution. There is no effective substitute for formaldehyde fixation of vertebrate materials. However, over the last several years, good techniques have been developed to eliminate formaldehyde off gassing once fixation is complete. Therefore, respiratory exposure to formaldehyde gas should not be a problem. Additionally, the

Anatomy & Physiology lab and the cadaver lab is ventilated with non-recirculating downdraft ventilation. This serves to provide the lab environment with a continuous supply of clean fresh air. In order for this system to work, windows are kept closed. Exposure through skin, however, is another matter. **DO NOT** handle any wet preserved specimen or materials without proper hand protection. Proper hand protection includes latex, vinyl, and/or nitrile gloves.

Air Quality and Testing: In order to insure that the lab facility is a healthful environment for both students and faculty, the Environmental Safety Officer of the college conducts regular air sampling and assays for specific chemicals utilized in tissue preservation. In this way, any problem associated with ventilation and/or air flow can be quickly identified and corrected. In addition, once a semester faculty wear dosimeters while working in the lab for extended periods. These are then sent out to a private testing lab for analysis.

A note about pregnancy: While we regularly monitor and record the air quality in the cadaver lab and are confident that the A&P lab facility is a safe and healthy environment for teaching and learning, we still ask that any female student who is pregnant (or becomes pregnant during the semester) inform her instructor and, more importantly, consult with her physician regarding participation in the cadaver experience. While there is no alternative to cadaver study available, it is possible that an arrangement can be devised that will award the student an incomplete grade for the current semester and allow her to complete the cadaver study portion of the lab in the following semester.

Dissection: While we generally do not dissect in the cadaver lab, there are occasional dissection activities that are conducted in the main A&P lab. Students should be aware of the following guidelines governing the use of dissection instruments. Scalpels and scissors are sharp. They are supposed to be. Also, in the anatomy and physiology lab, we use a variety of probes, some of which are very sharp. Always handle these instruments carefully. You should not only be cognizant of accidentally injuring yourself, but also, accidental injury to another student. Remember that injury to yourself or another can result from leaving dissection tools on the specimen table where they can easily become hidden under the cadaver or the cloth drapes that are used to cover the specimen. Always place dissection tools in a small tray when transporting them from one area of the lab to another. If you sustain any injury during lab, or experience any adverse reaction to any of the materials utilized in lab, be sure to report this to your lab instructor immediately.

Behavior: Maturity, professionalism and respect are the operative terms that define what is required of all students during the two semesters of anatomy and physiology study. Students must realize that this opportunity to explore and study a dissected human cadaver is a privilege that very few college underclassmen will ever be able to experience. Each of these specimens is a donation specifically for the purpose of furthering the education of students such as yourselves. When you consider that, this donation represents a remarkable gift that each of these individuals has made to us all. They have placed their trust in students and teachers whom they will never know. We, in turn, will come to know them in a way no one before has. **Therefore, treat these cadavers as you would want the body of a loved one treated... because they were and are surely very special to someone. And now they are very special to us. Their willingness to contribute to our education and the trust they have placed in us translates into a solemn responsibility that we honor their generosity and guarantee their dignity at all times. Truly the dead will teach the living. And for this chance we certainly must be thankful.**

Basic Operating Rules of the Cadaver (Anatomy) Lab - AB215:
The lab is to be maintained in a neat and clean condition by all those who are allowed to use the facility. Students are responsible for always acting in a manner that is in compliance with these rules.

- A. Students should leave outer coats, sweaters, etc. in the main A&P lab (AB 213). Valuables (purses, textbooks, class notes, and other belongings) can be stored in the cadaver (anatomy) lab. The instructor will indicate the cupboard that has been set aside for this purpose.

- B. Students must always wear protective gloves (latex, vinyl, or nitrile) when working with the cadavers or preserved organs. Students are required to purchase their own gloves from the College Bookstore or from an outside source. Students with any kind of allergy to powder or latex, etc. should consult their instructor for advice about possible options.

- C. Students must always wear a rubberized apron when working with cadavers. The college provides these and they are kept hanging in the cadaver lab. <u>Before</u> an apron is returned to its hanger after lab is concluded, its <u>outside surface must be sprayed with ethanol solution and wiped dry</u>. Ethanol solution is available in labeled spray bottles in the cadaver lab.

- D. When in the anatomy lab, students are encouraged to wear their own protective lab coats over their street clothes. Students may also purchase disposable (but reusable) lab coats and sleeve protectors in the College Bookstore. Such garments are not required, they are recommended. Specific cupboards in the main lab will be set aside and designated for the storage of these items. We recommend that a large zip-lock plastic bag be used to store each lab coat. No student belongings may be left in the cadaver facility.

- E. When performing dissections in the main lab, all tools (forceps, probes, clamps, etc.) that are used are to be transported and kept in a small tray. When finished with these tools, they should be carefully rinsed and returned to the appropriate designated storage bins. When instruments of any sort are used in the cadaver lab for either dissection or study, they should be placed in the detergent solution that is kept in one of the main sinks. No dirty tools should be placed in the drying rack or the drawers and no wet tools should be placed in the drawers.

F. Students must always exercise care in examining and exploring these specimens. Many of the structures on which you will be working are very delicate and can be easily damaged. This is especially true for structures such as serous membranes and many small vessels and nerves. In general, **look and think before you touch, and when you touch, be very gentle**. If unsure, seek guidance or assistance from your instructor before proceeding.

G. There are three different types of trash receptacles in the cadaver lab. Each is intended to contain a different type of material. Students must be careful not to mix these up.
   1) Each cadaver table is accompanied by a **numbered red plastic flip-top receptacle** (the number corresponds to the similarly numbered cadaver table). The **only** material that is placed in this container is **human tissue** from the cadaver with the same number. This tissue will eventually be returned to the medical school with its cadaver for cremation. It is very important that **no paper or other material be put into these containers**. Since there is typically no dissection being performed during A&P sessions, these containers are generally not out in the lab at these times.
   2) There are also special receptacles marked "**Soiled Waste**". These containers are for any waste materials that have been significantly soiled by preservative or body fluids from a specimen. These materials can include **soiled** paper towels, **soiled** tissue wipes, **soiled** protective gloves, **soiled** protective clothing, etc. Paper or non-paper waste that has not been soiled by such fluids should not be put into these containers.
   3) Lastly, there is/are one or two tall gray trash receptacles in the lab for all other regular, **unsoiled** refuse (e.g. paper towels from handwashing, used masks or face shields, relatively clean disposable protective clothing, and any other unsoiled paper or non-paper waste material).

   These distinctions are important. The material in each different type of container is disposed of by the college in a different manner. **Students and faculty must be diligent in placing all waste material into the appropriate designated containers.**

H. At the conclusion of any lab session, all specimens are to be returned to a normal position and all internal organs are to be carefully repositioned in their proper locations. Also, the body walls on all cadavers are to be closed up. Unless told otherwise by the instructor, any paper toweling left on the cadaver table or packed in body cavities must be removed and discarded. As this is done, the specimens are to be moistened with the wetting solution that is provided in sprinkle and spray bottles. This includes both internal organs and the outer surface of the cadavers. Students are advised to wear goggles or a face shield when completing this task. The specimens are then to be covered/wrapped in the canvas sheeting that is supplied after which the sheeting is also thoroughly moistened. When finished wetting the specimens, students should refill any empty or nearly empty solution bottles from the large container of wetting solution that is kept in the cadaver lab. Lastly, the specimens are to be covered with the rubberized canvas sheet (shiny rubberized surface down) and the sheet loosely tucked in around the edges of the cadaver. Note: Unless instructed otherwise by the instructor, students should always wet and wrap the specimens before departing… even if there is a lab immediately following. **No student should leave the cadaver room until all clean-up work is done or until given permission to do so by their instructor.**

I. Whether the cadaver tables are left open or closed, the outer rims must be sprayed with ethanol solution and wiped dry. This is to be done even if there is another lab immediately following. Lastly, if there is no lab immediately following and the instructor directs that the tables be closed, then the outside surfaces of the covers must also be sprayed with ethanol and wiped dry. On occasion, the instructor may lock each table before it is returned to the cooler. Students are expected to assist in returning the cadavers to the cooler, being careful not to bump the latch on the cooler door with the edge of the table. **Note: It is not possible to be inadvertently locked in the cooler. It can always be easily opened from the inside simply by pushing on the door.**

J. Unless told otherwise by the instructor, students should see that the drain valve under each cadaver table is kept in the open position both during use and during storage.

K. At the end of a session and before leaving the lab, students should spray all countertops with ethanol and wipe them dry. Students should also clean the handles of the surgical lights with ethanol and wipe them dry as well. If the handles of the paper towel dispensers are soiled, they too should be sprayed with ethanol and wiped dry. Students should likewise clean their clipboards with ethanol before returning them to their rack. Finally, each student must spray the outer surface of his/her apron with ethanol and wipe it dry before removing it and hanging it in its designated place. **Note: Clean-up is considered part of the check-off for each lab.**

L. After gloves have been removed and discarded in the soiled trash container, students should wash their hands and forearms with soap and water before leaving the lab.

M. There is a wealth of resource material stored in the anatomy lab for the use of students. These materials are divided into two categories... references that are soiled and must remain in the cadaver lab and references that are kept unsoiled and which may be used by students in AB 213-215.

1) The page edges of those soiled references that can be used as students work in the cadaver lab have been colored (blue or green or red) so they can be readily identified at a glance. Students may use these books even while wearing soiled protective gloves. There is no feasible way for these books to remain in clean "library" condition. When they are too soiled for continued use, they are simply discarded and replaced by new volumes.

2) Clean references, on the other hand, are kept in a cabinet in the anatomy lab (AB 215). Students may use these in either the Cadaver Lab or in the A&P lab. Some of these volumes are the property of the Life Science Department and some are the personal property of different members of the Life Science faculty. **These references cannot be removed from the A&P lab complex (AB 213-215) without an instructor's express permission.** These volumes are to be kept clean. They may not be used by students who are wearing soiled gloves. Likewise, they should not be placed on a soiled surface.

3) The college's holdings related to human anatomy are increasing. Students are directed to explore the Library's holdings on-line under the category of "anatomy".

4) A list of anatomical reference materials (authors, titles, ISBNs) may be obtained from any A&P faculty member. Any of these titles may be purchased on-line or through the College Bookstore by students with interest in expanding their personal reference libraries. **These are not required for A&P 1 or A&P2**. They are simply titles that a student with a particular interest in more detailed anatomy may find useful. Note: Some such references are very expensive.

Anatomy Lab Artwork

| 1 | 2 | 3 | 4 | 5 | 6 | 7 |

Presently there are seven framed art prints hanging within the Human Cadaver Lab. These prints depict various aspects of the rich history of anatomy and, we hope, convey a seriousness about our approach to the study of anatomy and the opportunity that cadaver access provides our students. Following are brief comments about each of the prints.

Print #1:
>"Dissection of a Cadaver", published in 1714 in Bartolomeo Eustachi's ***Tabulae Anatomicae*** depicts an interior view of an anatomical theater in which a cadaver dissection is being performed (presumably by Eustachi). Students are seated and standing around the table, observing the dissection. Eustachi first described the pharyngotympanic tube which we all notice whenever in a plane changing altitude. He also was the first to inject blood vessels with colored fluid to better visualize them, a practice that continues today in the form of colored latex-injected vessels in commercially available preserved biological specimens.

Print #2:
>[Human Skeleton] This version of a human skeleton woodcut, engraved by Thomas Geminus, was pirated from an earlier version of Vesalius' ***De Humani Fabrica Corporis*** and appeared in his ***Compendiosa totius anatomiae deleneatio*** that was published in 1545. It shows a full length standing skeleton viewed from the right side. The skeleton is leaning against a sarcophagus and with his head resting on his left hand (in a manner reminiscent of Rodin's famous ***Thinker*** sculpture). The right hand of the skeleton is resting on a skull that is on the surface of the tomb. Its lower legs are crossed. It is a very thoughtful and surprisingly lifelike pose.

Print #3:
>This print is of the frontispiece from ***De Humani Fabrica Corporis*** (***The Fabric of the Human Body***) by Andreas Vesalius, considered by many to be the "Father of Anatomy". It is perhaps the most famous print in that entire work and it forms the centerpiece of our small collection. It depicts Vesalius at work teaching. He is using a female cadaver to demonstrate some element of anatomy and he is surrounded by a throng of students and onlookers. A sense of interest and excitement pervades the scene. Prior to Vesalius, such anatomical instruction was very different with the teacher much more removed and aloof from the students. The model of Vesalius is one we try to emulate in our lab instruction.

Print #4:

[The Human Body and the Library as Sources of Knowledge] This work by Johann Adam Kulmus dates to 1732. It is an allegorical engraving which shows the inside of a library. Within the library are seen many books as well as a standing human skeleton, a human cadaver on a table and assorted surgical tools. The message is simple and appropriate for our facility… Knowledge can be found in books and within the human body.

Print #5:

[Musculature of the Human Body] This engraving by Thomas Geminus was also pirated from an earlier version of Vesalius' **Fabrica** and along with print #2 above appeared in his 1545 **Compendiosa totius anatomiae deleneatio**. It shows a full length standing, muscular male from the left side. The left arm is raised and the right points downward. Most of the weight is on the left leg. Superficial musculature is shown in considerable detail. Presumably this dissection was completed by Vesalius, and it is impressive for its clarity and accuracy.

Print #6:

"Woman Medical Student Dissecting the Leg of a Cadaver" This wood engraving was taken from Frank Leslie's Illustrated Newspaper. It is dated April 16, 1870. It shows a female student from New York Medical College for Women performing a dissection on the anterior lower leg of a cadaver. It is included in our collection to recognize the large number of our students who are female.

Print #7:

"The Anatomy Lesson of Doctor Tulp" This is a black and white print of the 1632 painting by Rembrandt. It shows a physician by the name of Nicolaas Tulp using a cadaver to demonstrate some aspect of human anatomy to a group of obviously interested students or colleagues. The level of seriousness and interest depicted serves as a model for us all to emulate, students and teachers alike.

Language of Anatomy   **Lab Worksheet 1**
                                                                                                             (Home Assignment)

Students should complete these exercises and be thoroughly familiar with the contents of this worksheet **prior to the week 2 lab exercise** (A-2). Week 2 is the first session dealing with the human specimens.

Introduction

The number of terms involved in anatomy and physiology can certainly seem overwhelming to a new student. However, it is very important to learn this new vocabulary. The language of anatomy and physiology allows you to talk with colleagues and write reports without confusion and errors. The terms used in anatomy and physiology allow us to communicate with precision and without ambiguity. These terms allow us to locate structures, both on the surface of the body and internally. They allow us to divide the body into clearly defined regions and subregions. Anatomical terminology provides us with the language that we need in order to understand body cavities and the numerous membranes associated with these body cavities. And, finally, anatomical and physiological terminology provides us with a way of visualizing the body as being composed of a series of planes (imaginary flat surfaces). These planes provide directions for sectioning or slicing the body or a specific structure. Each section or slice through a particular plane provides a unique view of internal structure. A series or progression of numerous sections or slices allows us to trace with precision changes in structure through the thickness of the body or a particular organ.

Most of the terms used in anatomy and physiology are derived from the classical languages of Latin or Greek. The use of these ancient languages as the basis for terminology provides an anatomy and physiology vocabulary that is largely universal. The femur is the bone of the upper leg to a German physician, an Italian physician, a French physician, a Spanish physician, or an English physician. Etymology is the study of the origins of words. Learning the language of anatomy and physiology is more interesting and can be made a bit easier if you pay attention to word origins. The Latin word "cauda" means tail. The Latin word "equina" means horse. Towards the end of the spinal cord is a large collection of nerve roots which spread out from the end of the spinal cord and have the appearance of a horse's tail. The name for this collection of nerves is the cauda equina. Many times terminology is modified by the use of prefixes and suffixes. These prefixes and suffixes are combined with a root word or stem. For example, "peri" is a prefix derived from Greek. It means around. "Osteon" is the Greek word for bone. A membrane called the periosteum is a sheet of connective tissue which typically surrounds a bone.

This worksheet is composed of a number of self-study exercises that you need to complete according to the directions provided by your lab instructor. In order to complete these exercises, use your textbook (glossary, index, and introductory chapter) and, if need be, refer to resources in the Library or on-line such as medical dictionaries and books or sites dealing with medical or anatomical terminology.

Part 1 – Anatomical Position

When describing body parts or body regions, terms are used in reference to a body orientation called anatomical position. For many such terms, the meaning is not changed or affected by body position but in some instances it can be. For instance, in the anatomic position the thumb is the most lateral digit. However, when the hand is rotated so the palm faces backward, it is the most medial. The anatomic position for a human or any bipedal (2-legged) organism is standing upright, facing forward, hands at the side with palms facing forward. This position thus becomes a reference position that will clarify some terms that would otherwise be ambiguous.

Not surprisingly, four-legged creatures have a different anatomical position. In the space provided, describe anatomical position as you think it would apply to a cat or any other four-legged creature.

_____

_____

Part 2 – Directional Terms

With the exception of right and left, general directional terms such as up, down, front, back, inside, outside are rarely, if ever, used in precise anatomy and physiology (or medical) applications. Such terms are replaced by about 15 important directional terms. For each term below, provide a brief one-sentence definition and, if possible, a term from the list which would be synonymous. You should be able to use each term correctly in a sentence. Note that the terms **right** and **left** always refer to the right and left sides of the subject (and not you, the observer). This is important when trying to follow dissection directions and when viewing anatomic images such as X-rays, MRIs, or CT scans.

Anterior _____

_____

Posterior _____

_____

Ventral _____

_____

Dorsal _____

_____

Superior _____

_____

Inferior

Cephalic

Caudal

Proximal

Distal

Medial

Lateral

Superficial

Deep

Part 3 – Body Regions and Body Cavities
The body is grossly divided into two main regions, axial and appendicular. The axial portion comprises the central axis of the body and consists of the head, neck, and trunk. Thinking more specifically in terms of bony structures, this includes the skull, vertebral column (spine), and the ribs.. The appendicular portion includes the upper and lower extremities and their associated limb girdles. The girdles are the bony structures to which to limbs are attached. Each of these major areas is composed of further subdivisions. For instance, one area of the trunk is of particular clinical importance and is typically subdivided into either four abdominopelvic quadrants or nine abdominopelvic regions.

From the following list of major body regions, indicate for each item on the list whether it best relates to the axial or appendicular region, and then provide the common name for that area of the body.

Common Name

Acromial   axial or appendicular   _____

Axillary   axial or appendicular   _____

Brachial   axial or appendicular   _____

Buccal   axial or appendicular   _____

Carpal   axial or appendicular   _____

Cervical   axial or appendicular   _____

Costal   axial or appendicular   _____

Coxal   axial or appendicular   _____

Cranial   axial or appendicular   _____

Cubital   axial or appendicular   _____

Digital   axial or appendicular   _____

Femoral   axial or appendicular   _____

Frontal   axial or appendicular   _____

Gluteal   axial or appendicular   _____

Inguinal   axial or appendicular   _____

Lingual   axial or appendicular   _____

Lumbar   axial or appendicular   _____

Mental   axial or appendicular   _____

Nasal   axial or appendicular   _____

Occipital	axial or appendicular	_____
Oral	axial or appendicular	_____
Orbital	axial or appendicular	_____
Patellar	axial or appendicular	_____
Pectoral	axial or appendicular	_____
Pedal	axial or appendicular	_____
Popliteal	axial or appendicular	_____
Pubic	axial or appendicular	_____
Sural	axial or appendicular	_____
Thoracic	axial or appendicular	_____
Umbilical	axial or appendicular	_____
Vertebral	axial or appendicular	_____

Part 4 – Abdominopelvic Quadrants and Regions

In medicine and nursing, the anterior abdomen is divided into four abdominopelvic quadrants. This allows internal structures to easily be related to surface landmarks and is of great assistance in physical assessment procedures. Refer to a reference and list the four abdominal quadrants.

_____   _____

_____   _____

What obvious surface landmark is used in locating the longitudinal and transverse reference lines?

_____

Using the torso model or diagrams available in your textbook or in another reference, identify a major organ (or significant specific portion of an organ) found in each of the abdominal quadrants.

Quadrant   Organ or Specific portion of an organ

_____   _____

_____   _____

_____   _____

_____   _____

Less common than the quadrants scheme is the division of the anterior abdomen into nine abdominopelvic regions. Refer to your textbook to list the nine regions by name. The nine region scheme utilizes two longitudinal and two transverse reference lines that will be part of next week's initial exploration of the human cadaver exercise. The longitudinal lines utilize the midpoints of the two clavicles (collarbones) for their origin. The more superior of the transverse lines uses the bottom of the rib cage on each side as a reference. The inferior transverse line uses the tubercles of the ilium as reference points. Both lines will be demonstrated and named in the first cadaver exploration exercise.

Using the torso model or diagrams available in your textbook or other reference volume, determine the name of each region and identify a major organ (or significant specific portion of an organ) found in each of these abdominopelvic regions.

Abdominopelvic region   Organ or specific structure contained within

_____   _____

_____   _____

_____   _____

_____   _____

_____   _____

_____   _____

_____   _____

_____   _____

_____   _____

Part 5 – Body Cavities

The body is composed of numerous spaces or cavities. Some of these cavities communicate directly with the outside environment. These would include cavities such as the nasal cavity, the oral cavity, the entire digestive tube, and the reproductive, respiratory, and urinary passages. However, there are large body cavities which have no direct connection with the outside environment and which house most of the vital organs of the body. The two major body cavities which meet these criteria are the dorsal body cavity (contained within the cranium and spinal column) and the ventral body cavity (occupying most of the space within the trunk). Both the dorsal and ventral body cavities are further subdivided.

Refer to your text or another reference and in the space provided develop a chart or illustration showing the subdivisions of the **dorsal** body cavity. For each subdivision, provide the name of the subdivision and representative organ(s) contained within that subdivision.

Again refer to your text or another reference and in the space provided develop a chart or illustration showing the subdivisions of the **ventral** body cavity. For each subdivision, provide the name of the subdivision and representative organ(s) contained within that subdivision.

Part 6 – Serous Membranes

Both body cavities or passages which open to the outside environment and body cavities which are sealed from and do not communicate directly with the outside environment have membranes associated with them. Those body spaces or passages which communicate with or open to the outside environment are generally lined with a type of membrane known as a mucous membrane. Those body spaces which are sealed from the outside environment (with the exception of the dorsal body cavity) possess a serous membrane lining. Serous membranes not only line the inside surface of such cavities but also generally cover the outer surface of the organs contained within these cavities. Serous membranes which line cavities are referred to as parietal (from a Latin word referring to walls). Those which cover the organs within the cavities are referred to as visceral (from the Latin word meaning internal organ). The space between parietal and visceral membranes define these cavities. These cavities are kept moist with small amounts of serous fluid which is able to pass through these membranes easily. The heart with the associated serous membranes covering its surface and lining the sac in which it is contained provides a good example of this association.

The concept of visceral and parietal membranes and the cavities between them is somewhat similar to what would happen if you were to push your fist into a soft balloon. The balloon deforms and forms a layer immediately around your fist. This layer is analogous to the visceral serous membrane. The air space within the balloon is now deformed and represents the serous fluid moistened cavity (although the amount of air in this example is far, far greater than the actual amount of serous fluid that would typically be found between these serous layers). Finally, the outside surface of this space is defined by the outer balloon surface. This represents the parietal membrane.

In the space that follows, draw the fist in the balloon example as described. Label the comparable visceral membrane, parietal membrane and moist serous cavity. In your drawing, extend the deformed portion of the balloon past the wrist onto the forearm.

Next, imagine that the wrist and arm degenerate so that the fist is now isolated in its own compartment. Let the balloon seal around the fist (where the wrist and forearm were). The fist is now suspended within the balloon attached to the outside of the balloon by a double layer that connects the visceral and parietal layers. This double suspending layer is analogous to a serous membrane structure called a mesentery. Now redraw and relabel the fist in the balloon example to illustrate the concept of a mesentery. Note: In the abdominal cavity, mesenteries generally help to anchor internal organs to the dorsal or lateral body wall or to anchor one organ to another. Because mesentery is both a general term and also can refer to a specific double-layered membrane, the use of the term mesentery will be reserved in this manual to specific structures which include the term mesentery or the prefix meso- as part of their names. When reference is being made to generic double-layered membranes, they will simply be referred to as double-layered serous membranes.

Many of these double-layered serous membranes which connect one organ to another are referred to as ligaments but you should realize that they are in no way <u>structurally</u> similar to the strong ligaments that hold bones together in moveable joints. Examples of these "ligaments" are the falciform ligament and the gastrocolic ligament to name just two. Refer to your text again and find reference to the lesser omentum. Based on the description you find, is the lesser omentum an example of a double-layered serous membrane that might be considered a serous ligament as well? Explain your answer.

Serous ligament? Yes / No _____

_____

Next, in the space below, draw and label an illustration that partitions the ventral body cavity into its 2 major subdivisions. Label the structure that divides the ventral body cavity. Then further subdivide the superior compartment. Each of these subcompartments that you illustrate is defined (lined) by a parietal serous membrane.

Now list the different serous membranes (parietal and visceral) associated with your preceding illustration of the compartmentalized ventral body cavity. Indicate the principal organ(s) found within each serous compartment.

Visceral & parietal _____ : Organ(s) _____

_____

Visceral & parietal _____ : Organ(s) _____

_____

Visceral & parietal _____ : Organ(s) _____

_____

Can an organ be located within the ventral body cavity but not within the peritoneal cavity? (Hint: Recall the cat exploration exercise during the first week.) If yes, provide one or several examples if you can.   Yes / No

_____

_____

What does it mean if an organ is referred to as being retroperitoneal?

_____

_____

Part 7 – Sections and Body Planes
As already mentioned, in anatomy we often visualize the body or a body structure as being composed of a series of planes (imaginary flat surfaces). These planes provide an orientation for slicing the body or a specific structure. Each section or slice through a particular plane provides a unique view of internal structure. A section is an incomplete view, one step in a journey. Sections can be made parallel to the long axis of the body or a structure (longitudinal section), perpendicular to the long axis of the body or a structure (transverse or cross section), or at an angle creating an oblique section. Any section provides a two dimensional view of a structure that has three dimensions (length, height, width). That means that any section provides an incomplete view of whatever structure is being examined. The dimension or perspective which is lost when the cut surface is viewed is the dimension that was cut in making the section. For each section listed below, circle your choice for the dimension that is lost.

Section type	Missing dimension/perspective		
Longitudinal	Height/length	Width	Depth
Transverse	Height/length	Width	Depth

In order to appreciate this fact, you will need to examine and carefully consider a number of different sections. A series or progression of sections or slices allows us to trace with precision changes in structure through the thickness of an organ. A good anatomist can visualize three-dimensional structure from the two dimensional information provided by a series of sections. This is essentially what happens when CT-scan images are examined. Carefully read about planes and sections in your textbook, consider the illustration below, and then attempt to answer the questions which follow.

Distinguish between a longitudinal section, a sagittal section, and a frontal or coronal section. Of these terms, which is the most general one that encompasses the others?

_____

_____

_____

Most general term is: _____

Distinguish between a sagittal, parasagittal, and a median or midsagittal section. Of these terms, which is the most general one that encompasses the others?

_____

_____

_____

Most general term is: _____

What is an oblique section? _____

_____

How many transverse sections through the thigh bone (femur) are possible?   1 / 2 / many

How many longitudinal sections through the thigh bone (femur) are possible? 1 / 2 / many

How many midsagittal sections through a human brain are possible? 1 / 2 / many

How many sagittal sections through a human brain are possible? 1 / 2 / many

How many parasagittal sections through a human brain are possible? 1 / 2 / many

How many oblique sections through the thigh bone (femur) are possible? 1 / 2 / many

How many frontal (coronal) sections through the head are possible? 1 / 2 / many

Consider the illustration of a piece of garden hose shown below. Draw and label a line that demonstrates the cut needed for a longitudinal section. … for a transverse section. … for an oblique section.

Next, in the space provided, draw the cut surface of this hose after it has been sectioned transversely. Note: Viewing the cut surface requires that the tube be rotated 90° from the plane of the cut.

In the space provided, now draw the cut surface of this hose after it has been sectioned longitudinally in the midline.

In the space provided, draw the cut surface of this hose after it has been sectioned obliquely. Remember to rotate the tube 90° from the plane of the cut.

Consider the following series of cross-sections (transverse sections) through this hypothetical solid structure. What you are seeing below is a series of <u>cut surfaces</u> that resulted from the transverse cuts. Once again, remember that in order to see the cut surface, the object must have been rotated 90° from the plane of the cut. That means that in order to draw the object as it existed before the cut, each of the images below must first be rotated back 90°. Draw the unsectioned object as you would see it from the side in the space to the right below.

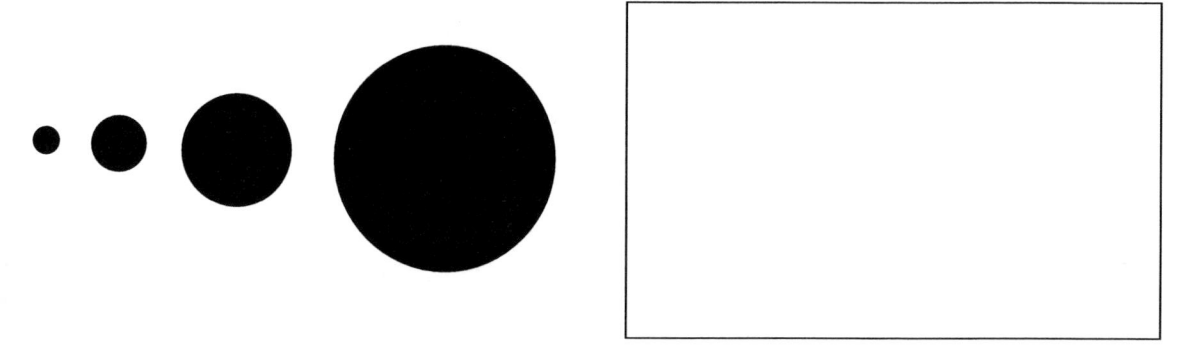

Lastly, imagine that you have sectioned the torso of a human cadaver (ignore the arms). Below is a crude stylized drawing of a torso without arms viewed from the front. In the spaces provided, draw the cut surfaces that would result from a midsagittal section and from a transverse section. That means two different drawings. Label each of the drawings using in each instance <u>only</u> those terms from the following list that apply: **right, left, anterior, posterior, superior, inferior**.

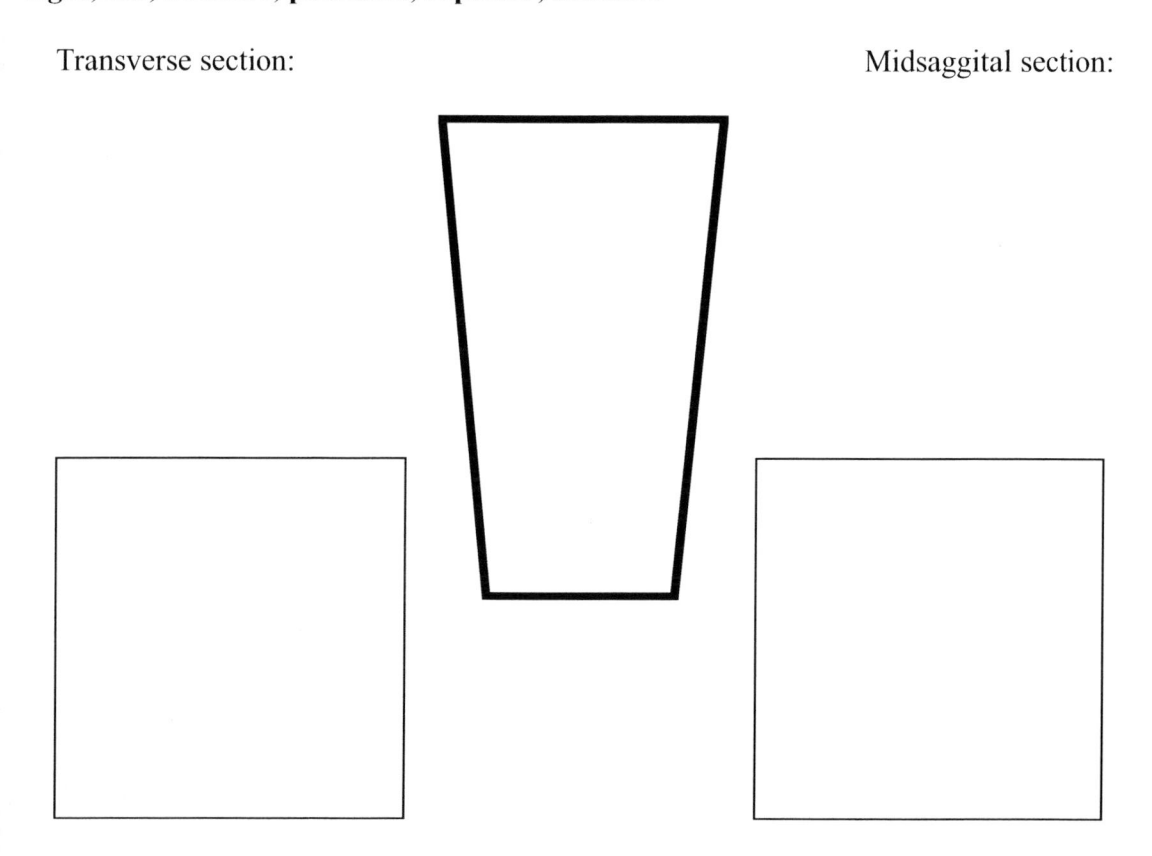

Transverse section: Midsaggital section:

Exercise A-1

Introduction to Dissection and Gross Anatomy:
Guided Exploration of the Cat

What are Dissection and Gross Anatomy?
Dissection and gross anatomy involve the study of structure at the macroscopic level. In fact, the word *anatomy* is derived from the Greek word meaning dissection. Generally, in gross anatomy we are concerned with those things which are visible to the naked eye. Gross anatomy may take a regional approach or an organ-system approach. In a regional approach, organs within a particular area or region of the body are studied. The structures exposed in any particular region will belong to a number of different organ systems. In an organ-system approach, the major organs of a particular system are exposed. Since many organ-systems are not confined to one particular location of the body, organ-system anatomy generally involves working with structures throughout the body.

The process of exposing organs and structures for study is called dissection, derived from the Latin word meaning to cut up . The dissection experience is like an off-trail hike through a wilderness area. On a backcountry hike, you would constantly look for landmarks and monitor the general features of the terrain in order to avoid becoming lost and to continue making progress toward your destination. Keep this analogy in mind as you dissect. Remember, dissection is not simply cutting and slicing. Dissection is exposing, sometimes with a blunt instrument. Dissection is exploring by touch. This means that you need to note the texture and consistency of structures that you uncover. Dissection involves visualizing details such as size, shape, and compartmentalization of structures. Dissection is performing simple tests on structures as you uncover them. This means determining strength, elasticity, and if a structure is solid or contains one or more cavities. Dissection involves using structural features to speculate on the functional capabilities of the tissues and organs. Finally, dissection and a knowledge of gross anatomy allow us to connect what is observed at the gross anatomical level with what can be visualized at the microscopic level.

Our commitment to the use of biological specimens and to dissection as a method of exploration and discovery is fully consistent with the Human Anatomy and Physiology Society's official position statement on Animal Use which is reproduced with permission at the end of this exercise).

About the Cats
Your first dissection experience will involve a necropsy of a cat. Necropsy is the animal equivalent of an autopsy. The cats used for this procedure were all provided by animal shelters to biological supply houses. If the biological supply houses had not purchased the bodies of these cats for use as dissection specimens, these bodies would have been cremated. Our use of preserved cats for study insures that the cat specimens which would otherwise simply be destroyed after they are euthanized will now be put to a worthwhile, educational use.

General Objectives

Anatomy & Physiology faculty feel that a major dissection experience early on in A & P is a valuable educational experience. As already mentioned, dissection is a discovery experience analogous to a journey into what should be new territory for all of you. There is a tendency among beginning students, and also among some Anatomy & Physiology teachers to reduce gross anatomy to an exercise which involves putting names or labels on structures. Indeed, learning the proper name of anatomical structures is extremely important. However, gross anatomy and dissection is much more than labeling. As you are performing this dissection exercise, here are some general things to keep in mind.

1. Listen to your instructor. He or she will be giving directions by using proper anatomical terminology. You should gain an appreciation of just how valuable the proper use of anatomical terminology is in a dissection experience, and by extension, in a surgical setting.

2. By the time you complete this dissection experience, you should have an excellent understanding of body cavities and how major body cavities are subdivided.

3. This dissection experience should also clarify your understanding of the different types of body membranes.

4. This exercise should solidify the concept of an organ and help you to realize how organs with similar jobs group together to constitute organ systems.

Preparation

The lab exercises contained in this manual are designed to fill the full 3 hours allotted for each lab. In order for a student group to be able to complete the entire exercise within the allotted time, each member of the group must arrive for lab each week having completed the necessary preparation for that exercise. What constitutes appropriate preparation will vary for each different exercise but there are common requirements that apply to all lab sessions and common reference materials that will be useful to all students as they work to complete the required preparation. First among useful references is your textbook, most especially the introductory chapter, the listing of word roots, the glossary, and the index. Second, any standard medical dictionary is extremely useful for determining the meaning of specialized directional or clinical terms, and for locating and describing general and specific anatomical structures. Your instructor may provide additional resources, some of them on-line, which may be of assistance in this as well.

1. <u>Prior to coming to lab each week</u>, you should <u>carefully</u> read the entire exercise in your lab manual and any additional materials provided in advance.
2. <u>Prior to coming to lab each week</u>, you should look up (and write down in your lab book) the meaning of any specialized term contained in the exercise. That means that there will be no need to refer to a reference other than your lab books simply to determine the meaning of any specialized word or phrase that is part of the day's exercise. This includes any term used as part of the directions for the exercise.

3. <u>Prior to coming to lab each week</u>, you must complete and be prepared to hand in any pre-test materials relating to the week's exercise.

The goal of lab preparation is two-fold. First, it is intended to transform your lab manual into a student-friendly resource that should facilitate your work in the lab. Second, it is intended to increase the likelihood that you and your group will be able to complete the entire assigned exercise in the time provided. Remember, adequate lab preparation <u>does not</u> require you to complete the exercise before you arrive. Rather, it just requires you to clarify <u>for yourself in writing</u> specialized terms that are part of the day's exercise. Lastly, realize that any individual instructor may modify what is required as preparation for any given exercise.

This close-up illustration is taken from the title page of the famous anatomic tome *De Humani corporis fabrica libri septum* by Andreas Vesalius. The *Fabrica* was published in 1543. A framed print of the entire frontispiece can be viewed hanging in our cadaver lab. What is noteworthy about this illustration is that it depicts the teacher (Vesalius) performing the actual dissection demonstration himself amidst his students. Prior to this, depictions of dissections and anatomic demonstration kept students and teachers apart. The interest of his students is apparent even in this small portion of the drawing. A look at the complete piece hanging in our lab communicates the interest and excitement that should be at the core of any real learning experience.

Specific Tasks and Your Observations

The following is a list of specific objectives that you should accomplish by the time you have completed the cat dissection. In each case you will be expected to make specific observations and/or answer specific questions. You should circle the appropriate responses or write your observations and answers in the spaces provided. Once you've completed the observations in each activity, check off either **Verify** ____ or **Refute** ____ to indicate your group's final consensus conclusion.

1. **Verify ____ or refute ____ this statement: Careful inspection of the oral cavity shows that its structure is specialized for the cat's hunting and killing (predatory) life style.**

    To make your inspection and assessment easier, first use a scalpel to completely and deeply cut the soft tissue (skin and muscle) at the corners of the cat's mouth. Then use wadded up paper towel to protect your fingers from the cat's sharp teeth and force the cat's mouth open as widely as possible. If this is not successful, it may be necessary for you to use the bone cutters that are available to crack the lower jaw at the corners of the mouth. This will allow the mouth of the cat to more easily be widely opened so you can see, feel and generally better observe the structures of the oral cavity. Again, be careful when you attempt to open the cat's mouth since some of the teeth may be very sharp. Ask your instructor for assistance if you experience any problems with this.

    Remember: you are observing **structural** detail. Initially, do not try to determine what the purpose of these structures or what they do. Simply list each item or detail of structure that any member of your group notices.

    For each of the indicated structures below, list any specific details of structure that you notice.

    Some structural details to consider (merely a help to get you started, not a complete list):

    Jaw: Length from hinge point to front of jaw compared to the width at the hinge point:
    _____

    Shape when viewed from below: U or V

    Anterior angle: $<60°$ $60°$ $>60°$

    Other observations: _____

    _____

Teeth: Length and location of different types of teeth: _____

_____

_____

Shapes of different teeth (sharp, rounded, flat, etc): _____

_____

_____

Other observations: _____

_____

_____

Tongue: Thickness: _____

Width: _____

Mobility: _____

Texture of surfaces: _____

Other observations: _____

_____

_____

Roof of mouth: Texture: _____

Consistent pattern or random design: _____

Other observations: _____

_____

_____

Only after all groups have recorded their observations about details of structure should individual groups try to make functional connections (to a predatory life style) that relate to the specific elements of structure that have been observed.

2. **Verify ____ or refute ____ this statement: Fascia is a generally distributed connective tissue within the body. Close inspection of its structure and its mechanical properties reveals a strong correlation between structure and function.**

A good example of fascia that is easily examined is the tissue which holds the skin in place. To observe this tissue you should first place the cat in the prone (belly side down) position. Then with both hands raise a longitudinal (lengthwise) fold of skin along the cat's back. Next, using either a scalpel or a pair of sharp scissors, carefully cut/snip a transverse (crosswise) opening in the skin fold at the midline on the back (dorsal surface). Remember that you should **not** cut too deeply and damage underlying muscle tissue. Once you can get under the skin, you can use a blunt probe or a closed blunt scissors to create a longitudinal path extending along the spinal column first up toward the neck and then down toward the base of the tail. Then with a scissors, cut the skin along this path. You may find it easiest to do this in smaller sections.

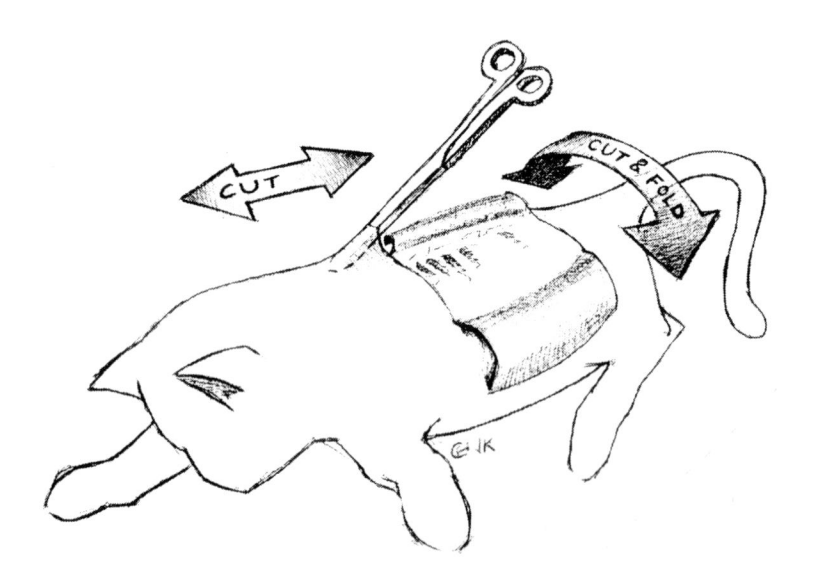

Once the skin is opened, pull the cut edges laterally and carefully examine the whitish tissue which you are stretching and probably tearing as you separate the skin from the body wall. Be careful in doing this because if you cut this tissue or completely tear it away from the skin, you won't have anything left to examine. The trick is to stretch it without tearing it so you can get a good close look at its structure. List several of your observations in the spaces provided. Do so as precisely as you can. Note: The illuminated magnifiers on the lab tables and the handheld magnifying glasses will be a great help in performing this inspection.

_____

_____

_____

Observe what happens when you stretch it and then release it.

_____

Hint: It is often helpful when trying to describe something you are examining to relate it to something with which you or others are very familiar. For example, think in terms like "It reminds me of…" or "It looks like …" as you try to articulate your observations. An actual anatomical example of this approach involves the tiny bones of the middle ear. The one that is attached to the ear drum is called the <u>malleus</u> because it looks like a hammer. Try the approach below.

The fascia holding the skin in place reminds me of _____

3. **Verify ____ or refute ____ this statement: Without entering the main body cavity within the torso (ventral body cavity), it is possible to make some accurate observations or reach specific conclusions about internal organs (viscera).**

   <u>At this time, do not make any cuts or incisions in your specimen.</u> Rather you should examine the belly side of your specimen first by carefully looking and then by touching, pressing, and feeling… a technique called palpation. Palpation is one of the assessment techniques that your doctor uses when he/she conducts a physical exam.

   First, determine the sex of your specimen.   Male   Female
   On what do you base your conclusion about sex?

   _____

   If female, do you think this cat has been pregnant before?   Yes / No
   On what do you base your conclusion about previous pregnancy?

   _____

   By palpation, can you tell where the chest cage ends and the abdominal wall begins?   Yes / No

   Are the lower (inferior) limits of the chest cage at the same level on the belly side of the cat as they are at the sides of the cat?   Yes / No
   If not, describe (or draw) the difference.
                                                                        Drawing
   _____

   _____

33

Internal organs can be placed into one of two categories: solid or hollow. Consider the liver which is located toward the top of the abdominal cavity on the right side of the specimen, just under the inferiormost extent of the rib cage. Try to locate the liver on your specimen by palpation.

How would you categorize the liver?   Solid   Hollow

Now try to determine how far inferiorly (toward the groin) it extends. Place a pin vertically into the abdomen of the cat at the inferiormost edge of the liver to indicate your finding. Note: The pins will be supplied by your instructor.

Based on your examination, does the liver cross the ventral midline?   Yes / No

Use another pin to indicate the furthest <u>leftward</u> extent of the liver toward or over the midline. Note: References to right and left always refer to the specimen's right or left side.

Be prepared to demonstrate your answers to your instructor. In the next activity you will open the ventral body cavity of the cat and be able to visualize the liver. You will then be able to evaluate the accuracy of your assessment.

Next consider the stomach which is located toward the top of the abdominal cavity on the left side, beneath the inferiormost extent of the rib cage. Try to locate the stomach on your specimen by palpation. Describe how it feels compared to the liver.

_____

Based on this, how would you categorize it?   Solid   Hollow

Lastly, try to determine by palpation whether the condition of the stomach.
                                                        Full   Empty

In many specimens, this may be very difficult to discern. Again, when you open the main body cavity of the cat, you will be able to evaluate the accuracy of your assessment.

4. **Verify ____ or refute ____ this statement: The large body cavity of the torso (ventral body cavity) is divided into a number of discreet compartments.**

You should now open the abdominal portion of the main (ventral) body cavity of the cat from groin to neck. To do this, first cut through a fold of abdominal wall with a scissors or a scalpel. The approach is much the same as was done in the previous activity dealing with observation of fascia, only now you are working on the belly side of the specimen. Also, in this instance, you are to make a deeper cut so that the inner body cavity is exposed. Then with a <u>blunt-ended</u> scissors, extend the cut inferiorly to the groin and superiorly <u>just **to the inferior tip**</u> of the breastbone (sternum). Be careful to **NOT** enter the chest cavity at this point in the exercise.

Before proceeding any further, reflect the wall of abdomen back to expose the liver. To do this, make 2 transverse (crosswise) cuts on each side as described below. One cut should extend from the edge of the midline incision along (but not through) the lower edge of the rib cage. that means you will be using the observations you made earlier about the edges of the rib cage to make this first cut. The second cut should begin at the midline near the groin and extend obliquely toward the top of the pelvic bone (iliac crest). Repeat these cuts on the opposite side of the specimen. Now you should be able to flap open the abdominal cavity without tearing or stretching anything. These cuts should greatly improve the exposure of abdominal organs.

Now you can evaluate your work on the previous activity (#3) where you tried to determine the margins of the liver by palpation.

How did you do? _____

If your observation by palpation alone was in error, you can now close the body wall and palpate the liver again to determine if you can now successfully and accurately feel the borders of the organ. Do not be discouraged if you were initially in error. Like any assessment technique, palpation requires practice if you are to master the approach. Doctors and other clinicians practice these techniques a great deal before they become expert.

Once you've done that, you can explore the abdominal cavity gently with a gloved finger. Can you pass your finger directly into the chest cavity? Yes / No

If not, what seems to be preventing passage?

_____

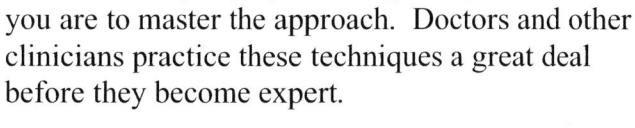

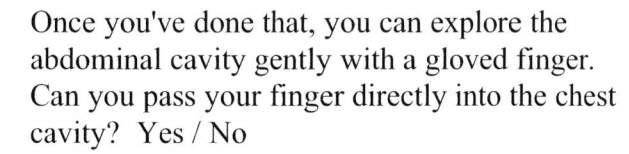

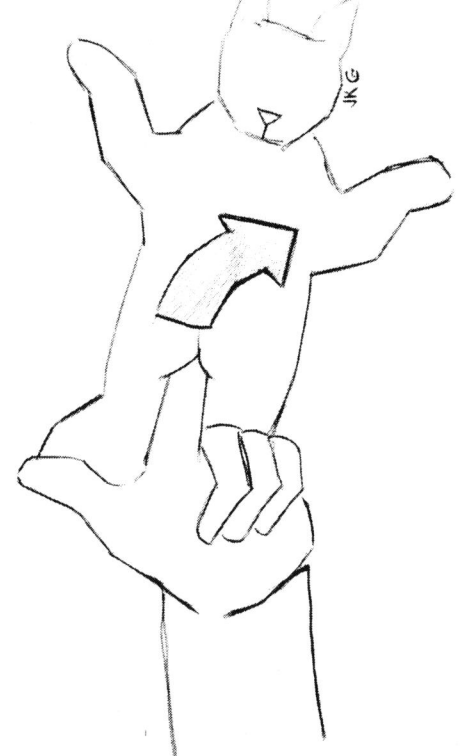

Now you can continue the longitudinal cut completely through the breastbone, extending it all the way to the neck. Once the longitudinal incision is complete and **before** you spread it open, you should carefully use your scissors to free the diaphragm from the inside of the body wall.

If you open the incision widely before doing this, you will split the middle of the diaphragm from front to back. This will make your observations about compartments a bit more difficult. If you are confused or unsure about what to do, ask your instructor for further direction before you proceed.

Now that you have access to the entire ventral cavity, please <u>try to be gentle</u> and systematic in your observation. Don't cut any organs or membranes. Rather, move or reflect them carefully so as not to cause any damage as you try to check for the presence of separate compartments within the ventral cavity.

Does the chest (thoracic) cavity seem to be divided into separate smaller compartments?   Yes / No
If yes, indicate in the spaces provided below any such compartments, chambers, containers, or enclosures by indicating the organ(s) that are contained within each.

_____

_____

5. **Verify _____ or refute _____ this statement: Serous membranes cannot effectively stabilize the position of internal organs or limit the mobility or extent of the movement of internal organs.**

Once the specimen is opened, the ventral body cavity is exposed and internal organs are readily visible. Anything you touch is actually touched <u>through</u> a serous membrane that either covers an organ (visceral) or lines a cavity (parietal). Serous membranes are very thin and made up of a single layer of flat cells anchored or supported by a thin layer of loose connective tissue much like the tissue you've already examined in activity #2. Sometimes the thinness of a serous membrane is not readily apparent because it is "glued" to a more substantial underlying tissue or structure.

To address the statement above, gently move or try to move various organs.
Are all the internal organs equally mobile or immobile?   Yes / No
If any organs are limited in their movement, what structure(s) seem(s) to be responsible for this?
_____

Also, you can change the position of the entire specimen (ie. turn the cat so the belly surface faces down) and observe the internal organs during this maneuver. Do serous membranes limit their movement during this maneuver?   Yes / No

When the specimen is returned to its supine (belly up) position, do the organs generally return to their original positions/locations?   Yes / No

6. **Verify ____ or refute ____ this statement: Any organ that is contained within the abdominal cavity must also be contained within the peritoneal cavity (the cavity within the sac formed by the intact parietal peritoneum).**

The smooth serous membrane associated with the abdomen and its organs is named the peritoneum. The abdominal cavity is <u>lined by</u> a parietal peritoneum that is seemingly "glued" to the inside surface of the abdominal wall. This membrane folds back on itself and then covers (is likewise "glued" to) the organs of the abdominal cavity as a visceral peritoneum. It is probably helpful to think of the intact parietal peritoneum as a closed sac within the abdomen containing the individually wrapped abdominal organs.

A useful analogy might be that of a plastic liner inside a trash can. The trash can represents the abdominal wall and the liner represents the parietal peritoneum. If we placed an apple between the liner and the trash can, it would be in the can (ie. within the abdominal cavity) but not contained within the liner (ie. not within the peritoneal sac). Now imagine that you are blindfolded and you have to find the apple **by feel** and decide whether its in the sac or between the sac and the can. Simply transfer the same process to the cat.

By careful inspection and palpation of the abdominal cavity, you are to determine whether there are any organs that are within the abdominal cavity (inferior to the diaphragm) which are not also contained within the sac that is formed by the parietal peritoneum. Note that when you are touching the inside surface of the abdominal wall, your finger is on the <u>inside</u> of the peritoneal sac (along with ~~the~~ many abdominal organs). The outside surface of the peritoneal sac is touching (glued to) the muscle that makes up the wall of the abdominal cavity.

Based on your examination, are all abdominal organs contained within the peritoneal cavity (sac)? Yes   No

If your answer to the above is no, show your instructor. Such an organ not contained within the peritoneal sac is generally considered extraperitoneal (outside the peritoneum) or more specifically retroperitoneal (if it is behind the peritoneum). In either case, your instructor will indicate whether you are correct or not.

How does the mobility of organs contained within the peritoneal sac generally compare with the mobility of any organs that are outside the peritoneum (that is, between the parietal peritoneum and the body wall)?

_____

_____

_____

7. **Verify ____ or refute ____ this statement: There is no characteristic pattern of fat distribution within the body of the cat.**

In order to establish a pattern, you need to do two things. First, you must carefully and thoroughly examine your specimen and compile a list indicating all the places where you can see that fat is deposited. Do not only look in the abdominal cavity. Examine the thoracic cavity and various areas beneath the skin as well. Second, you must then examine several other specimens to determine if the sites of fat deposition in these cats correspond to the same locations you identified in your specimen. If the answer is yes… then you have identified a pattern.

Areas where fat is found:	Your specimen	Other specimens
	_____	Yes / No
	_____	Yes / No
	_____	Yes / No
	_____	Yes / No
	_____	Yes / No
	_____	Yes / No
	_____	Yes / No

Based on this, does a pattern of fat distribution exist?   Yes / No

8. **Verify ____ or refute ____ this statement: Cats of approximately the same size show individual differences in various details of the structure of their internal organs.**

In order to complete this assignment, select several specific organs in your specimen. We suggest that you choose from among the following: lungs, liver, stomach, gall bladder, spleen, small intestine, kidneys. Your instructor can help you to identify any of these with which you are not familiar. Examine each of them carefully. Do this visually and by palpation. Only after having done this should you proceed to other specimens of similar size and examine the same selection of organs.

Record your observations in the designated spaces on the next page.

Organ viewed in your specimen	Structural differences in other cats
_____	Yes / No
_____	Yes / No
_____	Yes / No
_____	Yes / No
_____	Yes / No
_____	Yes / No

Based on this, do differences in structural
detail generally exist in different specimens?   Yes / No

9. **Verify ____ or refute ____ this statement: Organs of the main body cavity (ventral body cavity) can be broadly divided into two groups: hollow or solid.**

Hollow organs are those which contain a single large internal chamber (or several such chambers). Solid organs do not possess a large central cavity or a single lumen (that is, big enough for a finger or a probe to enter) but may, however, contain one, two, several or even many tiny hollow structures. Note: By what assessment technique can you <u>initially</u> determine (or try to determine) whether an organ is solid or hollow?

_____

_____

Be sure to examine organs in <u>both</u> the chest cavity and the abdominal cavity.

Organ examined	Solid	Hollow	Not sure
_____	____	____	____
_____	____	____	____
_____	____	____	____
_____	____	____	____
_____	____	____	____
_____	____	____	____

10. Verify _____ or refute _____ this statement:
It is not always readily apparent whether an organ is hollow or solid.

For this assignment, a list of organs for you to examine has been provided. You should also consider the organs from the previous activity which you included in the "Not sure" category.

Organ examined	Difficult to determine	Final conclusion
Liver	_____	Solid / Hollow
Gall bladder	_____	Solid / Hollow
Small intestine	_____	Solid / Hollow
Heart	_____	Solid / Hollow
Urinary bladder	_____	Solid / Hollow
Lungs	_____	Solid / Hollow
Stomach	_____	Solid / Hollow

Based on your examination, what structural feature(s) can make a hollow organ appear to be solid?

_____

When unsure about the nature of an organ, by what examination technique can you conclusively (without doubt) verify whether it is solid or hollow?

_____

For any organ that you found the determination to be difficult or inconclusive, perform this technique to come to a final conclusive answer. Enter your final answer in the far right column above.

11. **Verify _____ or refute _____ this statement: Some tubular organs within the body have a thin collapsible wall structure, whereas other tubular organs have a thick or reinforced, noncollapsible wall structure that maintains the patency of the lumen.**

For this activity, confine your exploration to the chest cavity. In order to make your observations in the chest, use a scissors to carefully remove the heart and each of the lungs. This will provide you with a much clearer view of several different tubular organs which run in a longitudinal direction within the chest. For this activity, you have complete freedom to expose, section, and examine any tubular organs (air passage, blood vessel, food tube) you can find in the thorax.

Include your observations in the spaces provided below. Check with your instructor if you are not sure of the name of a structure that you wish to include in your results.

Tubular organ	Collapsible wall	Reinforced wall
_____	_____	_____
_____	_____	_____
_____	_____	_____
_____	_____	_____
_____	_____	_____

12. **Verify _____ or refute _____ this statement: Some organs and body structures have particularly well-developed elastic properties.**

Elasticity requires not only that something can be stretched but also, more importantly, that it returns to its original shape when it is released or the stress placed on it is removed. Among the organs/structures that you can consider in addressing this problem are the ears, chest wall, trachea (windpipe), esophagus, aorta, lungs, small intestine, and subcutaneous fascia. If you decide to examine a tubular organ, with a scissors sever the tube transversely (crosswise) and then cut a ring of tissue (akin to a small rubber band) from the end of the tube. Then you can secure the ring of tissue in a dissecting tray with a probe or closed scissors and test it for elasticity by stretching and releasing the ring using another probe or a forceps.

If you decide to examine the lungs, you will need to cut the trachea transversely. You can then insert a small breathing tube into the trachea through which you may inflate the lungs with a manual breathing bag. You will need assistance from your instructor for this. Observe the behavior of the lungs during both inflation and during deflation.

You may select any organ or body structure to examine for elasticity. For some, you will have to devise your own technique for assessing this property.

Organ	Possesses elasticity
_____	Yes / No
_____	Yes / No
_____	Yes / No
_____	Yes / No
_____	Yes / No

13. **Verify ____ or refute ____ this statement: Glandular organs, regardless of where they are found in the body, share some common anatomic features.**

    Since at this point you have no background that would allow you to recognize glandular structures, your instructor will assist you by exposing and/or pointing out several such glandular organs in the specimens being studied or that have been selected and collected from other specimens for this purpose. Once you have access to a selection of organs, address the statement above and record your observations below. For this activity, the large illuminated magnifiers or the small handheld magnifying glasses will prove helpful.

Organ	Anatomic features
_____	_____
_____	_____
_____	_____
_____	_____

    What is the most consistent structural feature shared by glands?

    _____

14. **There are many examples of structural details or specializations which serve to increase the surface area (and therefore the functionality) of an organ, system, or structure.**

Surface area may be increased by such structural modifications as creases, folds, projections of tissue, wavy attachment surfaces, alterations of shape and dimensions, and various other features. As you search for specific examples of increased surface area, you should examine the shapes of the various organs you have exposed. Carefully open or section some of them and examine their internal surfaces. Your instructor may set up a dissecting microscope demonstration of a stained portion of small intestine wall for you to examine. You might also carefully examine any of the various human (or feline) skulls available in the lab.

Structure that increases surface area	Found in…

Human Anatomy & Physiology Society
Position Statement on Animal Use
(Adopted July 28, 1995)
(Modified January 2001)

It is the position of the Human Anatomy and Physiology Society that dissection and the manipulation of animal tissues and organs are essential elements in scientific investigation and introduce students to the excitement and challenge of their future careers.

The Human Anatomy and Physiology Society (HAPS) is a national organization of science educators dedicated to the task of providing instruction of the highest quality in human anatomy and physiology. A fundamental tenet of science is the ordered process of inquiry requiring careful and thoughtful observation by the investigator. As subdivisions of biology, both anatomy and physiology share a long history of careful and detailed examination, exploration and critical inquiry into the structure and function of the animal body. Consistent with the origins and nature of scientific inquiry, HAPS endorses the use of animals as essential to the laboratory experiences in both human anatomy and human physiology.

Historically, the principal tool of investigation in anatomy has been dissection. A properly directed dissection experience goes beyond naming structures and leads the student to conclusions and insights about the nature and relatedness of living organisms that are not otherwise possible. To succeed in their future careers, students must become thoroughly familiar with anatomical structures, their design features and their relationships to one another. Dissection is based on observational and kinesthetic learning that instills a recognition and appreciation for the three-dimensional structure of the animal body, the interconnections between organs and organ systems, and the uniqueness of biological material. While anatomical models, interactive computer programs, and multimedia materials may enhance the dissection experience, they should not be considered as equivalent alternatives or substitutes for whole animal dissection. HAPS supports the use of biological specimens for anatomical study provided their use is in strict compliance with federal legislation and the guidelines of the National Institutes of Health and the United States Department of Agriculture and that such use fulfills clearly defined educational objectives.

Physiology experiments involving live animals provide an excellent opportunity to learn the basic elements specific to scientific investigation and experimentation. It is here that students pose questions, propose hypotheses, develop technical skills, collect data, and analyze results. It is here that they learn to remain focused on the details of procedure and technique which may influence the outcome of the experiment and the responses of the animal. When faced with unexpected and even erroneous results, students develop and improve their critical thinking and problem solving skills. Computer simulations and video programs are useful tools that help students acquire a basic understanding of physiologic principles. However, due to the inherent variability and unpredictable nature of biological responses, such programs fail to fully depict the uniqueness of living organisms and should not be viewed as equivalent alternatives or substitutes for live animal experiments. HAPS supports the use of biological specimens in physiology experiments provided their use is in strict compliance with federal legislation and the guidelines of the National Institutes of Health and the United States Department of Agriculture and that such use fulfills clearly defined educational objectives.

Science educators have in common a respect and reverence for the natural world and therefore have a responsibility to share this with their students. They must communicate the importance of a serious approach to the study of anatomy and physiology. HAPS contends that science educators should retain responsibility for making decisions regarding the educational uses of animals. Furthermore, it opposes any legislation or administrative policy that would erode the educator's role in decision making or restrict dissection and animal experimentation in biology.

Exercise A-2

Human Cadaver Exploration

Now that the initial exploration and dissection of the cat is completed, we can progress to an initial examination of the prosected human cadaver. Over the course of the two semesters of lab work, you will have the opportunity to examine and explore in some depth the structure of each of the body's systems. Today begins the examination of actual human anatomy which will take you through two full semesters of laboratory work.

Policies and Rules

During the first lab session, the philosophy, policies and rules that pertain to the cadaver facility and experience were outlined and discussed. This serves to reinforce the major points that were made at that time.

1. The human cadavers in our lab were donated by individuals specifically for the purpose of expanding and enhancing your education. Obviously, the individuals whose bodies you will now study placed a very high value on learning. **Consider them your teachers**.

2. Your access to this anatomy lab and your participation in this special laboratory experience is a rare privilege. Showing respect for these specimens and maintaining their dignity is an absolute requirement of all us who will take part. No exceptions will be tolerated. As has already been discussed, failure to do so will result in your removal from the course.

3. Students are allowed in the cadaver lab only when a supervising faculty member or other authorized individual is present. Times when such access is possible will be determined and posted outside the lab early in the semester.

4. The basic rules which apply when working with human specimens are included at the start of this manual. You should reread these carefully. In the *Exploring A&P* CD that accompanies this lab manual, there is a QuickTime video that introduces students to the cadaver facility and summarizes many of the policies and procedures governing its use and the conduct of human cadaver study. Remember that you are responsible for always acting in a manner that is in compliance with these rules.

Cadaver Exploration

As a result of your previous exploration and dissection of the cat and because you have also completed the "Language of Anatomy" home assignment, you should now have a basic familiarity and understanding of the mammalian body plan and its associated cavities, membranes, and organs. Today you will for the first time examine and explore actual human anatomy using a preserved cadaver. The approach to this will be careful and deliberate.

Our commitment to the use of human cadavers as the primary study specimen for study of human anatomy and its functional correlations is fully consistent with the Human Anatomy and Physiology Society's official Position Statement on Cadaver Use which is reproduced with permission at the end of this exercise.

Initial Activity

Students will be placed into one of three or four groups and will perform the series of tasks described below. The purpose of this exercise is twofold. First it is intended to begin to make you more comfortable with touching and manipulating human specimens. Second, it is intended to familiarize you with a number of anatomical structures, landmarks, and reference points and lines that you will utilize in later cadaver explorations. Your instructor will review and check off each exercise once completed by each group. You should keep your notes and study them. Once this exercise is completed, you will be expected to know and be able to demonstrate and use any of these terms at any time throughout the rest of this course (that means this semester or next). So learn them now.

The lines or spaces provided are for you to jot down a definition, brief note, or reminder that will help you to locate the structure or landmark and/or to use the term correctly. Using the glossary of word roots from your text or any other reference (medical dictionary, A&P or nursing textbook, Internet) will prove very useful for this exercise.

1. Using the cadaver to which you are initially assigned, demonstrate the following <u>longitudinal</u> reference lines located on the surface of the torso.

    ventral midline _____

    mid-clavicular line _____

    anterior axillary line _____

    mid-axillary line _____

    R&L sternal margins _____

2. Using the complete skeletons and the cadaver to which you are initially assigned, demonstrate the following landmarks or structures located on the surface of the thorax (chest).

    axillary fossa _____

    costal cartilages _____

    costochondral junction _____

sternochondral
junction _____

costal margin _____

sternum
  manubrium _____

  body _____

  xiphoid _____

sternal notch
(jugular notch) _____

sternal angle
(angle of Louis) _____

xiphisternal junction _____

first rib
(sternal junction) _____

You should also practice so that you can identify individual ribs and individual intercostal spaces by number.

3. Combine longitudinal and transverse reference lines to precisely navigate the surface of the chest.

Once you have done this, you will be able to pinpoint or locate precise spots on the thorax by combining individual ribs, intercostal spaces or any other transverse surface reference line with any of the longitudinal reference lines listed in #1 above. Some common points on the anterior chest relate to a clinician's ability to clearly hear various sounds originating from the heart. For example, each of the four heart valves is best heard by placing the head of a stethoscope at a specific point on the chest as listed below. Find each spot and be able to demonstrate it to your instructor.

Bicuspid (mitral) valve: 5th intercostal space on the left, just medial to the midclavicular line. This is also the preferred site for listening to heart rate with a stethoscope, sometimes referred to as the point of maximum intensity (PMI).
Tricuspid valve: 5th intercostal space at the right sternal margin.
Aortic semilunar valve: 2nd intercostal space at the right sternal margin.

Pulmonic semilunar valve: 2nd intercostal space at the left sternal margin.

Finally, a thorough understanding of surface anatomy landmarks and reference points will allow you to better appreciate the location of various internal organs you will be studying during the course.

4. Using the complete skeletons and the cadaver to which you are initially assigned, demonstrate the following abdominopelvic landmarks/structures.

    epigastric fossa _____

    umbilicus _____

    linea alba _____

    anterior superior iliac spine (ASIS) _____

    anterior inferior iliac spine (AIIS) _____

    iliac crest _____

    tubercle of iliac crest _____

    symphysis pubis _____

    greater trochanter of femur _____

    ventral gluteals _____

    (Note: This clinical term used by practicing nurses refers to the gluteus medius & minimus collectively and is an important reference for administering injections in the buttock region.)

5. Using the cadaver to which you are initially assigned, demonstrate the following transverse reference lines.

    subcostal line (Use the inferiormost point on the lateral costal margin.)

    _____

transpyloric line (This reference line runs transversely through the pylorus of the stomach and is slightly superior (1-2 finger widths) to the subcostal line. For our purposes it can be approximated by the subcostal line.)

___

transtubercular line (Use the tubercles of the iliac crest.)

___

6. Using the cadaver to which you are initially assigned, name and demonstrate the four abdominopelvic quadrants. What surface landmark do you use in order to define the four quadrants?

___

At this time, you should list at least one internal organ or major portion of an organ that is contained within each quadrant. <u>Later</u> you will open the abdominal cavity and be expected to demonstrate at least one significant internal organ or major portion of an organ in each of the four quadrants.

Quadrant	Organ or portion of an organ
___	___
___	___
___	___
___	___

7. Using the cadaver to which you are initially assigned, name and demonstrate the nine abdominopelvic regions.

___   ___   ___

___   ___   ___

___   ___   ___

What longitudinal reference lines do you use in order to define the nine regions?

___

What transverse reference lines do you use in order to define the nine regions?
_____

At this time, you should list at least one internal organ or major portion of an organ that is contained within each of the nine regions. <u>Later</u> you will open the abdominal cavity and be expected to demonstrate to your instructor at least one significant internal organ or major portion of an organ in each of the nine regions.

Abdominopelvic region	Organ or portion of an organ
_____	_____
_____	_____
_____	_____
_____	_____
_____	_____
_____	_____
_____	_____
_____	_____
_____	_____

8. In the clinical setting, particularly in viewing radiographic images (X-rays, CT scans, MRIs), anatomic structures and landmarks are related to specific vertebral levels. Use any of the real bone skeletons to determine the vertebral level for the following structures.

Structure/Landmark	Vertebral level
angle of Louis	_____
xiphisternal junction	_____
iliac crest	_____
umbilicus	_____
subcostal line	_____

9. Precise location of the heart: In each of the cadavers, the heart has been returned to its normal anatomic position within the thorax. Carefully expose it by removing the chest plate and, using proper terminology and reference to specific landmarks on the thoracic (chest) surface, describe its location and extent (superior, inferior, and right and left lateral margins) as precisely as you can. Describe your directions for defining each margin in the spaces below. You should reach a consensus among members of your group on your final answers. Following your directions <u>precisely</u> should allow us to place our hands on the <u>closed</u> chest in a way that defines a box (a rectangle) which surrounds only the heart when the chest plate is removed.

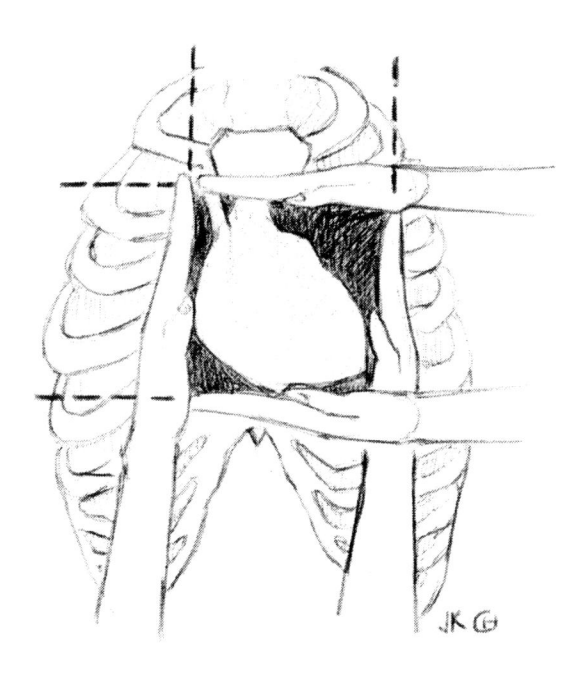

superior margin   _____

                       _____

inferior margin   _____

                       _____

right lateral margin   _____

                       _____

left lateral margin   _____

                       _____

10. From previous exercises, you should already be familiar with serous membranes. Using the cadaver to which you are assigned, demonstrate for your instructor the visceral and parietal pleurae, the visceral and parietal pericardium, and the visceral and parietal peritoneum. Once you have shown that you recognize the difference between the visceral and parietal serous membranes, focus your attention on the serous membranes of the abdomen.

Verify ____ or refute ____ this statement: The parietal peritoneum of the abdomen is not an extension of or connected to the visceral peritoneum.

As you consider this statement, place your finger on some area of parietal peritoneum that covers the dorsal surface of the abdominal cavity. If you can now slide your finger along the parietal membrane and eventually find that you are touching visceral membrane, then the above statement is false and you should refute it. If, on the other hand, you find that your finger consistently encounters a definite separation dividing the parietal membrane from the visceral, then the above statement is true and you should verify it.

Verify ____ or refute ____ this statement: The serous membranes found in the abdomen can be followed without interruption or separation to the serous membranes within the chest.

To start, place your finger on the peritoneum which covers the liver. Slide your finger toward the underside of the diaphragm. If you are able to follow the serous membrane through the intact diaphragm and find that your finger is now within the chest cavity, then the above statement is true and you should verify it. If you find otherwise, then the above statement is false and you should refute it.

In addition as was previously discussed, reflections of the parietal peritoneum form double-layered membranes called mesenteries. Carefully explore the abdominal cavity and demonstrate any of these double-layered membranes which are still intact. As you are aware, depending on the cadaver, some of these double-layered serous membranes have been cut and/or wholly or partially removed.

Please note: If any membranes are intact, they are very fragile and can be easily torn. You must be **very gentle** as you explore. Examine the abdomen and try to find examples of such double-layered membranes. At this point, naming is not part of the exercise. Based on your observation, consider carefully and then verify or refute the following statements. Be prepared to demonstrate your findings to your instructor.

A. **Verify ____ or refute ____ this statement:** There are double-layered membranes (or portions of these membranes) that do not provide support or stability to internal organs.

B. **Verify ____ or refute ____ this statement:** There are double-layered membranes (or portions of these membranes) that connect organs to the body wall.

C. **Verify ____ or refute ____ this statement:** There are double-layered membranes (or portions of these membranes) that connect organs to other organs.

Now you are in position to attribute names to some of the serous membranes you have found. Be prepared to demonstrate the following double-layered membranes for your instructor. For each of the double-layered membranes named below, indicate which of the three categories listed above (A, B, or C) most accurately describes the membrane. You can also include some information that will help you to remember each specific membrane in the space provided.

_____ free edge of the greater omentum _____

_____ gastrosplenic ligament _____
_____

_____ falciform ligament _____

_____ lesser omentum _____
_____

_____ gastrocolic ligament _____
_____

_____ transverse mesocolon _____
_____

_____ sigmoid mesocolon _____
_____

_____ mesentery of the small intestine _____
_____

10. **Verify ____ or refute ____ this statement: In general, while the overall human body plan is consistent among individuals, there are many specific details of anatomy which differ from one individual to another.**

   Start with a careful examination of the ventral body cavity (abdomen and thorax) of your assigned specimen. Notice details of structure involving the cavities and their enclosed membranes, the viscera and the body walls. After ten minutes, move to a different cadaver and perform the same examination.

   First verify or refute that the overall plan is the same. Second, find and document 10 specific <u>anatomical</u> differences or variations that are present in these different specimens. Be sure that your group agrees on each one of these observations. Do not consult with members of another group as you do this.

   As you work on this task, remember that observation is more than simply looking. You should also palpate the same structures on the two specimens you are comparing. Don't limit yourself to just one area or one type of structure. Look for differences in surface landmarks, bony structures, muscular structures, abdominal organs, thoracic organs, serous membranes, etc. Record your observations on the facing page. Your instructor may collect these observations for separate evaluation.

11. **Individual organ descriptions and comparisons:** An important element of the laboratory experience in anatomy and physiology is the development of skill in observing structures accurately and completely. Careful, thoughtful observation involves looking, palpating, and manipulating structures and requires an open, active mind to process and interpret the information that is obtained in the activity. Related to this (actually dependent on it) is the ability to describe, compare, and contrast the design and appearance of those body structures that are being examined. In the cadavers before you, several internal structures have been pinned or otherwise indicated. Your instructor will indicate the two structures that each student group will be required to first describe, and then to compare, and contrast. These are not the same thing. Naming the pinned structures is **not** a part of this exercise. If there is time, your instructor may require you to perform this exercise twice.
   Describe in detail the structure and appearance of each organ.
   How are these two structures <u>anatomically</u> similar?
   How are these two structures <u>anatomically</u> different?

   Record your observations on the separate page provided. Your instructor may elect to collect these for separate evaluation as well.

Name: _____
Lab Worksheet (Human Cadaver Exploration)
Put your comments/answers in the spaces below.

Cadaver comparisons:

1) Cad # ___ _____

   Cad # ___ _____
===
2) Cad # ___ _____

   Cad # ___ _____
===
3) Cad # ___ _____

   Cad # ___ _____
===
4) Cad # ___ _____

   Cad # ___ _____
===
5) Cad # ___ _____

   Cad # ___ _____
===
6) Cad # ___ _____

   Cad # ___ _____
===
7) Cad # ___ _____

   Cad # ___ _____
===
8) Cad # ___ _____

   Cad # ___ _____
===
9) Cad # ___ _____

   Cad # ___ _____
===
10) Cad # ___ _____

    Cad # ___ _____
===

11. Individual organ descriptions and comparisons:

Organs/structures to be compared:
Organ 1 _____ Organ 2 _____

Structure and appearance of organ 1 _____
_____

Structure and appearance of organ 2 _____
_____

Anatomical similarities: _____
_____
_____

Anatomical differences: _____
_____
_____

===

Organs/structures to be compared:
Organ 3 _____ Organ 4 _____

Structure and appearance of organ 3 _____
_____

Structure and appearance of organ 4 _____
_____

Anatomical similarities: _____
_____
_____

Anatomical differences: _____
_____
_____

Position Statement on Cadaver Use (Human Anatomy & Physiology Society) Adopted: January 2001

It is the position of the Human Anatomy and Physiology Society that the use of cadavers is the preferred method for the study of human anatomy.

The Human Anatomy & Physiology Society (HAPS) is a national organization of science educators dedicated to the task of providing instruction of the highest quality in human anatomy and physiology. A fundamental tenet of science is the ordered process of inquiry requiring careful and thoughtful observation by the investigator. As subdivisions of biology, both anatomy and physiology share a long history of careful and detailed examination, exploration, and critical inquiry into the structure and function of the body.

Mindful of the constraints imposed by specimen availability, limited facilities and underfunding, HAPS endorses the use of cadavers as consistent with the origins and nature of scientific inquiry and views the proper use of cadavers as an ideal laboratory experience in human anatomy and physiology. While animal dissection may approach the ideal, cadavers provide opportunities that cannot be duplicated by animal dissection.

The mastery of human anatomical structures, their design features, and their relationships to one another are at the core of human anatomy and physiology. The opportunity to observe and wonder at the complexity of the human body, the impact of disease on human structure, the effects of age and life style on anatomy, and structural variations related to development are unique attributes of a cadaver experience. There is no better way to educate our students about human anatomy than through carefully and thoughtfully developed laboratory experiences using cadaver dissection and/or the exploration and examination of prosected cadavers. These laboratory experiences should be based on observational and kinesthetic learning that instills a recognition and appreciation for the three-dimensional structure of the body, the interconnections between organs and organ systems, and the structural uniqueness of the human organism. While anatomical models, interactive computer programs, and multimedia materials may enhance the laboratory experience, they should not be considered as equivalent alternatives or substitutes for a hands-on cadaver experience.

HAPS supports the use of cadavers for anatomical study provided their use is in strict compliance with federal legislation, the guidelines of the National Institutes of Health, and the body donor program from which the cadavers were acquired, and that such use fulfills clearly defined educational objectives.

Science educators have in common a respect and reverence for the human body and therefore have a responsibility to share this with their students. They must communicate the importance of a serious approach to the study of human anatomy and physiology. HAPS contends that human anatomy and physiology educators should retain responsibility for making decisions regarding the educational uses of cadavers. Furthermore, HAPS opposes any legislation and/or administrative policy that would erode the educator's role in decision-making.

Exercise A-3

Gross Anatomy of the Digestive System

This week's lab exercise deals with the gross anatomy of the digestive system. We will be using human organs in the prosected cadavers, excised organs (both wet preserved and plastinated), and a few selected models. Be sure that you are mindful of the philosophy, policies, and rules that pertain to the cadaver facility. Be sure to abide by all policies and procedures at all times. The first part of the exercise involves general impressions and observations about the gross anatomy of the digestive system. You should attempt to answer all questions dealing with Part I activities using the cadaver to which you are initially assigned. Part II involves detailed identification of a number of digestive system organs and structures. Initially, you should attempt to make all Part II observations and identifications on the cadavers to which you have been assigned. If unsuccessful, visit other cadavers. Keep in mind that no one particular specimen may exhibit all the structures you are required to master. Organs have been disturbed and in some cases may even be removed during the dissection process in some specimens but not (or in different ways) in others. An individual may have had a surgical procedure that resulted in the removal of a digestive structure such as a gall bladder, an appendix, or a portion of the intestinal tract. Individual variation often results in a structure being more easily recognized and identified in one specimen than is the case in another. Lastly, in several instances structures you are required to identify have not been exposed on any of the cadavers but have been dissected and exposed on the separate organ specimens. Your instructor will be helpful in directing you toward those specimens that best illustrate these specific structures.

For these reasons and to reinforce your knowledge of structure, attempt to identify all structures on different cadavers and available specimens.

Part 1:   Initial Cadaver Exploration

1. Examine the serous membrane which lines the abdominal cavity. This is the peritoneum which you explored in the initial cadaver exploration exercise. It is divided into two parts, a visceral peritoneum which covers organs and a parietal peritoneum which lines the cavity. Identify both parts of the peritoneum and be prepared to point these out to your instructor. Recalling your first cadaver exploration, is the visceral peritoneum anatomically distinct and separate from the parietal peritoneum or are these membranes different portions of the same continuous sheet of tissue?

   _____

2. Digestive organs of the ventral body cavity may be characterized as peritoneal or retroperitoneal. Peritoneal organs are surrounded by a visceral membrane and are located within the sac formed by the parietal membrane. Such peritoneal organs are connected to the abdominal wall by a double-layered membrane referred to previously as a mesentery. These double-layered membranes have also been previously studied in the cadaver exploration exercise. On the other hand, an organ which is retroperitoneal is not contained within the sac and is not supported by a double-layered membrane (mesentery). Rather it is covered only anteriorly (and possibly laterally but not posteriorly) by peritoneum, technically parietal peritoneum.

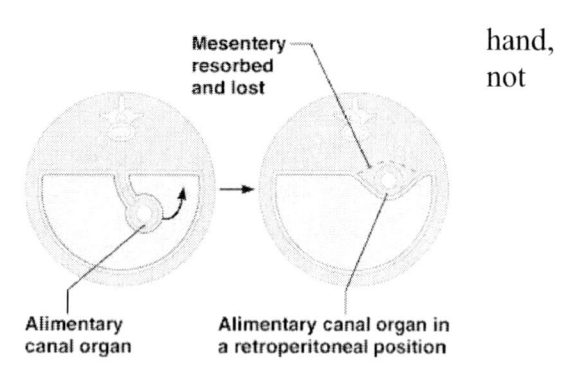

   An excellent example of a retroperitoneal organ (although not a digestive organ) is the kidney. In the cat exploration exercise, you found that the kidney was contained within the abdomen but not within the sac formed by the parietal peritoneum. Many textbooks include an illustration of a medial view of serous membranes as seen in a sagittal section. To the left is such an illustration (without labels) taken from your textbook. This perspective is very helpful in understanding the difference between peritoneal and retroperitoneal organs. Label the retroperitoneal space on the illustration. It will also help you in trying to better understand the double-layered membranes called mesenteries that you will be studying shortly.

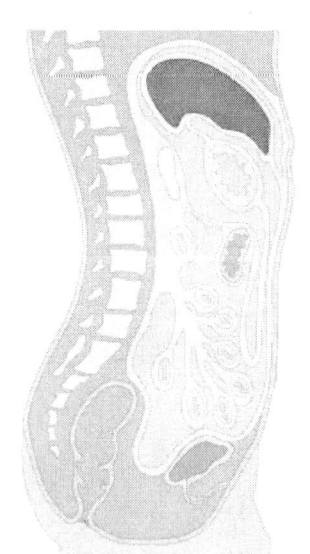

   You should be able to find several examples of each type of **digestive** organ and be prepared to demonstrate each to your instructor if asked. Peritoneal digestive organs are numerous and should be easy to recognize. Retroperitoneal organs are less obvious. It is possible for only one or several portions of an organ to be retroperitoneal, with the rest of the organ being within the peritoneal cavity. For example, there are three separate portions of the large intestine that are considered retroperitoneal. Also, one of the three segments of the small intestine is retroperitoneal as is one glandular digestive organ closely associated with it. Examine your cadaver and other cadavers carefully to try to locate these retroperitoneal organs.

Based on your observation, compare the mobility of peritoneal and retroperitoneal organs within the ventral body cavity. Are they equally mobile?   Yes / No
If not, which are less mobile?   Peritoneal   Retroperitoneal

What might be an advantage associated with this? _____

_____

3. If the dissection of your specimen allows, carefully remove the lungs and heart from the thoracic cavity and place them in a plastic bag. (The heart is often left intact within the thorax. If only one lung is removeable, it is more likely the right lung.) Note their position before you remove them since you will be required to replace them properly. Be prepared to demonstrate to your instructor the midline tubular digestive structure that you have exposed within the thorax immediately ventral to the vertebral column. Although it may not be obvious or easily determined by gross observation, there is <u>no peritoneum</u> (or outer serous membrane) associated with this structure.

Identify this digestive structure. _____

Use proper anatomic, directional terminology to describe the relationship of the superiormost portion of this structure to the larynx.

_____

Do likewise to describe its position relative to the trachea.

_____

_____

Does the tube extend through the diaphragm?   Yes / No

4. A number of digestive structures function as exocrine glands. Exocrine glands empty their contents on to an epithelial surface and are often referred to as "ducted" glands. Examples of exocrine secretions include serous (watery) fluid, mucus, oil, digestive enzymes, acidic or alkaline fluids. A number of different

exocrine glands have been exposed on the specimens. Identify those exocrine glands of the digestive system which have been exposed on your cadaver. For each gland, list the <u>type</u> of product it secretes. Types of exocrine products include serous (watery) fluid, mucous, a mixture of serous fluid and mucous, or an oily secretion. Since the information about glandular product must be found in a reference and is not able to be determined by observation, complete this portion of the following table either before lab or after. During lab, only indicate whether the listed structures were or were not found on your cadaver.

Found?	Exocrine gland	Type of exocrine product
Yes / No	Parotid gland	mucous serous mixed oily
Yes / No	Submandibular gland	mucous serous mixed oily
Yes / No	Sublingual gland	mucous serous mixed oily
Yes / No	Pancreas	mucous serous mixed oily
Yes / No	Liver	mucous serous mixed oily

Of those structures identified above as exocrine glands, which ones show the classic, broken texture characteristic of a gland?

_____

Be prepared to demonstrate these glands to your instructor if asked.

5. You have already examined the peritoneal folds called mesenteries that either attach organs to the abdominal wall and attach one or several organ(s) to another. Recall that such mesenteries are <u>doubled-layered</u> serous membranes. Examine them carefully again so that you clearly understand their "double" nature. By letting your finger pass from the parietal peritoneum of the dorsal body wall to and around the small intestine and back to the dorsal surface, you should be able to verify the double-layered nature of these serous membranes. By palpation and visual observation, what tissues or structures appear to be housed within these double-layered membranes?

_____

_____

Consider all that you have observed, hypothesize as to the various functions of these double-layered membranes.

_____

_____

_____

_____

Be prepared to demonstrate double-layered membranes (mesenteries) to your instructor and to justify your answers by pointing out specific aspects of anatomy associated with these folds.

6. The main space within the peritoneal cavity is called the greater peritoneal sac. However, there is a smaller space known as the lesser peritoneal sac or omental bursa. If all serous membranes are intact, the lesser sac may only be entered through a small passageway in the right upper quadrant called the epiploic foramen of Winslow. By careful palpation, try to find and navigate the foramen of Winslow into the lesser sac. It is located dorsal to the hepatoduodenal ligament and the common bile duct. If you are successful in doing this, answer the questions which follow based on your exploration. If you have been unsuccessful, use the reference books which are available in lab to determine where this space is and to answer the following questions.
From the following list of organs, select the organ(s) which fit each statement:
liver - spleen - pancreas - transverse colon - greater omentum - stomach

What organ forms its ventral border? _____

What organ forms its dorsal border? _____

What organ forms its superior border? _____

What organ forms its inferior border? _____

What organ forms its extreme left lateral border? _____

When your finger is positioned within the lesser sac, where is it relative to the greater omentum?
　　　___ Dorsal to it?　___ Ventral to it?　___ Between its layers?

Be prepared to demonstrate the lesser sac and its boundaries to your instructor.

7. In the Language of Anatomy worksheet you were introduced to the concept of a mesentery, what we have been calling a double-layered membrane for clarity. Direct your attention to the double-layered membrane (mesentery which anchors and supports the small intestine. It may not be fully intact on all cadavers. Depending on the extent of ventral body cavity dissection in your specimen, it may have been cut and partially (or completely) destroyed. This double-layered membrane which anchors the small intestine originates from the parietal peritoneum on the dorsal body wall and <u>continues around</u> the small intestine before returning to the dorsal body wall. This dorsal connection, the root of the mesentery, extends diagonally left to right from superior to inferior. It is best viewed from the left side of the cadaver after reflecting the small intestine toward the right side. By careful inspection, you should be able to determine the abdominopelvic regions in which the superior and inferior ends of the root are found.

Superior end of root: _____

Inferior end of root: _____

Approximately how long (inches) is the root of the mesentery? _____

What would be the consequence if the mesentery failed to develop at all?

_____

You should be prepared demonstrate the root of the mesentery and its extent to your instructor.

The intestinal border of the mesentery actually connects to the entire length of the jejunum and ileum. First locate the start of the jejunum by locating the superior end of the root of the mesentery. This is the point at which the duodenum emerges from behind the parietal peritoneum and becomes the jejunum. Follow the jejunum and ileum from proximal to distal and roughly estimate the length of the intestinal border in feet? There are rulers available for you to use in doing this. How does this compare to the length of the root of the mesentery? As a result of this considerable difference in length between the root of the mesentery and the intestinal border of the mesentery, how is the small intestine arranged within the abdominal cavity?

_____

8. Examine the entire intestinal tract (from proximal to distal) in your specimen. Can you distinguish between the large and the small intestine? Yes / No
What is the main structural feature that you notice to distinguish large from small intestine?
_____

Demonstrate for your instructor where the small intestine ends and the large intestine begins. What is the name given to this junction point?

_____

Describe the appearance of the small intestine. _____

_____

_____

Describe the appearance of the large intestine. _____

_____

_____

Compare the two.
How are they <u>structurally</u> similar? _____

_____

_____

_____

How are they <u>structurally</u> different? _____

_____

_____

_____

67

9. This next is a difficult assignment. The small intestine is composed of three different regions (duodenum, jejunum, and ileum) which may not appear obviously different on gross inspection. Since the duodenum is retroperitoneal, we will ignore it for this assignment. Carefully trace the small bowel from proximal to distal and try to determine whether there is/are some observable difference(s) in appearance that will allow one portion (jejunem) to be distinguished from the other (ileum). Come to consensus within your group and record your findings below. Be prepared to share your insights with your instructor.

Listed below are structural features you might consider in your examination. Circle your choices.

Diameter - which is greater?   jejunem / ileum / can't tell

Wall thickness - which is thicker when pinched between 2 fingers?   jejunem / ileum / can't tell

External wrinkles or creases - which has more?   jejunem / ileum / can't tell

Thickness of the mesentery - which is thicker?   jejunem / ileum / can't tell

Amount of adipose along the border - which has more?   jejunem / ileum / can't tell

Is the diameter of the jejunum consistent along its entire length?   Yes / No

Is the diameter of the ileum consistent along its entire length?   Yes / No

Is there a clear, distinct and abrupt transition from jejunum to ileum or is there a more subtle, gradual transition from one to the other?

            ___ abrupt and distinct   ___ subtle and gradual

Lastly and only if time allows, examine a second cadaver. Are the findings from your specimen consistent with those from a different specimen?   Yes / No

10. Lastly, there are a number of organ specimens (wet preserved and plastinated) and models on display in the laboratory which include structural modifications that serve to increase surface area, and by doing that, increase the functional efficiency of a given digestive organ. Such things as folds of tissue, wrinkles, projections, creases, increases in length all can increase surface area. Describe each of the listed structures which are being displayed here.

   Rugae of the stomach _____

   Plicae circulares of small intestine _____

   Villi of small intestine _____

   Papillae of tongue _____

   Which digestive organs use length as a means to increase surface area?

   _____

Part 2: Location, Identification, and Demonstration of Specific Organs and Structures

The following is a list of specific digestive system structures for which you are responsible. Some of these structures are not exposed on any of the cadavers and must be observed on a model or a separate preserved specimen. Some of these structures are visible on all of the cadavers, and a few may be visible only on two or even just one of the cadavers. You should proceed through this exercise as efficiently and quickly as possible using your assigned cadaver. Once you have located and identified all the structures that you can using your specimen, proceed to the separate specimens and to other cadavers to complete the exercise.

Important: You **must** come to this lab having already "located" each of the following structures in your text, lab manual, or other reference. Each student is expected to have already compiled information on each of the listed structures (what they are, where they're located, what they connect, etc.) so that the actual work with the specimens can be completed within the allotted time. There is space provided on the pages which follow for you to jot down your notes as you are preparing for this lab. These notes will be invaluable in allowing you complete this assignment.

Note: **Students who are unprepared and, because of this, adversely affect the progress of their group in completing this exercise may be asked to leave. Such students will be given a zero for the assigned work of the day.**

Structures You Must Be Able to Name and Identify

A. Head and Neck:
Use either the preserved sagittal sections of the head and neck or the sagittal section model of the head to find the following structures. Note: This portion of the exercise may be put off to last since you can have very easy access to the sagittal head models and specimens at any time that the lab is open. Use the lined spaces provided to enter any details or observations that will help you to better remember each structure and locate it in the future. The unlined space to the right allows you to add drawings (if you choose) that will help you to remember the structures you are studying.

hard palate _____

soft palate, uvula _____

_____

tonsils (see models for palatine and pharyngeal tonsils)
    palatine _____

    pharyngeal _____

    lingual _____

tongue _____

_____

    papillae _____

pharynx
    oropharynx _____

    nasopharynx _____

    laryngopharynx (hypopharynx) _____

opening for Eustachian tube _____

_____

epiglottis _____

_____

origin of esophagus _____

    upper esophageal sphincter _____

parotid gland _____

    parotid duct _____

submandibular gland _____

B. Ventral Body Cavity
Although each cadaver's ventral body cavity is opened and accessible, some of the listed organs that you must locate and examine may not be exposed in the full cadavers. For such organs/structures, you will need to utilize special specimens that your instructor will make available. As above, use the lined spaces provided to enter any details or observations that will help you to better remember each structure and locate it in the future. The unlined space to the right allows you to add drawings (if you choose) that will help you to remember the structures you are studying.

esophagus _____

diaphragm _____

    esophageal hiatus _____

greater omentum _____

stomach _____

    cardia _____

    fundus _____

    body (corpus) _____

    pylorus _____

    pyloric sphincter _____

    greater curvature _____

    lesser curvature _____

        rugae _____

   duodenum _____

        plicae circulares _____

        villi _____

        hepatoduodenal papilla (major duodenal papilla)

_____

_____

liver _____

_____

        falciform ligament (remnant) _____

        round ligament (ligamentum teres) _____

        left lobe _____

        right lobe _____

        caudate lobe _____

        quadrate lobe _____

        porta hepatis _____

_____

        coronary ligaments (remnants) _____

_____

        bare area of liver _____

_____

lesser omentum (remnants) _____

_____

biliary system
- gall bladder _____
- cystic duct _____
- hepatic duct _____
- common bile duct _____

pancreas _____
_____
- head _____
- body _____
- tail _____
- pancreatic duct system _____

spleen (not a digestive organ) _____
_____
- diaphragmatic surface _____
- visceral surface _____
- hilum _____
- gastrosplenic ligament _____

greater omentum _____

gastrocolic ligament _____

small intestine _____
_____
_____
- duodenal jejunal junction _____
- jejunum _____

ileum _____

mesentery of jejunum and ileum _____

ileocecal junction _____

_____

large intestine _____

_____

_____

cecum _____

vermiform appendix _____

ascending colon _____

transverse colon _____

transverse mesocolon _____

descending colon _____

sigmoid colon _____

sigmoid mesocolon _____

hepatic flexure _____

splenic flexure _____

haustrae _____

teniae coli _____

epiploic appendages _____

rectum. _____

Exercise A-4

Human Skeletal System

Introduction

During today's lab exercise you will begin work on the human skeletal system. Your approach to this material is twofold.

The "Identification Responsibilities" sheets of this exercise list the details and structures of skeletal anatomy which you are required to master and identify. Please note that mastery of these structures often goes beyond simply placing a name with an item to be identified but may also include an ability to correctly orient a particular element of skeletal anatomy.

Each week's work also involves a collection of short assignments designed to guide you and challenge you in your inspection and analysis of the skeletal materials. Each student is responsible for completing these questions/assignments before leaving lab. It is not necessary to hand them in. Rather, your instructor will assess your progress on these tasks as the lab progresses and require each of you to demonstrate mastery of isolated portions of the overall exercise.

Skeletal Lab A-4 Part 1: First week

Today's work will concentrate on the general structure of vertebrae and the vertebral column, the sternum, and ribs. If time allows, you should also begin the identification of individual skull bones, both separately and in intact specimens, and determine right/left orientation for four specific skull bones.

Skeletal Lab A-4 Part 2: Second week

During the second week, you will continue with your study of the skull and identify selected processes, depressions, cavities, and foramina as required. You will also study the appendicular skeleton (the limb girdles and the upper and lower extremities).

Exercise A-4 Part 1 - Axial Skeleton

The Spinal Column: The central axis of the body is formed from a column of individual irregular bones called vertebrae. This column is divided into several regions. The portion of the spine comprising the neck is the cervical region (7 vertebrae). The portion associated with the rib cage is the thoracic spine (12 vertebrae). The lower back is the lumbar region (5 vertebrae) and the portion that is included as part of the pelvic girdle is the sacrum (5 fused vertebrae). The most inferior portion of the spine is the tiny tail bone or coccyx (4 fused vertebrae). When viewed from the side, the spine is not a straight vertical column. Rather from top to bottom, it is composed of a series of alternating (anterior-posterior-anterior-posterior) curvatures. These curves make the spinal column a more stable central axis and a more efficient anchor for muscles that move the trunk and allow us to maintain an upright posture.

1. You will be provided with a tray of selected vertebrae. In the space provided and based only on your observation of the actual specimens available in lab, list five structural features that you observe these vertebrae have in common. Initially for this task, do not use any reference to complete this activity. Simply look at the bones and identify and describe any common structures (even though at this point you cannot name these structures). Write your 5 observations in the spaqces provided below. After you have described 5 structural similarities, open a reference (an atlas, not a textbook) to name the structures you have just described. Be prepared to share these observations with your instructor when asked.

    1) _____
    2) _____
    3) _____
    4) _____
    5) _____

2. You will be given a small tray containing 4 vertebrae representing the cervical, thoracic and lumbar regions. By comparing each with the vertebrae on the skeletons or on the intact spinal columns, you should be able to assign each to one of the three spinal regions. As before, do not use a reference to assist you with this activity. Once you have done that, check with your instructor to insure that your observations are correct.

    Next, in the space provided and again based only on your observation of the actual specimens, list at least one distinguishing structural feature that you found for each of the three types of vertebrae (cervical, thoracic, lumbar). Basically, your task here is to devise an approach that will allow you to identify cervical, thoracic, and lumbar vertebrae with 100% accuracy. This is easier than it may seem initially but it requires that you look carefully at vertebrae and come to a clear understanding about what truly distinguishes vertebrae of one region from another. Hint: Look at each region and think what do vertebrae of that region have (or lack) that those in the other two regions have (or lack). Again, <u>do not use a reference to complete this activity</u>. Be prepared to demonstrate these to your instructor if asked. Also, expect to be given vertebrae at random and asked to categorize them.

cervical _____

_____

_____

thoracic _____

_____

_____

lumbar _____

_____

_____

3. Examine a representative rib from the collection provided and identify its parts. Orient it so that you can identify its superior and inferior edges and its anterior and posterior ends. Determine if this rib is from the right side or the left side of the body. Record in the spaces below what details of structure you key on to orient a rib. Be sure you can do this with any other rib in the collection. Use any of the skeletons to verify your answers.

Superior edge _____

Inferior edge _____

Anterior end _____

Posterior end _____

Now examine the rib further to determine the number of points at which the rib contacts the vertebral column. You should probably start by examining one of the middle ribs on an intact skeleton to see how the rib connects to the vertebral column. Note: Whenever bones meet or join, there will be a smooth articular facet. How many such facets can you find? (Be sure to examine both the end of the rib and the tubercle of the rib.) Be prepared to point it/them out to your instructor if asked.

Number of articulation facets <u>on a middle rib</u>.   1   2   3   4   5

Now examine a vertebra from the upper or middle thoracic region.
Can you find facets <u>on the vertebra</u> where it contacts a rib? Yes / No
How many facets are there on one side?   1   2   3   4

How many vertebrae does one rib articulate with?   1   2   3

Record the precise location of each facet on the vertebra.

_____

_____

Using one of the skeletons as a guide, determine precisely how a rib attaches to the vertebral column. For this do not use vertebrae or ribs from the very top or bottom of the thoracic region. Complete the following statement:

The head of the rib articulates with the _____ of the vertebra(ae)

and the tubercle of the rib articulates with the _____ of the vertebra

Demonstrate for your instructor as specifically as you can how a rib attaches to a thoracic vertebra. Pay particular attention to the articular portion of the rib's tubercle.

4. Identify the costal groove of the rib. Describe its location on the rib.

_____

What anatomic structures can be found within this groove?

_____

To assist you in this, there may be a cadaver or a separate spinal column which has been prepared specifically to illustrate the groove and its accompanying structures. If available, examine these specimens carefully. Be prepared to demonstrate this structure to your instructor if asked.

In the clinical setting it is sometimes necessary to insert a tube through the chest wall (on the midaxillary line) to evacuate air, blood, or other fluid that has collected within the chest but outside the lung. In performing this procedure, the surgeon uses the top of a rib as a guide in making the incision and inserting the tube. The insertion instrument rubs along the top of the rib as it passes through the chest wall. Based on what you now know of the anatomy, does this make sense? Yes / No

Explain. _____

_____

5. Using one of the human sternums available in the lab, draw in the space below an illustration that indicates as specifically as you can whether and where each of the following bones attaches to the sternum. Be prepared to demonstrate these articulations to your instructor if asked.

       clavicle
       scapula
       first rib
       second rib
       4th rib
       12th rib

6. By making two simple measurements of the sternum, it is possible to make an informed "guess" about the sex of the individual to whom the bone once belonged. Remember that a determination that evaluates one such skeletal characteristic is not foolproof and does not definitively determine the gender of the individual from whom this bone came. Rather it provides one isolated piece of evidence supporting a particular gender.

First, identify the three parts of the sternum (manubrium, body, xiphoid process). In the space below and to the right, draw and label a simple diagram.
Do different sternums show consistent structure?
Size   Yes / No
Thickness   Yes / No
Texture   Yes / No
Shape   Yes / No

Use the following guidelines to assess the sex of the paired sternums in our collection and those on the real bone skeletons.

Likely Male:
2X length of manubrium < Body of sternum

Likely Female:
2X length of manubrium => Body of sternum

Likely sex of the sternums:

Sternum # ____   Body _____ cm   Manubrium _____ cm   male / female

Sternum # ____   Body _____ cm   Manubrium _____ cm   male / female

Sternum # ____   Body _____ cm   Manubrium _____ cm   male / female

Sternum # ____   Body _____ cm   Manubrium _____ cm   male / female

7. Next identify all skull bones (including the mandible) using intact skulls as well as the disarticulated skull bones. You will find the color-coded and labeled plastic skulls and the exploded skull specimens very helpful for this as you start. Once you feel sure that you have the bones of the skull mastered, demonstrate this for your instructor.

8. Each student is expected to be able to determine the side of the body to which selected paired skulls bones belong. These are the temporal, parietal, and zygomatic bones, and the maxillae.

By matching individual disarticulated bones with the intact or exploded skulls, you should first determine whether the bone you are evaluating is from the right or the left side. Once you are satisfied that you are correct, you should then determine what structural cues will allow you to accurately repeat this determination. Be prepared to describe your approach and demonstrate this determination for your instructor if asked.

Indicate the structures you key on or the approach you use in determining side for each of these bones.

Maxilla: _____

_____

_____

Temporal: _____
_____
_____

Parietal: _____
_____
_____

Zygomatic: _____
_____
_____

Exercise A-4 Part 2: Skull (continued) and Appendicular Skeleton

1. There are a number of fetal skulls available in lab. Examine them carefully. Identify the four different fontanels (2 are paired, 2 are unpaired). Use the box below on the right to illustrate these fontanels.

   _____

   _____

   _____

   _____

   Look at the unpaired bones of the skull on the exploded adult skulls, specifically the occipital bone, frontal bone, and mandible. Then carefully examine these same unpaired bones on the fetal skulls. Which, if any, initially develop from 2 separate bones which fuse during development.

   Occipital bone: develops from   1 bone / 2 bones

   Frontal bone: develops from   1 bone / 2 bones

   Mandible: develops from   1 bone / 2 bones

   Lastly, examine the state of closure for each of the fontanels you have now identified. Based on your findings, arrange the skulls in order (by letter) from least developed to most developed. Be prepared to explain the basis for your order to your instructor.

   Most developed _____   Least developed _____

   Once you have completed this, you should determine from this sequencing which fontanel typically closes first and which fontanel typically closes last.

   Fontanel closure: First _____

                       Last   _____

   Be prepared to demonstrate these determinations to your instructor if asked.

2. Each student should locate and identify the structural components of the skull that are listed below. You should also know the basic functional significance for each. For example, you might indicate the muscle that uses a particular process as an attachment point or the vessel or nerve that passes through a particular foramen. Be prepared to demonstrate these structures to your instructor if asked and to describe the function of each.

crista galli _____

mandibular condyle _____

orbital fissure _____

foramen magnum _____

jugular foramen _____

hypoglossal canal _____

hypophyseal fossa _____

dens (odontoid process) _____

optic foramen _____

mastoid process _____

3. The paranasal sinuses are air-filled cavities in some bones of the skull. They are lined by mucous membranes and help to moisten inspired air and lighten the skull. Fluid that collects in these chambers drains into the nasal cavity by tiny openings beneath the conchae. Sinus infections are often accompanied by characteristic pain symptoms or patterns. Use the sectioned skulls and disarticulated skull bones to identify the following sinuses: maxillary, sphenoidal, frontal, ethmoidal. Based on this, which sinus is likely inflamed when an individual experiences:

what appears to be a toothache in an upper tooth? _____

pain above the eyes? _____

pain or pressure between the eyes? _____

4. Sexual Dimorphism of the Skull:
It is well documented that there are significant and consistent differences in skull anatomy between males and females. This is referred to as sexual dimorphism. Therefore, using a variety of anatomical landmarks and details, it is possible to make an "educated guess" as to the sex of a human skull. Below is a list of anatomical features to use in this determination and a simple scoring scheme to use in completing this exercise. The most reliable determination is made using all of these features.

You will be assigned a pair of skulls to analyze. Determine the likely sex of each specimen by evaluating and scoring each of the features listed below. Use the score sheet which follows to record your observations.

Trait	Male	Female
General Appearance	rugged, bumpy, irregular	delicate, smooth
Cranium		
Parietal eminences	smaller	larger
Supraorbital (brow) ridges	medium/large	medium/small
Orbit		
Shape	squared	rounded
Margins	rounded, blunt edges	sharp edges
Cheekbones		
Size	larger	smaller
Zygomatic ridge	extends beyond external auditory meatus	extends to external auditory meatus
Palate	broad, U-shape	narrow, parabola
Mandible		
Size & Shape	large, squared chin	small, pointed chin
Angle	< 125 degrees	> 125 degrees
Inferior Surface		
External Occipital Protuberance	marked, obvious	slight, indistinct
Mastoid Process	larger	smaller

Adapted from Krogman (1962) and Bass (1987)

Name: _____

Exercise A-4 Part 2 (#4)

Put your scores for your selected skulls in the spaces below. Your instructor may elect to collect your sheet.

Sexual Dimorphism of the Skull
Score Sheet
Assign +1 if male; -1 if female; 0 if unclear.
Total >0 indicates male; <0 indicates female.

Skull ID	_____	_____	_____
General Appearance	_____	_____	_____
Cranium			
Parietal eminences	_____	_____	_____
Supraorbital ridges	_____	_____	_____
Orbit			
Shape	_____	_____	_____
Margins	_____	_____	_____
Cheekbones			
Size	_____	_____	_____
Zygomatic ridge	_____	_____	_____
Palate	_____	_____	_____
Mandible			
Size & Shape	_____	_____	_____
Angle	_____	_____	_____
Inferior Surface			
External Occipital Protuberance	_____	_____	_____
Mastoid Process	_____	_____	_____
Total Score	_____	_____	_____
Interpretation	_____	_____	_____

adapted from R. Smoes

5. Sexual Dimorphism of the Pelvis

It is well documented that there are significant and consistent differences in pelvic structure between males and females. That of the female is of course modified to facilitate the childbirth process while that of the male is designed to serve as a strong base to support much of the body's weight and as a firm anchor for some of the body's strongest muscles. Refer to your text or some other suitable reference to obtain a list of structural features that you can use to distinguish a male pelvis from that of a female. Then, using the pair of the human pelves provided, determine which specimen is more likely from a male and which is more likely from a female. In doing this, you should be able to identify and score all the structural features which are referenced in the grid which follows. You should be prepared to demonstrate these to your instructor if asked.

Sexual Dimorphism of the Pelvis

Trait	Male	Female
General Appearance		
Bone Thickness	Thicker	Thinner
Muscle Attachments	Prominent, obvious	Less prominent
Pelvic Inlet (Brim)	Heart-shaped	Oval or kidney bean shaped
Sacrum		
A-P Curvature	Pronounced ventrally	Straighter/less curved
Sacral Promontory	More ventral	Less pronounced
Pelvic Outlet		
Ischial tuberosities	Oriented medially	Oriented laterally
	Closer together	Farther apart
Subpubic Angle (Angle of Pubic Arch)	$> 90°$	$< 90°$
Acetabula		
Size	Larger	Smaller
Greater Sciatic Notch	Wider	Narrow
	Loose around thumb	Tight around thumb
Iliosacral Space	Wide; > 2 fingerwidths	Narrow; < 2 fingers

Exercise A-4 Part 2 (#5):
Sexual Dimorphism of the Pelvis Score Sheet
        Assign +1 if male; -1 if female; 0 if unclear.
        Total >0 indicates male; <0 indicates female.

Pelvis ID   _____   _____   _____

General
   Bone Thickness   _____   _____   _____
   Muscle Markings   _____   _____   _____

Pelvic Inlet (Brim)   _____   _____   _____

Sacrum
   A-P Curvature   _____   _____   _____
   Sacral Promontory   _____   _____   _____

Pelvic Outlet
   Ischial tuberosities   _____   _____   _____

Subpubic Angle   _____   _____   _____
(Angle of Pubic Arch)

Acetabula
   Size   _____   _____   _____

Greater Sciatic Notch   _____   _____   _____

Iliosacral Space   _____   _____   _____

Total Score   _____   _____   _____

Interpretation   _____   _____   _____

    In addition to the pelves which are provided there are several pairs of os coxae and human sacrums. Using the pelves which you have already "sexed" as references, your instructor may direct you to try to determine the sex of these bones as well. In doing so, focus your attention on those structural features from the preceding list that relate to these specific bones.

    Sacrum ID _____   Male / Female   _____

    Sacrum ID _____   Male / Female   _____

    Os coxa ID _____   Male / Female   _____

    Os coxa ID _____   Male / Female   _____

6. Variations in Long Bone Anatomy
For this activity, there are several pairs of long bones that have been set aside for your examination. Some of these bones are separate, disarticulated specimens while others have been labeled on one or more of the real human skeletons that are displayed in the lab. For paired bones from the same individual, we will use the skeletons. For paired bones that came from different individuals, we will use the disarticulated specimens. For each pair of bones, one or two questions are posed which require you to carefully examine elements of structural detail. Compare them and make an educated guess. Be prepared to share your answers with your instructor <u>and to defend your conclusions</u>.

Tibia
Which bone likely came from the taller individual? _____

Which bone was likely acted on by the stronger quadriceps muscles? _____

Humerus
Which bone likely came from the taller individual? _____

Humerus
Which bone likely indicates this person's dominant side? _____

Radius
Which bone likely came from a female? _____

Which bone was likely acted on by the stronger biceps muscle? _____

7. Bones of the Upper and Lower Extremities: Distinguishing Right from Left
You should also be able to determine right or left for any of the individual bones of the extremities if asked. The best way to start developing your skill at this is to take an individual bone and match it to its equivalent on one of the skeletons. Once you are sure of what side it belongs to, you can key on specific structural elements that relate to each of its three dimensions. First pick out something that lets you distinguish proximal from distal or superior from inferior. Then find a structure (maybe it's the same one) that lets you distinguish anterior from posterior and then pick one that separates medial from lateral. If you orient the bone exactly based on the above, you should consistently come to the correct conclusion.

Another helpful approach you might consider once you feel that you are pretty successful in determining right or left is to place individual bones in a bag. This is not a requirement for you, merely an approach to help you to fine tune your powers of observation. If you can identify the bone and whether it's right or left by feel, you have truly mastered this part of the exercise. Document what you "key" on in determining right or left for each of the bones of the extremities.

Lower Extremity:

    Os coxa _____

_____

    Femur _____

_____

    Tibia _____

_____

    Fibula _____

_____

Upper Extremity:

    Scapula _____

_____

    Humerus _____

_____

    Radius _____

_____

    Ulna _____

_____

Bones of the Upper and Lower Extremities: Constructing an Extremity
Now using the sets of bones that have been selected by your instructor, you should assemble a complete upper and a complete lower extremity (not including the wrist/hand or ankle/foot). Completing this task will require that you not only know which bones you need for an upper and for a lower extremity but also that you can orient each one as to right and left. That means that you must be able to recognize bones that do not belong with that limb or with that side of the body. You should be prepared to demonstrate this for your instructor if asked.

Assembling an upper/lower extremity: Indicate the bone IDs in the spaces below.

Upper extremity: Right / Left ____ ____ ____ ____

Lower extremity: Right / Left ____ ____ ____ ____

Skeletal System
IDENTIFICATION RESPONSIBILITIES

Questions concerning the skeletal system material concern: General skeletal plan, including the names of most bones and the proximal and distal articulations of all long bones. Note: Your instructor may choose to add other structures to this list.

Axial Skeleton
Skull:
all individual bones except wrist/hand & ankle/foot (separately and in intact specimens);
right/left orientation of maxilla, temporal, parietal and zygomatic bones;
major sutures (sagittal, frontal/coronal, lamdoidal, squamosal)
fontanels (anterior/frontal, posterior/occipital, anterolateral/sphenoidal, posterolateral/mastoid);
sinuses (frontal, maxillary, sphenoidal, ethmoid air cells).

processes/ridges/eminences
parietal eminences - external occipital protuberance - occipital condyles - mastoid process - supraorbital (brow) ridge - zygomatic process - zygomatic arch/ridge - mandibular symphysis - mandibular ramus - mandibular condyle - crista galli, perpendicular plate of ethmoid.

depressions/cavities/foramina –
foramen magnum - superior/inferior orbital fissure - optic foramen - foramen ovale - jugular foramen - hypoglossal canal, external auditory meatus - internal auditory meatus - hypophyseal fossa - cribiform plate.

Vertebrae:
atlas (C1), axis (C2), sacrum, coccyx
generic cervical, thoracic and lumbar vertebrae

processes/ridges/eminences - body, spinous process, transverse process, pedicles, odontoid process (dens), laminae, superior and inferior articulating facets, sacral promontory.

depressions/cavities/foramina - spinal (vertebral) foramen, intervertebral foramen, transverse foramen, sacral canal, dorsal sacral foramina.

Other Bones:
sternum - manubrium, body, xiphoid, sternal (jugular) notch, sternal angle of Louis, xiphisternal junction; male/female.
ribs - R/L, articular facets, articular portion of tubercle, costal groove).
hyoid.

Appendicular Skeleton
- Shoulder and Upper Extremities:

    clavicle, scapula, humerus, radius, ulna [right or left, proximal/distal portion, anterior/posterior surfaces, medial/lateral surfaces].

    carpals, metacarpals, phalanges (generally by group only).

    processes/ridges/eminences/ depressions/cavities/foramina:
    - scapula - spine, acromiom process, coracoid process, glenoid cavity, axillary/vertebral border.
    - humerus - head, greater/lesser tubercle, deltoid tuberosity, medial/lateral epicondyle, olecranon fossa, coronoid fossa, intertubercular groove.
    - radius - head, radial tuberosity, styloid process
    - ulna - olecranon process, coronoid process, radial (semilunar) notch, styloid process.

- Pelvis & Lower Extremities:

    os coxae (ilium, ischium, pubis), femur, tibia, fibula, [right or left, proximal/distal portion, anterior/posterior surfaces, medial/lateral surfaces].

    tarsals, metatarsals, phalanges (calcaneus & talus by name; others only generally by group).

    processes/ridges/eminences/depressions/cavities/foramina:
    - os coxa - symphysis pubis, acetabulum, iliac crest, tubercle of iliac crest, anterior superior iliac spine, anterior inferior iliac spine, greater sciatic notch, ischial spine, ischial tuberosity, puboischial ramus.
    - femur - head, neck, greater/lesser trochanter, intertrocanteric line/crest, gluteal tuberosity, linea aspera, patellar groove, lateral/medial condyles.
    - tibia - lateral/medial condyles, tibial tuberosity, medial malleolus.
    - fibula - head, lateral malleolus.

Exercise A-5

A Representative Bony Articulation: The Knee

Introduction

Joints are sites where two or more bones meet. Some joints allow no movement at all. Cranial sutures and tooth sockets are examples of this type. Others allow only a very small amount of movement. The symphysis pubis is an example of this functional category. The last and largest category are freely moveable synovial joints and are represented by a number of different specific designs ranging from ball and socket joints (hip and shoulder) to hinge joints (elbow and knee) to pivot joints (radius and ulna), among others. Rather than try to explore the entire range of bony articulations in one session (something that could occupy an entire semester of lab by itself), we will focus on the knee joint as a representative freely moveable joint.

The knee is an ideal joint for study in a human anatomy lab experience because it is a joint that is easily accessible on cadaver specimens without undue disruption of neighboring muscles and tendons. Also, because the specimens tend to be from older individuals and because the knee is a joint that "takes a pounding" during everyday activities, the knees that are available for student study often exhibit a wide range of normal variation, changes due to "wear and tear", and pathology. Because the movements of the knee joint are limited, it is easier for students to understand the specific role of each ligament in providing the mix of stability and mobility that characterizes the knee. The four ligaments that hold the knee together are distinct entities, each separate from the other, unlike what is seen in some joints (ie. shoulder) where some ligaments seem to merge with others and are much more difficult to isolate and identify, especially if trying to minimize associated muscle damage. Lastly, because it is so easy to enter the joint capsule without damaging the four main ligaments of the knee, it is also possible to selectively cut one of the ligaments and allow students to assess for themselves the impact of such an injury.

We are fortunate to have available for our examination of the knee plastinated human knee joints in addition to a number of working plastic models. Students will begin their study of the knee using these to identify the relevant bones, muscles, tendons, ligaments, and cartilaginous structures. A list of the essential structures that each student must master follows: quadriceps muscle, quadriceps tendon, patellar ligament, medial meniscus, lateral meniscus, anterior cruciate ligament, posterior cruciate ligament, tibial (medial) collateral ligament, fibular (lateral) collateral ligament, transverse ligament, and articular cartilages.

1. Examine the plastinated specimens and the models which are available. For each, indicate whether it is a right or a left knee.

2. Examine the bony components that make up the knee joint. It is essentially a bone with a rounded distal end resting atop a bone with a flat proximal end. Because of this, it is a joint held together entirely by soft tissue structures. Besides the ligaments, are there any structures which enhance the stability of the joint by keeping the 2 bones together and properly positioned? Yes / No
If yes, identify them and describe how they enhance stability.

_____

_____

_____

Be prepared to share your observations with your instructor.

3. Now turn your attention to the four ligaments that hold the knee together. For each you should be able to describe how it stabilizes the joint. More specifically, be able to describe how it prevents the femur from moving on the tibia and also how it prevents the tibia from moving under the femur.

   Medial collateral ligament:
       What movement of the tibia is prevented? _____

       What movement of the femur is prevented? _____

   Lateral collateral ligament:
       What movement of the tibia is prevented? _____

       What movement of the femur is prevented? _____

   Anterior cruciate ligament:
       What movement of the tibia is prevented? _____

       What movement of the femur is prevented? _____

   Posterior cruciate ligament:
       What movement of the tibia is prevented? _____

       What movement of the femur is prevented? _____

   Be prepared to demonstrate these using the plastinated specimens or plastic models if asked.

4. Often when a collateral ligament is torn, there is an accompanying meniscal injury (tear). Examine the medial and lateral collateral ligaments and their associated menisci. Based on your examination of the anatomy, is a meniscal tear more likely to accompany a tear of the medial collateral ligament or the lateral collateral ligament. Or do you think a meniscal injury is equally likely with each?

   ____ more likely with medial collateral ligament injury
   ____ more likely with lateral collateral ligament injury
   ____ equally likely with either injury

5. Next examine several dissected knees on the cadavers. In most specimens both knees are opened. Be able to identify the articular surfaces, tendons, ligaments, and menisci. Based on your examination, are both knees healthy or do one or both of them show degenerative signs of aging and/or disease? Describe your findings.

   _____

   _____

   _____

   Anterior collateral ligament injury: Often one knee will remain with all ligaments intact while the other will have one of the four (usually the ACL) purposely severed. Injury to a ligament will disrupt stability of the knee. Since the ACL is likely cut on at least one of the specimens, you should focus on it.

   Based on your examination of the knee, develop an approach to assessing the anterior cruciate ligament to determine if it is intact.

   _____

   _____

   _____

   What would be the assessment findings in the case of an intact ACL vs and injured (torn) ACL?

   _____

   _____

   Patella:
   Sesamoid bones are ones which develop within tendons. Based on your examination, is the patella an example of such a bone?   Yes / No
   Describe the position of the patella when the knee is in the extended position and when the knee is flexed.

Extended _____

Flexed _____

Along what bone does it move? _____

If an individual had a difference in the relative strengths of the vastus lateralis and the vastus medialis, could the tracking of the patella be impacted? Yes / No
If yes, what might be the consequence?
_____

Exercise A-6

Muscles of the Trunk and Shoulder

Introduction

The skeletal musculature of the human includes something in excess of 600 different muscles. Your study of muscles will focus on a relatively small selection of these, most of which tend to be more central or proximal in location. In the course of your work with these muscles, you will be expected to identify them, their proximal and distal (or medial and lateral) attachments, and the movements caused by their contraction. Remember that muscles can only do one thing - contract. When they contract, they therefore pull on a bone or other attachment structure. Because of this, skeletal muscles work in opposing pairs or groups. Muscles in different regions of the body and involving different joints will be pinned for your study. To facilitate your work, some of the more superficial muscles have been cut so that they may be easily reflected and deeper muscles can be exposed, viewed and manipulated.

Also, as you determine attachment points for the various muscles you will study, realize that you will be expected to master specific elements of skeletal anatomy. The preceding list of skeletal landmarks and details contained in exercise 4 includes many (probably not all) of the specific structures that act as points of attachment for the muscles you will be studying. You can utilize your textbook or other resources to determine origins and insertions but you are probably best served if you **first** try to determine attachment points by careful observation and palpation. Understanding and appreciating subtle movements caused by muscle contraction requires that you be familiar with precise points of attachment and the path by which the muscle fibers reach these points. Be focused and precise in your observations. When finished, you should be prepared to demonstrate for your instructor your answers to the many questions that are posed during this exercise.

Also in preparation for lab exercise, you should review the information in your textbook pertaining to the muscles listed below.

Muscles of the Anterolateral Neck
    Sternocleidomastoid
Muscles of Thorax
    External Intercostals   Internal Intercostals
Muscles of the Anterior & Lateral Abdominal Wall
    External Oblique   Internal Oblique
    Rectus Abdominis   Transverse Abdominis
Muscles of Anterior & Posterior Thorax: Movement of the Scapula
    Trapezius   Pectoralis Minor   Serratus Anterior
    Levator Scapulae   Rhomboideus Major   Rhomboideus Minor
Muscles Crossing Shoulder Joint: Movement of the Arm
    Pectoralis Major   Deltoid   Latissimus Dorsi
    Subscapularis   Supraspinatus   Infraspinatus
    Teres Major   Teres Minor

1. Prior to lab, you should look up and be familiar with the following terms:

Agonist _____

_____

Antagonist _____

_____

Origin _____

Origins tend to be: lateral / medial   proximal / distal
                           extensive / focused   multiple / single

Insertion _____

Insertions tend to be: lateral / medial   proximal / distal
                              extensive / focused   multiple / single

Action _____

Flexion _____

_____

Extension _____

_____

Adduction _____

_____

Abduction _____

_____

Pronation _____

_____

Supination _____

_____

2. **Selected Muscles Visible on the Posterior Trunk**

   Before considering the names of each of the indicated muscles, do the following. Determine a possible action for each of the labeled muscles. Consider only <u>direct</u> actions. That means that the <u>muscle must attach to a structure in order to move that same specific structure</u>. At this point, keep it simple. Notice that there are several muscles on your specimen which have been highlighted with sewn on letters. Do not concern yourself with the names of these muscles <u>yet</u>. Simply indicate <u>by letter</u> possible actions for each muscle as one or more of the following:

   a. movement of the <u>arm</u> at the shoulder joint (To select this category, a muscle must insert on the humerus);

   b. movement of the head (To select this category, a muscle must insert on some bone of the skull, not the spine);

   c. movement of the scapula (To select this category, a muscle must insert on some bone of the skull, not the spine);

   d. bending or twisting of the spine (To select this category, a muscle must insert on one or several vertebrae);

   Here is some advice about approaching this portion of the exercise in a step-by-step fashion.
   a) Select a muscle.
   b) Identify its points of attachment by sight and by feel… and <u>then</u> name the bone(s).
   c) Decide which of these is the origin (proximal or medial or more extensive attachment site) and which is the insertion (distal or lateral or more focused attachment site).
   d) Based on your conclusions in "c" above, decide which bone or structure will move when the muscle contracts. Put the letter designating this muscle in the appropriate category (1, 2, 3, or 4).
   e) Next, consider what would happen if other muscles held what you consider the insertion fixed and immobile. Could the origin now become moveable? That is, could the origin now become the new insertion? If no, move on to the next muscle and start at "a" again. If yes, then put the letter designating this muscle in an additional appropriate category (1, 2, 3, or 4). Move on to the next muscle.

   Once you complete this task, be prepared to share the results with your instructor.

Now that you have associated muscles (by letter) with specific movements, you must learn the names of these same muscles. First, focus on just those muscles which you identified as moving the scapula. What is the name of the large, superficial, triangular, muscle (A) which inserts on the scapula?

Muscle A: _____

By palpation of your specimen and by referring to the human skeleton, determine by name the <u>specific</u> parts of the scapula to which this muscle inserts.

_____

Besides the scapula, to what other bone(s) does this muscle attach? Consider both its origin and its insertion.

_____

Notice that this muscle has been cut along its medial margin. This margin constitutes the origin of the muscle. What is the precise superior and inferior extent of the origin of this muscle?

To determine its most inferior point of attachment, you must be able to count vertebrae. To help with this, realize that the seventh cervical vertebra is commonly referred to as "vertebra prominens" because it is so noticeable when the base of the neck is palpated. Start there as you try to count vertebrae. Record your answer.

    From _____ to _____

For some muscles, the origins and insertions can sometimes switch. Muscle A is such an example. If the scapula was fixed (held stationary) by other muscles, the origin and insertion of A would switch. What action would contraction of just the superior portion of this muscle cause?

_____

Reflect this muscle from medial to lateral. If you look closely, you should see nerves and blood vessels entering/exiting it from the deep surface. Would you expect that these types of structures would typically apply themselves to the deep side of a muscle?   Yes / No
Would you expect to find these same structures typically associated with every muscle?   Yes / No
Explain the reasons for your answers.

_____

_____

Identify by name the three labeled (B, C, D) deep muscles which underlie muscle A and which insert on the scapula.

Muscle B: _____

Muscle C: _____

Muscle D: _____

Scapular movements: Movement of the scapula is complex and involves the combined action of a number of muscles. Besides the muscles we have visualized here from the posterior approach, there are additional muscles which insert on the scapula that are best studied from the anterior view. Muscles which move the scapula can have a significant impact on the range of motion of the arm at the shoulder joint. Your ability to extend (lower) and flex (raise) your arm at the shoulder is influenced by the six distinct movements of the scapula. These are:

elevation	depression
retraction	protraction
inferior (downward) rotation	superior (upward) rotation

The terms that describe the movements of the scapula require clarification.
- a) When the scapula moves <u>toward</u> the midline, it is being retracted. Retraction of the scapula is therefore adduction of the scapula. Add an arrow to the illustration below to indicate retraction of the scapula.

- b) Movement of the scapula <u>away from</u> the midline, that is, laterally, is protraction. Protraction is equivalent to abduction of the scapula. Add an arrow to the illustration below to indicate protraction of the scapula.

c) Elevation involves lifting or moving the entire scapula upward. Add an arrow to the illustration below to indicate elevation of the scapula.

d) Depression involves lowering the position of the entire scapula. Add an arrow to the illustration below to indicate depression.

e) Rotation of the scapula involves changing the relative position of the glenoid cavity. It involves turning the scapula as if a nail had been driven through it to hold it securely to the dorsal surface of the torso. Add an arrow to each of the illustrations below to indicate scapular rotations.
- Upward or superior rotation involves a pivoting movement that redirects the glenoid in a superior direction.

- Downward or inferior rotation involves a pivoting movement that redirects the glenoid in an inferior direction.

Using one of the plastic scapular models or one of the plastic skeletons provided, be prepared to demonstrate each movement to your instructor if asked.

Here's a hint that should prove helpful: Use a piece of paper toweling, string or ribbon to represent the muscle you are considering. Precisely duplicate its origin and insertion. Hold the material firmly at the insertion point and pull the material from the origin. Doing this will allow you to duplicate the precise movements caused by contraction of each individual rotator cuff muscle. See the illustration below to better visualize the approach.

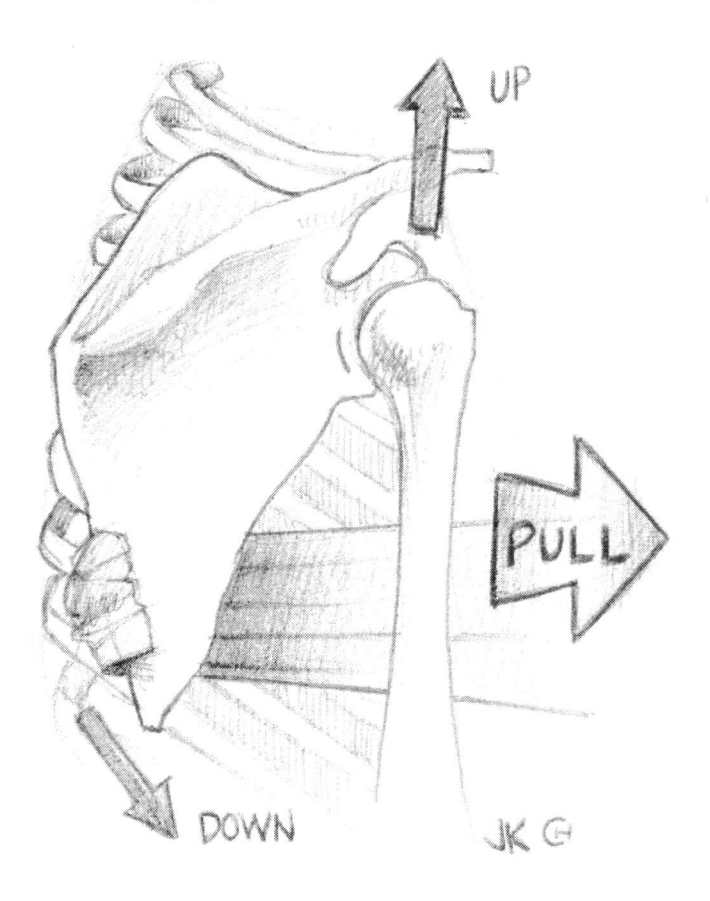

Consider these different scapular movements and the muscles which have been examined thus far. What is a common action shared by all of the labeled scapular muscles which have been exposed in this posterior view.

___

Which of these muscles (if any) rotate(s) the scapula in a downward direction?

___

Which of these muscles (if any) rotate(s) the scapula in an upward direction?

___

Lastly, in addition to the muscles that you have already identified, there is one additional large superficial muscle of the posterior torso that has been labeled (E). Even though this muscle does not directly insert on the scapula, it can cause scapular movement. Name the muscle. _____

Describe its origin (proximal attachment) and insertion (distal attachment).

Origin: _____

Insertion: _____

What <u>direct</u> movement is caused by contraction of this muscle? _____

Demonstrate the specific movement of the scapula that contraction of this muscle indirectly causes. Do this by simply abducting the arm of the cadaver until this muscle is tense. Do this <u>slowly and carefully</u> so that the muscle is not stretched too far causing it to tear. Now slowly adduct (lower) the arm until it is again at the side. As you do this, be careful to observe the movement of the scapula. Be especially attentive to the movement of the inferior angle of the scapula.

What indirect scapular movement did you observe? _____

Having done this simple maneuver with muscle E, you have probably noticed a very useful fact that should help you in trying to determine the specific actions of other muscles. <u>When you passively move a structure in a direction that causes a particular muscle to tighten, that muscle will cause the opposite or antagonistic action when it contracts.</u>

3. **Selected Muscles of the Shoulder Joint Visible from the Posterior View**
   There are six additional labeled muscles (F-K) that originate on the scapula and insert on and move the arm.

   Rotator cuff muscles: Four of the six are considered elements of a muscle complex called the rotator cuff. The rotator cuff muscles, in addition to moving the arm, surround the head of the humerus and work together to stabilize and strengthen the shoulder joint. Name the four rotator cuff muscles.

   _____   _____

   _____   _____

   Examine carefully the insertions of the rotator cuff muscles. What do they all have in common?

   _____

On quick glance because these four muscles all originate on the same bone and insert on the same bone, you might simply assume that they share a common action. What is your prediction at this point? _____

Carefully palpate the origins and insertions of the four muscles. Refer to the skeletons in the lab to assist as you describe each insertion point in detail. The differences in the movements or roles of these four muscles are subtle. Keeping their <u>specific</u> attachments sites in mind, consider how each muscle would exert force on the upper arm during contraction. The various movements of the arm possible at the shoulder include flexion (raising) and extension (lowering), adduction and abduction, and lateral and medial rotation. Rotation of the humerus is best demonstrated with the arm bent at the elbow to ninety degrees. Keeping the upper arm against the side of the torso and the elbow bent, move the forearm so that it lies across the the front of the abdominal wall. In this position, the humerus is rotated medially or inwardly. Duplicate this with the upper extremity of the skeleton. Now swing the forearm out away from the ventral surface (upper arm is still against the body and elbow is still bent). In this position, the humerus is rotated laterally or outwardly.

Now, before referring to an atlas or a text reference, try to predict how each might specifically move the arm. Once you have done that, test your predictions using the plastic skeletons. For this we recommend using the plastic skeletons because the arms on them have greater mobility than the arms on the real bone skeletons. As described previously, use a piece of paper toweling, string or ribbon to represent the muscle. Precisely duplicate the origins and insertions of each of the rotator cuff muscles. Hold one end of the material firmly at the insertion point and pull the material from the origin. This will duplicate the precise movements caused by contraction of each individual rotator cuff muscle.

Rotator cuff muscle 1   Letter ____   Name _____

   Origin _____   Insertion _____

   Predicted Action _____

   Actual Action _____

Rotator cuff muscle 2   Letter ____   Name _____

   Origin _____   Insertion _____

   Predicted Action _____

   Actual Action _____

Rotator cuff muscle 3   Letter _____ Name _____

    Origin _____   Insertion _____

    Predicted Action _____

    Actual Action _____

Rotator cuff muscle 4   Letter _____ Name _____

    Origin _____   Insertion _____

    Predicted Action _____

    Actual Action _____

As already mentioned, the rotator cuff muscles also function as stabilizers of the shoulder joint, keeping the head of the humerus nestled snugly in the glenoid cavity. Because of the location of their tendons, one type of shoulder dislocation is much less likely than others. Examine these insertion points carefully.

Which do you think is less likely?   __ superior dislocation   __ inferior dislocation

Focus now on the remaining two labeled muscles of the shoulder that move the arm. One originates entirely on the scapula. The other originates mostly from the scapula but has attachment from the lateral portion of the clavicle. Identify each by name and letter. Place your answers in the spaces provided below.

By observation and palpation, determine the proximal and distal attachments of each muscle. Keeping their specific attachments sites in mind, carefully consider and predict how each muscle will exert force on the upper arm when it contracts. Write your predictions for actions in the spaces below.

Now use the skeletons as before to actually determine and demonstrate the true actions of these muscles. Describe how each will move the arm at the shoulder.

    Remaining muscle 1   Letter _____ Name _____

    Origin _____   Insertion _____

    Predicted Action _____

    Actual Action _____

Remaining muscle 2   Letter _____   Name _____

Origin _____   Insertion _____

Predicted Action _____

Actual Action _____

Lastly now that your investigation of the musculature of the posterior body wall is completed, consider this one last item. On occasion, a single muscle can perform different and even opposite actions? That is, on occasion one muscle can cause a specific movement at one time and then at another time cause the opposite or antagonistic movement. This is most likely to occur with larger muscles possessing extensive origins. Two such muscles are the trapezius and deltoid muscles. Consider each of these muscles individually. Carefully examine the full extents of their respective origins. By doing so you may be able to divide each muscle into separate regions, each of which causes an individual action. Once you have done this, predict the opposing actions that each muscle is able to cause.

Deltoid: _____   _____

Trapezius: _____   _____

Selected Muscles Visible on the Anterior Trunk

Before considering the names of each of the indicated muscles, do the following just as you did in initially examining the muscles of the posterior torso. Without using a reference volume, predict a possible action for each of the labelled muscles. At this point as in the previous sections, keep it simple. Just indicate by letter the possible direct action for each muscle listed below. Record your answers in the space provided and then share your answers with your instructor.

a. movement of the arm through the shoulder joint (To select this category, a muscle must insert on the humerus);

_____

b. movement of the scapula (To select this category, a muscle must insert on the scapula);

_____

c. movement of the head (To select this category, a muscle must insert on a bone of the skull);

_____

d. movement of the rib cage (To select this category, a muscle must insert on the one or more ribs);

_____

e. compression of the abdomen (This is a tough category to appreciate. Muscles that wrap the abdomen may insert on bone and/or sheets of fascia. If a muscle runs between the thorax and pelvis, it will bend or twist the abdomen. If it inserts near the middle of a sheet of fascia, it will compress the abdomen. If the muscle is extensive and covers a large area, it may do both.)

_____

First, notice the long straplike muscle (L) which extends from the top of the thorax to the skull just posterior to the ear. Please describe its specific superior and inferior attachment points. For this muscle it will be helpful to identifying the origin by determining which attachment (superior or inferior) is the more extensive. Remember the rule: origins are more extensive and insertions are more focused.

Superior attachment _____

Inferior attachment _____

Now that you see its attachments, its name should come easily. The names of many muscles indicate first the origin and then the insertion. Based on this, what is the name of this muscle?

_____

What movement will be caused if both the right and left muscles contract simultaneously?
_____

If only the right or left muscle contracts by itself, how will this movement be changed. Describe the direction the head will rotate relative to the active muscle by indicating whether the chin will point toward or away from the active side. Be prepared to demonstrate the resulting movement for your instructor.

Active muscle: R or L   Chin points toward: R / L

Next, identify the large superficial muscle (M) of the anterior chest which inserts on the humerus. This muscle has two medial sources of origin. Identify each of these origins.
    Origins: _____

_____

Move the arm carefully to represent the possible arm movements at the shoulder (adduction, abduction, flexion, extension, medial rotation, lateral rotation) and pay attention to whether these movements cause muscle M to stretch. Based on your observations, you should be able to indicate the actions of muscle M below.

    Actions at shoulder: flexion   extension   neither

                                        adduction   abduction   neither

                                        medial rotation   lateral rotation

Reflect muscle M laterally. You should now be able to clearly identify two deeper muscles that insert on the scapula. One muscle (N) is small and visible on the anterior chest. The other (O) is more lateral, large, fan-shaped, and composed of a number of individual slips that radiate over the lateral rib cage and converge as they proceed in a posterior direction to connect to the scapula.

Identify each of these muscles. For each one, indicate as specifically as you can its points of origin and insertion.

Muscle N: Name: _____

                Specific origin: _____

                Specific insertion: _____

Muscle O: Name: _____

   Specific origin: _____

   Specific insertion: _____

As previously defined, rotation of the scapula involves changing the orientation of the glenoid. Superior rotation redirects the glenoid in an upward direction and inferior rotation redirects the glenoid in a downward direction. Again, use some paper toweling to represent each of these muscles on one of the plastic skeletons available in the lab. Once you clearly visualize the muscle, move the scapula at its insertion in the direction of its origin to mimic the movement caused by contraction of N. Repeat this with O. Which of these muscles is involved in superior rotation of the scapula? Which is involved in inferior rotation of the scapula?

   Superior rotation: ___ Muscle N   ___ Muscle O

   Inferior rotation: ___ Muscle N   ___ Muscle O

Remember that besides rotation, other movements of the scapula include elevation, depression, protraction and retraction. What other of these scapular actions might these two muscles cause? Circle your choice(s).

   Muscle N: elevation   depression   protraction   retraction

   Muscle O: elevation   depression   protraction   retraction

A number of the muscles labeled in this view have a role in the process of breathing. Two muscle groups (P & Q) run obliquely in the spaces between ribs. The more superficial group which is situated more laterally and does not extend completely to the sternum pulls the ribs in a superior direction. The deeper group that is visible more medially and extends all the way to the sternum acts to depress the ribs (moves them in an inferior direction). Identify and name both of these groups and determine which group is involved in inhalation and which is involved in exhalation.

Muscle P: Name: _____

   ___ Inhalation   ___ Exhalation

Muscle Q: Name: _____

   ___ Inhalation   ___ Exhalation

There are four sheetlike muscles that cover the abdomen and make up the anterior/lateral abdominal wall. Two of these muscles run obliquely and are oriented at right angles to each other. The other two abdominal muscles are also oriented at right angles to each other with one muscle running transversely and the other longitudinally. Superficial muscles must be reflected in order to expose deeper muscles. In different ways, these muscles share a connection with or attachment to a common longitudinal mid-ventral, fibrous structure. This midline landmark does not necessarily serve as the origin or insertion for each.

Identify this structure/landmark by name. _____

Based on your observation of the orientation of these four muscles, which of these abdominal muscles is likely the most important in performing sit-ups or "stomach crunches"? Identify this muscle by label and name.

Label _____   Name _____

Trace the extent of this muscle. It extends:

    from _____

    to _____

During a sit-up (that is, when lifting the head and torso upward from the supine position), what is its origin and what is its insertion?

    Origin: _____

    Insertion: _____

Now turn your attention to the remaining three sheetlike abdominal wall muscles. Careful inspection will show that they are layered. Identify each first by letter and then by name, starting with the most superficial and ending with the deepest of the three. For each muscle, indicate on the accompanying diagram of the torso, the orientation of its fibers. For clarity, a linea alba has been included in each diagram.

Most Superficial
Label _____   Name _____

Middle
Label _____   Name _____

Deepest
Label _____   Name _____

Based on your examination of these muscles (S, T, U), indicate by letter which of them will contribute to the movements or effects listed below? For each movement, pick all that apply.

Compress the abdominal viscera	S	T	U
Assist in a bowel movement	S	T	U
Elevate the rib cage	S	T	U
Flex the torso forward	S	T	U
Pull the spine back	S	T	U
Help with a cough	S	T	U
Pull the rib cage down	S	T	U
Take a deep breath in	S	T	U
Pull the shoulder back	S	T	U

Exercise A-7

Student Musculoskeletal Presentations

This week in lab, each student will participate in a group presentation on one of the topics listed below. The members of your group and your specific presentation topic must be approved by your instructor **in advance**. Group size will be between 2 and 3 students each. All members of the group must have *active* roles in the presentations. Generally, all members of the group will receive the same grade. However, if one or more members of the group are obviously unprepared or relying on the efforts of classmates, their grades will reflect their lack of effort. Each presentation is worth the equivalent of a regular lab quiz.

Note: In each presentation, some muscles are suggested. Your instructor may increase or decrease the size of this list.

Suggested Presentation Topics:

1. **Muscles that Lift and Depress the Mandible and Operate During Mastication.**
   Demonstration of these movements;
   All relevant bone anatomy;
   Origin, insertion, and action of selected muscles which lift the mandible;
   Origin, insertion, and action of selected muscles which depress the mandible;
   Demonstration of how selected muscles accomplish the grinding action needed in mastication;
   Discussion of temperomandibular joint dysfunction.

   Some suggested muscles:
Masseter	Temporalis
Medial pterygoid	Lateral pterygoid
Buccinator	Digastricus
Platysma	

2. **Muscles that Flex and Extend the Forearm at the Elbow Joint**
   To include:
   Demonstration of these movements;
   All relevant bone anatomy;
   Origin, insertion, and action of selected muscles which flex the forearm;
   Origin, insertion, and action of selected muscles which extend the forearm; and
   Demonstration of the influence of the pronated, supinated, and midway forearm positions on determining the muscles most influential in flexion and extension at the elbow.

   Some suggested muscles:
Biceps brachii	Brachialis
Brachioradialis	Pronator teres
Triceps brachii	Anconeus

3. **Muscles that Flex and Extend the Hand at the Wrist and the Digits**
To include:
Demonstration of these movements;
All relevant bone anatomy;
Origin, insertion, and action of selected muscles that flex the wrist and digits;
Origin, insertion, and action of selected muscles that extend the wrist and digits;
Demonstration of the nature of and the muscle(s) involved in "tennis elbow"; and
Demonstration of the impact of wrist flexion on digital flexion.

   Some suggested muscles:
Flexor carpi radialis	Flexor carpi ulnaris
Palmaris longus	Flexor digitorum superficialis
Flexor digitorum profundus	Flexor pollicis longus
Extensor carpi radialis longus	Extensor carpi radialis brevis
Extensor carpi ulnaris	Extensor digitorum

4. **Muscles that Supinate and Pronate the Forearm and Hand**
To include:
Demonstration of these movements;
All relevant bone anatomy;
Origin, insertion, and action of selected muscles which supinate the forearm;
Origin, insertion, and action of selected muscles which pronate the forearm; and
Demonstration of how a paralyzed biceps brachii would affect the resting position of the forearm and hand.

   Some suggested muscles:
Biceps brachii	Brachioradialis
Suppinator	Pronator teres
Pronator quadratus	

5. **Muscles that Adduct and Abduct the Thigh**
To include:
Demonstration of these movements;
All relevant bone anatomy;
Origin, insertion, and action of selected muscles which adduct the thigh;
Origin, insertion, and action of selected muscles which abduct the thigh; and
Demonstration of muscle malfunction(s) that yield a positive Trendelenburg's sign.

   Some suggested muscles:
Sartorius	Tensor fascia latae
Gluteus medius	Piriformis
Adductor magnus	Adductor longus
Adductor brevis	Pectineus

6. **Muscles that Flex and Extend the Thigh at the Hip Joint**
   To include:
   Demonstration of these movements;
   All relevant bone anatomy;
   Origin, insertion, and action of selected muscles which flex the thigh;
   Origin, insertion, and action of selected muscles which extend the thigh;
   Demonstration of how paralysis of the gluteus maximus and the gluteus medius/minimus each adversely affect different simple activities of daily living (eg. walking, rising from the seated position, etc.).

   Some suggested muscles:
Iliopsoas	Rectus femoris
Sartorius	Tensor fascia latae
Adductor longus	Adductor brevis
Pectineus	Adductor magnus
Gluteus magnus	Biceps femoris
Semitendinosus	Semimembranosus

7. **Muscles that Rotate the Thigh**
   To include:
   Demonstration of these movements;
   All relevant bone anatomy;
   Origin, insertion, and action of selected muscles which medially rotate the thigh;
   Origin, insertion, and action of selected muscles which laterally rotate the thigh; and
   Demonstration of the impact on resting position and movement of injury that eliminates either type of rotational movement.

   Some suggested muscles:
Sartorius	Gluteus maximus
Piriformis	Quadratus femoris
Biceps femoris	Semimembranosus
Semitendinosus	Gracilis
Adductor magnus	Adductor longus
Adductor brevis	Pectineus

8. **Muscles that Flex and Extend the Leg at the Knee Joint**
   To include:
   Demonstration of these movements;
   All relevant bone anatomy;
   Origin, insertion, and action of selected muscles which flex the thigh;
   Origin, insertion, and action of selected muscles which extend the thigh;
   Demonstration of the impact of a pulled hamstring on thigh flexion; and
   Demonstration of the contribution of the quadriceps femoris to walking.

   Some suggested muscles:
Rectus femoris	Vastus lateralis
Vastus intermedius	Vastus medialis
Sartorius	Gracilis
Biceps femoris	Semitendinosus
Semimembranosus	Gastrocnemius

9. **Muscles that Cause Plantar Flexion and Dorsiflexion at the Ankle**
   To include:
   Demonstration of these movements;
   All relevant bone anatomy;
   Origin, insertion, and action of selected anterior compartment muscles which dorsiflex the foot;
   Origin, insertion, and action of selected posterior compartment muscles which plantar flex the foot; and
   Demonstration of how nerve damage to the muscles of the anterior compartment impacts movement of the foot and walking.

   Some suggested muscles:
Tibialis anterior	Extensor digitorum longus
Fibularis tertius	Extensor hallicus longus
Fibularis longus	Fibularis brevis
Gastrocnemius	Soleus
Plantaris	Flexor digitorum longus
Flexor hallicus longus	Tibialis posterior

10. **Structure and Function of a Representative Joint** (knee joint is to be used only if this has not previously been discussed or demonstrated in lab)
To include:
    All relevant bone anatomy;
    Identification of relevant cartilagenous structures;
    Identification of ligaments which stabilize the joint and how each accomplishes this;
    Identification of selected tendons and muscles which cause movement at the joint; and
    Demonstration of mechanisms of ligament injury and the consequence of such injuries on joint function.

Suggestions for a Different Approach to Musculoskeletal Presentation Topics:
Presentation topics in this list focus on specific movements or motor activities with which students are all familiar. Students are required to determine which muscles are involved in the completion of the movement. The presentation then becomes an opportunity to demonstrate how various muscles and muscle groups participate/cooperate in effecting the movement in question. The number of muscles to be included in the presentation should not be fewer than 7 nor greater than 10 individual muscles.

Possible topics include:
A. Pitching/throwing a baseball
B. Pitching a softball
C. Tennis serve
D. Tennis backhand swing
E. Tennis forehand swing
F. Straight ahead field goal kick
G. Soccer-style kick
H. Two-hand chest pass
I. Basketball jump shot
J. Dunking a basketball
K. Jumping jacks
L. Rolling from supine to prone
M. Walking
N. Walking downstairs
O. Climbing a ladder
P. Cannonball dive off a board
Q. Blowing out candles on a cake
R. Baseball swing

Exercise A-8

Gross Anatomy of the
Human Endocrine System

This week's lab exercise deals with the gross anatomy of the endocrine system. You will be using wet and dry preserved human organs and a few selected models in addition to the prosected cadavers.

Although many organs of the body have endocrine function, in this week's lab you will examine and consider the four classical non-gonadal endocrine structures of the body. These include the pituitary gland, the thyroid gland, the parathyroid glands, and the adrenal glands. At least one of the cadavers has been prepared and positioned to facilitate the in-situ study of the pituitary because the calvarium has been cut and removed, exposing the cranial floor. This view provides the necessary access in order to understand the placement of the pituitary gland as well as its relationship to the bony anatomy of the cranial floor. The other cadavers have been positioned in the supine which allows for observing the anatomy of the three remaining endocrine glands.

Pituitary

For this portion of the exercise, you must work with a cadaver in which the brain has been removed. The sagittal head sections are also very helpful and provide a different but very helpful perspective as you work through this exercise.

Observe the cranial floor in one of the specimens. In Exercise 4 you were required to find and identify several cranial foramina. Among these were the foramen magnum, jugular foramen, orbital fissure, optic foramen, and hypoglossal foramen. Find these same foramina in your cadaver. You may find it helpful to reexamine one of the human skulls to refresh your memory. What general types of structures are passing through these foramina? For this, you are not expected to name different specific structures.

_____

_____

Be gentle as you explore… these structures are delicate and can be easily torn and lost.

Direct your attention to the sphenoid bone. By careful observation and gentle palpation, identify the sella turcica (Turkish saddle), the bony structure which forms the hypophyseal fossa in which the pituitary gland sits. As you can see from any reference material you have consulted, the pituitary gland "hangs" from the ventral surface of the brain and rests in the fossa of the sphenoid. This is best appreciated by viewing the sagittally sectioned head. The pituitary is composed of a stalk-like infundibulum and a pea-shaped body which is divided into two lobes, one anterior and the other posterior. Find the infundibulum (or its remnant).

Approximately how long is the portion that remains in millimeters?
_____

Be prepared to point it out to your instructor.

Examine the pituitary carefully. Is it freely moveable within the cranium or it is held securely in place?
        ___ freely moveable   ___ held securely

Characterize the tissue which "packages" the pituitary. Which term most accurately describes the tissue? Circle your choice.

        ___ mostly adipose   ___ loose/flimsy   ___ dense tough

If the covering tissue has been removed or can be reflected to allow close examination of the gland itself, try to determine if the pituitary shares the texture you have previously observed with other glandular structures.   Yes / No
Based on the view which you have of the gland, are the two lobes clearly distinct from one another?   Yes / No

Although the pituitary appears to be located in a very inaccessible location, it is possible to perform surgery on this gland. Based on your examination of it and the related skeletal anatomy, describe what you feel would be a possible surgical approach to removing a growth from the pituitary gland.
_____

_____

_____

Thyroid
Find the thyroid gland on the anterior neck region of the cadaver. Use appropriate anatomical terminology to describe the location of the thyroid relative to the jugular notch.
_____

Do likewise to describe its position:
    relative to the heart   _____

    relative to the larynx   _____

    relative to the trachea   _____

    relative to the esophagus.   _____

The thyroid gland is composed of two lateral lobes joined across the anterior midline by a bridge of tissue called the isthmus. Identify each of these components of the thyroid gland. In the space below, draw the thyroid <u>as it appears on **your** specimen</u> and be prepared to point its components out to your instructor.

Sometimes a small remnant of thyroid tissue is visible extending superiorly from the isthmus. This is actually a remnant from the developmental path taken by the thyroid as it branches from the primitive gut tube. If present, it is called the pyramidal lobe. Look carefully to see if one is present.

	Pyramidal lobe present
Specimen # _____	Yes / No
Specimen # _____	Yes / No
Specimen # _____	Yes / No
Specimen # _____	Yes / No

If there is a pyramidal lobe present on one of your specimens, draw it in the box below.

As you do so, remember it is functional thyroid tissue so it will appear just like the tissue of the rest of the gland. If you see one, be sure to include it in your drawing above and be prepared to demonstrate it for your instructor. Is the texture of the thyroid gland consistent with that which you have previously described for other glands?   Yes / No
If not, how is it different?

The vagus nerve runs in a superior-inferior direction just lateral to the lobes of the thyroid on both sides of the neck. Try to find it. If you think you have it, be prepared to point it out to your instructor.

Does the vagus extend beyond the neck into the thoracic cavity?   Yes / No

Parathyroid glands

The parathyroid glands (from the Greek root *para* meaning near or beside) are particularly difficult to locate and recognize. They are generally composed of four small bodies, two on the right and two on the left. Each body is slightly oval and generally not larger than 5 mm in diameter. They generally lie on the posterior surfaces of the lateral lobes of the thyroid and are divided into two superior and two inferior glands. However, there is considerable variability in their positions and at times even in their numbers.

You may find it easier to locate a parathyroid gland by palpation than by looking. If you cannot find one on your specimen, check one of the other cadavers. Based on your observation, are the parathyroid glands appropriately named?   Yes / No
Please explain.

_____

_____

If you cannot find a parathyroid on one of the specimens, identify the parathyroid glands on one of the laryngeal models that are also available in the lab. Indicate the location of any parathyroids that you find on your drawing of the thyroid above. Be prepared to demonstrate it/them for your instructor.

Pancreas

You are already familiar with the pancreas from your study of the digestive system. Review the anatomy of the pancreas, including its three anatomical regions (head, body, and tail). Draw them in the space below and if asked, show them to your instructor on one of the specimens available in lab.

By what specific digestive organ is the head of the pancreas surrounded?

_____

Likewise, what <u>non</u>-digestive organ does the tail of the pancreas contact?

_____

Demonstrate these on one of the available specimens for your instructor if asked.

Using the cadavers, various surface landmarks of the thorax and abdomen with which you became familiar early in the semester, and the skeletons available to you in the lab, you should be able to locate the pancreas very precisely. Determine the vertebral level(s) at which the superior margin of the pancreas lies.

Be prepared to demonstrate this to your instructor.

Adrenal Glands

The adrenal glands are paired glands that are closely associated with the superior surfaces of the kidneys. Each gland consists of an outer cortex and an inner medulla but this will not be apparent to you on gross inspection. If your specimen has been dissected to expose the adrenals, find them. On which side is the gland larger?   Right / Left
What might account for this difference in size?

_____

_____

Indicate the position of the adrenal glands relative to the parietal peritoneum.

        ___ peritoneal   ___ retroperitoneal

The right adrenal gland is particularly susceptible to infections which involve the liver. With what specific area of the liver's surface (identified and discussed as part of exercise A-3) is the right adrenal most directly associated? Hint: Consider their positions relative to the serous membranes in the area.

_____

How does this association contribute to the susceptibility of the right adrenal to infection?

_____

_____

_____

_____

Look for evidence of a vascular supply and a nerve supply to each adrenal gland. Note, the ability to draw reasonable conclusions regarding the vascular and nervous supplies to the adrenals is very much dependent on the type, quality and precision of the dissections performed on the specimens. Carefully examine an adrenal gland that is exposed on one of the specimens. If there is no specimen with a well exposed adrenal, your instructor may refer you to one of the anatomy atlases available in the lab.

Is each adrenal supplied by a single artery or several arteries?

                                         ___ one artery   ___ several arteries

Is each adrenal supplied by a single nerve or several nerves?

                                         ___ one nerve   ___ several nerves

Be prepared to demonstrate your answers to your instructor if asked.

Exercise A-9

Gross Anatomy of the Human Reproductive System

This exercise deals with the gross anatomy of the reproductive system. We will be using human organs in the prosected cadavers, excised organs (both wet preserved and plastinated), and a few selected models. Be sure that you are mindful of the philosophy, policies, and rules that pertain to the cadaver facility. Be sure to abide by these policies and procedures at all times. This week's exercise involves gender-specific activities as well as comparisons between male and female structures. You should answer all questions posed in the lab exercise and observe and identify all structures presented. Your quiz on the anatomy of the reproductive system will be based on your knowledge of its structure and the insights you gain by thoughtfully answering the questions that make up this exercise.

Make your observations and identify structures (as applicable based on gender and to the extent possible due to differences in dissection extent and approach) on all cadavers. Any particular specimen may lack some of the structures you are required to recognize and master. Organs may have been disturbed and in some cases even removed during the dissection process. Individual variation often results in a structure being more easily recognized and identified in one specimen than is the case in another. For these reasons and to reinforce your knowledge of structure, do not hesitate to move among cadavers in order to answer the questions posed and to reinforce your command of structural plan and anatomic detail.

Some anatomical details have not been exposed on any of the cadavers. Therefore, in some instances you will need to use excised human organs, models and/or animal materials to answer questions and observe the specified structures. These materials may be examined either in the main lab or the cadaver lab. Working with them in close proximity to the cadavers may help you to clarify specific anatomical questions such as the proper orientation of an organ *in situ*.

Once you complete a portion of the lab exercise, you should be prepared to answer questions and/or demonstrate specific structures for your instructor. Your ability to answer questions and to demonstrate specific elements of anatomy will serve as the basis for grading your performance in this exercise.

Part A: Gross Anatomy of the Female

1. The major organs within the female pelvis are the rectum, uterus, urinary bladder. A portion of the sigmoid colon is also within the pelvis. Identify rectum, uterus, urinary bladder within the supine cadaver and determine their relative positions from anterior to posterior.

   Anterior   Middle   Posterior

   _____   _____   _____

   Be prepared to demonstrate these structures and answer related questions for your instructor.

2. Look for evidence of the broad ligament. This peritoneal membrane forms from ~~as~~ the parietal peritoneum as it pulls away from the pelvic wall during development. The largest portion of the broad ligament is the mesometrium. It is associated with the uterus medially. Observe the extent of the broad ligament carefully. Does it join directly to another internal organ or does it simply extend to the pelvic wall?
   ___ joins another organ   ___ joins the pelvic wall

   Be prepared to demonstrate these structures and answer related questions for your instructor.

3. The round ligament is a fibrous cord which extends from the uterus transversely along from the mesometrium to the labia majorum. Find it and follow it carefully towards the labia majora. Through what passage does it pass in leaving the ventral body cavity?
   _____

   Be prepared to demonstrate these structures and answer related questions for your instructor.

4. Superiorly, the broad ligament becomes involved with both the ovary and oviduct (also referred to as the fallopian tube, the salpinx, or the uterine tube). Find the ovaries and the oviducts. Identify the portion of the broad ligament which is associated with the ovaries. It is called the mesovarium. The third portion, mesosalpinx, is associated with the oviduct. Be prepared to demonstrate these structures and answer related questions for your instructor.

5. Find the ovaries. Depending on the age of your specimen, these organs may be very large and obvious or quite small. Each ovary is suspended by two ligaments. One ligament (ovarian ligament or ligament of the ovary) joins the ovary to the uterus. Developmentally it is actually a short extension of the round ligament. The other (the suspensory ligament) is a collection of blood vessels and connective tissue that anchors the ovary to the dorsal body wall. Find these two

ligaments. Be prepared to demonstrate these structures and answer related questions for your instructor.

6. The male has a similar structure to the round ligament that passes through the same opening? Determining just what structure that is requires a focus on the developmental process. Consider that in the female, the round ligament (along with the ovarian ligament) extends from the female gonad to the adult structure that develops from the embryonic labioscrotal swelling. In the male, a structure extends from the male gonad (testis) to the male structure which develops from the labioscrotal swelling. Therefore the equivalent male structure is the:

_____

You will need to examine a male cadaver in the second half of this exercise to demonstrate your answer this question. For that reason, you may postpone addressing this element until then.

7. Find the oviducts. Each oviduct has four segments: a distal, funnel-shaped infundibulum; a wide and long middle ampulla; a short, thick-walled isthmus that reaches the uterus; and a short intramural uterine segment which is found within the wall of the uterus. Examine the oviducts and try to distinguish these specific portions. This is best done using one of the several separate specimens that are available.

Observe first the infundibulum. At the distal end of the oviduct, what special structural modification(s) does it show?

_____

What is the functional significance of this specialized structure?

_____

Next identify both the isthmus and the ampulla. Lastly, as you already know, intramural means "within the wall". Select a specimen that shows clearly this portion of the oviduct.

Be prepared to demonstrate these structures for your instructor.

8. Find the uterus. It has three major anatomical parts: fundus, body (corpus), and cervix. The inferior constricted neck of the uterus which projects into the vaginal lumen is the cervix. The rounded superior portion between the fallopian tubes is the fundus. The middle substantial portion is the body (corpus). Although the boundaries between the parts of the uterus are sometimes indistinct, you should be able to distinguish each and to demonstrate these structures for your instructor.

By careful observation, you should notice that the uterus is bent along an antero-posterior plane. Relative to the cervix, in what direction is the rest of the uterus bent?

_____

Now carefully close the ventral body cavity of the cadaver you are working with and attempt to locate the fundus by palpation. This is something that is routinely done by an examining clinician during the course of a pregnancy. Assume that your finding is typical of all non-pregnant females. Based on your efforts, do you think palpation of the fundus is a potentially useful assessment technique in a non-pregnant or elderly woman?   Yes / No

Immediately following delivery (postpartum), manual massage of the uterine fundus is important in order to stimulate the uterus and help constrict uterine arteries. This minimizes blood loss following delivery.

The cervix contains a canal (endocervical canal) which opens at both ends. The openings are the internal os and the external os. Os is the Latin word for mouth. Find each. The internal os may not be visible *in situ*. To see it, you will likely have better success examining one of the separate preserved uterus specimens in which the cavity of the uterus has been opened. Be prepared to demonstrate these structures and answer related questions for your instructor.

In your specimen based on what you observe, are the ovaries, oviduct and uterus located entirely within the ventral body cavity? ... within the abdominal cavity? ... within the pelvic cavity?

	Ventral cavity	Abdominal cavity	Pelvic cavity
Ovaries	Yes / No	Yes / No	Yes / No
Fallopian tubes	Yes / No	Yes / No	Yes / No
Uterus	Yes / No	Yes / No	Yes / No

9. Posterior to the inferior portion of the uterus, the peritoneum is reflected onto the anterior surface of the rectum. This forms a space or recess, the rectouterine pouch of Douglas. It is also referred to as the posterior *cul-de-sac*. It is the most inferior (gravity-dependent) point in the peritoneal cavity. What are the anterior and posterior boundaries of this pouch of Douglas?

   Anterior boundary _____

   Posterior boundary _____

Be prepared to demonstrate this recess for your instructor.

10. Using the cadaver and the skeleton, describe and distinguish between the true pelvis and the false pelvis. _____

Trace the boundary between true and false pelvis with your finger and demonstrate this to your instructor. What bony structures form the boundary or division between the two?
_____

Notice and indicate which reproductive structures of the female are completely contained within the true pelvis.
_____

Be prepared to demonstrate these structures for your instructor.

11. Examine the vagina. Describe its structure briefly. _____

Describe the junction between the cervix and vagina. Does the vagina protrude into the cervix or does the cervix protrude into vagina?

_____ vagina into the cervix   _____ cervix into the vagina

Recesses formed by the junction of the cervix and the vaginal lumen are called fornices (singular, fornix). By extending your finger into the vaginal canal, it is possible to palpate the cervix, the external os, and the anterior and posterior fornices. This exam is easier however on one of the separate uterine specimens. Based on your examination, which fornix is deeper/larger?

_____ anterior fornix   _____ posterior fornix

In a procedure called a posterior colpotomy (culdocentesis), a physician can gain access to the most inferior portion of the peritoneal cavity, the pouch of Douglas or posterior *cul-de-sac*, by passing a needle through the wall of the vagina. To enter the pouch of Douglas from the vagina, the needle must penetrate the vaginal wall at what specific location?
_____

Be prepared to demonstrate these structures and answer related questions for your instructor.

12. Proper female hygiene involves wiping from the front towards the back following urination. Consider the orifices and their order from front to back in the female perineum. List these openings in order in the spaces provided.

   Anterior   Middle   Posterior
   _____   _____   _____

   Based on this, what is the anatomical basis for this practice? _____
   _____

   Be prepared to demonstrate relevant structures and answer related questions for your instructor.

13. A possible complication of any procedure which involves vaginal access to the uterus is infection within the pelvic cavity caused by gram negative bacteria associated with feces. How is this complication related to the anatomy of the female system?
   _____
   _____

14. The perineum is a diamond shaped area visible from an inferior perspective. Using an available skeleton or a plastic pelvis, determine its specific bony boundaries?
   Bony landmarks:
       Anterior _____

   Lateral _____   _____

       Posterior _____

   The perineum can be divided by a line connecting the two lateral bony landmarks into an anterior urogenital triangle and a posterior rectal triangle. Are there external reproductive structures within the anterior triangle? Yes / No
   If yes, what are they?
   _____

   Are there external reproductive structures within the posterior triangle? Yes / No
   If yes, what are they?
   _____

Be prepared to demonstrate these structures for your instructor.

14. The vulva (female genitalia) are found within the boundaries of the perineum. Find as many of the following structures as are visible on this specimen:

mons pubis	Yes / No	clitoris	Yes / No
labia majora	Yes / No	vestibule	Yes / No
labia minora	Yes / No	urethral orifice	Yes / No
vaginal orifice	Yes / No		

The vestibular glands also open to the outside within this area but their external openings are very small and not likely visible in your specimen.
Are they visible in your specimen?   Yes / No
If yes, verify them with your instructor and then describe their location.

_____

Be prepared to demonstrate these structures and answer related questions for your instructor.

Part B: Gross Anatomy of the Male

1. Indicate which of the following major internal organs of the male pelvis are visible or palpable within the cadaver in the supine position… rectum; bladder; prostate.
List them from anterior to posterior.

Anterior	Middle	Posterior
_____	_____	_____

Be prepared to demonstrate these structures for your instructor.

2. Identify the peritoneum at the pelvic floor and follow it posteriorly along the urinary bladder. Between the posterior bladder and the anterior rectum, the peritoneum folds to create a space or recess, the rectovesical pouch. Is this space continuous with the peritoneal cavity? Yes / No

Be prepared to demonstrate this structure and answer related questions for your instructor.

Is there a comparable space or recess in the female? Yes / No
Explain your answer.

_____

_____

131

3. Direct your attention to the urethra. It has three parts. From proximal to distal, they are: prostatic urethra, membranous urethra, and penile (spongy) urethra. Which portion(s) of the urethra is/are visible on your cadaver?

_____

Use a torso model, the cadavers, and any separate specimens to visualize all three parts of the urethra. Notice the curves in the penile urethra. This can make insertion of a urinary catheter painful, difficult, or both. What simple maneuver can straighten the urethra and make the insertion of such a catheter less problematic?

_____

Why do you think the urethra in the penis is also called the spongy urethra? Careful observation will be helpful here.

_____

Be prepared to demonstrate relevant structures and answer related questions for your instructor.

4. Find the prostate. Describe its position relative to the:

rectum _____

symphysis pubis _____

urinary bladder _____

penile urethra _____

It is common for the prostate to enlarge after age 50. What associated structure would be most impacted by this hypertrophy?

_____

What functions or capability might be negatively impacted by this hypertrophy?

_____

Is it possible to examine the prostate in an intact male by palpation? Yes / No
If not, why not? If yes, by what anatomical approach?

_____

Be prepared to demonstrate these structures and answer related questions for your instructor.

5. The diamond-shaped area between the thighs of the specimen is the perineum. What are its four bony boundaries?
Bony landmarks:

   Anterior _____

   Lateral _____   _____

   Posterior _____

   Draw an imaginary line between the ischial tuberosities to define the anterior (urogenital) triangle of the perineum. What external structures are contained within this triangle?

   _____

   _____

   The posterior half of the perineum is the rectal triangle. What external structure is contained within this triangle?

   _____

   Be ready to demonstrate these structures for your instructor.

6. Observe the testes and what remains of the scrotum. During development, the scrotum originates from paired labioscrotal swellings which fuse. Remnants of this fusion form the scrotal (perineal) raphe. Can you find evidence of the line of fusion on this specimen?   Yes / No
   If yes, demonstrate it for your instructor.

   The paired labioscrotal swellings are also present in the female early in uterine development. How does the course of their development into mature structures in the female differ from that just described in the male?

   _____

   What is the result? _____

   Be prepared to demonstrate these structures and answer related questions.

7. Examine the testis in what remains of the scrotal sac. Look for evidence of a ligament or connective tissue band that attaches and secures each testis within the sac. This scrotal ligament is the remnant of the gubernaculum. For what important developmental process is an intact gubernaculum essential?

   _____

   Be prepared to demonstrate this structure and answer related questions.

8. Attached to each testis is a spermatic cord composed of a number of distinct, smaller structures. What different <u>types</u> of structures comprise the spermatic cord?

_____

The cord appears to suspend the testis from the ventral body wall. Follow the cord superiorly to the superficial inguinal ring in the ventral body wall. This external ring is the outer opening of a passage leading through the body wall into the peritoneal cavity. This passage is called the inguinal canal. Verify the presence of the superficial ring by palpation and take note of its diameter relative to that of the finger you use in palpation. An intact, undamaged superficial ring should feel snug around an average adult-sized index finger.

Diameter of the superficial ring: _____

Next, examine the <u>inside</u> of the body wall just superior and lateral to the superficial ring to locate the deep inguinal ring. Verify its presence on the inside surface of the body wall by palpation and again take note of its diameter.

Diameter of the deep ring: _____

For what male developmental process is the inguinal canal required?

Compare the inguinal canals bilaterally on the male specimens. Sometimes the canal enlarges and allows other structures or tissue to pass through which normally should not be present, a condition called an inguinal hernia. Did you find any evidence of such a hernia in any of these specimens?   Yes / No
If yes, be prepared to demonstrate the hernia to your instructor.

Does the female specimen possess an inguinal canal?   Yes / No
If yes, what structure, if any, passes through it?

_____

9. Study the spermatic cord carefully and closely. Start with its covering. Notice that there are muscle fibers visible in the coverings of the cord. Follow these fibers in a superior direction.
Do they seem to pass through the inguinal canal?   Yes / No
From what specific muscle group do these fibers seem to be originating?

_____

Based on the orientation of the muscle fibers which are visible on close inspection, how is the position of the testis affected when the fibers contract?

_____

Name this muscle. _____

Be prepared to demonstrate it and answer related questions.

Within the spermatic cord are a variety of different structures including the vas (ductus) deferens, testicular artery, pampiniform venous plexus, and nerves. The vas deferens is the most obvious and most posterior tube within the cord. Try to identify it. Be prepared to demonstrate it.

What does the word plexus mean? _____

Within the spermatic cord, there is a venous plexus associated with the testis? Note: Veins are very thin walled vessels with large lumens. Because of this, blood tends to pool in them after death. As a result, They tend to be more obvious than arteries and their walls often appear dark because the color of the coagulated blood shows through. For what purpose is there a venous plexus associated with the testis? Hint: Remember the direction of blood flow in arteries versus veins and then consider that this venous plexus surrounds an artery.

_____

_____

Be prepared to demonstrate this structure.

10. The testis has two coverings; an outer, thin, double-layered tunica vaginalis and an inner thicker and fibrous tunica albuginea. The deep layer of the tunica vaginalis is difficult to appreciate because it is firmly adherent to the outer surface of the tunica albuginea. The reflection of the vaginalis into two layers forms a bare area on the testis which is not obvious (between the epididymis and the posterior surface of the testis). You are not expected to find this region on the specimens. In association with what organ of the digestive system did we previously observe a bare area?

_____

The thick tunica albuginea forms inner-directed septae (walls) which partition the testis into lobules which contain the seminiferous tubules. What would you need to do to an <u>intact</u> testis in order to demonstrate this division of the testis into separate compartments?

_____

Examine the testes on your specimen in search of these septae. You may find one of the handheld magnifying glasses helpful in making this observation. In addition, your instructor may set up a dissecting microscope to allow a better view of these structures. Be prepared to demonstrate these structures to your instructor.

Based on your examination, briefly describe the seminiferous tubules.

_____

11. The epididymis lies largely over the bare area of the testis. It has three parts: a superior head, a middle body which covers the bare area, and an inferior tail. Try to identify these regions of the epididymis on your specimen.

    The epididymis receives sperm from the testis, stores them, and later delivers them to the vas (ductus) deferens for eventual expulsion. Of the three regions listed above, which specific portion of the epididymis (of the three listed above) receives the sperm directly from the testis?

    _____

    Which specific portion of the epididymis leads directly into the vas deferens?

    _____

    Be prepared to demonstrate these structures for your instructor.

12. Identify the following superficial structures of the penis: dorsal surface, ventral surface, root, body, glans, external urethral orifice. Note: Dorsal and ventral surfaces of the penis are best understood by visualizing the penis in the erect state. The ventral surface is also sometimes referred to as the urethral surface.

Was your specimen circumcised?	Yes / No
Is the prepuce present?	Yes / No
If the prepuce is present, is it complete and intact?	Yes / No

    Be prepared to demonstrate these structures for your instructor.

13. In a specimen where the penis has been transversely sectioned, identify the dorsal vessels and nerves, the tunica albuginea, urethra, corpus spongiosum, and the two corpora cavernosa with the septum running longitudinally in the middle. The corpus spongiosum, and the two corpora cavernosa are classified as bands of erectile tissue. Describe this tissue as it appears on gross inspection. For a closer view, use the handheld magnifiers.

    _____
    _____

    Carefully spray or pour a small amount of wetting solution onto this tissue. Now squeeze it and release it. Describe what you observe.

    _____

What structure that you have already identified contributes to the septum that divides the corpus cavernosum? Note: If the penis on your specimen has been sectioned longitudinally, not all of the above structures will be visible. You should still, however, be able to add the wetting solution and make the necessary observations.

_____

What type of tissue occupies the interior of the glans penis?

___ muscle   ___ epithelium   ___ connective   ___ epithelium

To what penile structure that you just identified does this tissue belong?

_____

For the vessels that are visible, can you distinguish between veins, arteries, and nerves?   Yes / No   If yes, what is the basis for your choice?

_____

Be prepared to demonstrate these structures and answer related questions.

14. Deep to the skin between the root of the penis and the anus is an area, the pelvic diaphragm, within which lie thin muscles associated with the penis, the bulb of the penis, and the crura (singular, crus) of the penis. Find a specimen where the penis has been dissected to allow these structures to be viewed or palpated. Of what band of tissue that you've already identified is the bulb of the penis a part?

_____

Likewise, to what band of tissue that you've already identified do the crura belong?

_____

Exercise A-10

**Gross Anatomy of the
Central Nervous System - 1
The Brain**

This week's lab exercise begins your examination of the gross anatomy of the nervous system. Your investigation of the nervous system will start with the examination of the central nervous system which includes the brain and spinal cord. Today you will focus your attention on the anatomy of the brain and the associated membranes that surround it. Working in groups of two or three, you will start by examining the sheep brain. You will not only make observations; you will also section it. Labeled line drawings of the sheep brain accompany the instructions for this exercise to aid you in your study. Note that the level of detail indicated by the labels goes beyond the level of structural detail for which you will be held accountable.

Upon completion of the sheep brain study, you will move to the study of the human brain. Human brain specimens are limited, extremely fragile, and for obvious reasons very valuable. Treat them with the utmost care and respect. Handle them gently and do not section or dissect them. The human brain specimens that are available for your study include traditionally wet preserved human brains and brain sections, a plastinated human brain, and museum mounts of sagittal and frontal sections. As with the sheep, labelled line drawings of the human brain accompany the instructions for this exercise to aid you in your study.

Part 1: The Sheep Brain

Meninges:
1. The outer fibrous covering of the brain is the dura mater. It is similar to and closely associated with periosteum. You may wish to reexamine the sample of sectioned, preserved bone which your instructor can provide. Examine the periosteum. Dura is derived from this membrane. It is not likely that there is any dura visible on your sheep brain. However, if suitable specimens are available, your instructor may provide you with the opportunity to examine sheep dura. Note: If the specimens provided for dissection possess a complete and intact dura, do not proceed any further until you get specific direction from your instructor. He/she will guide you through the removal of the dura so that you will not destroy the cranial nerves.

2. With the ventral surface of the brain facing downward, examine the cerebrum.

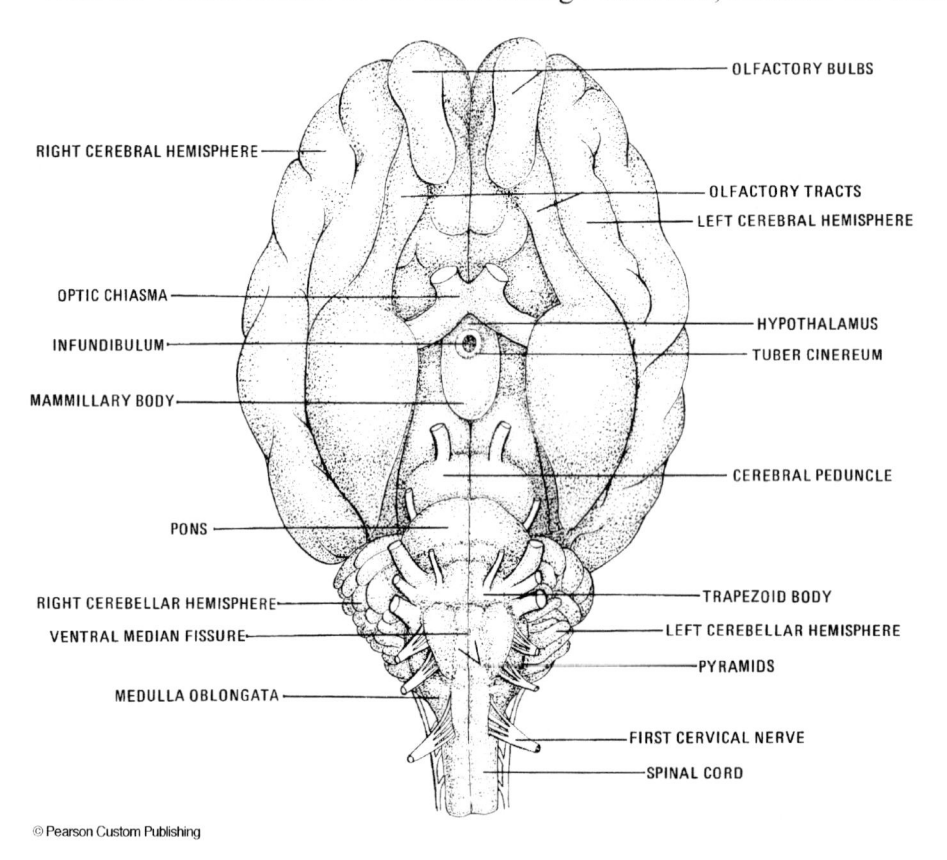

SHEEP BRAIN, VENTRAL VIEW

The cerebrum is the largest area of the brain. It is likely to be covered by a delicate membrane, the arachnoid mater. With a dissecting needle, carefully try to separate the arachnoid form the underlying brain tissue to which it adheres.

Based on your inspection, are there any blood vessels associated with this membrane?   Yes / No

The root word from which arachnoid is derived means spider. Based on your inspection, please try to explain why this membrane is called the "arachnoid"?

_____

_____

Look at all surfaces (dorsal, ventral, lateral) of your specimen.
Is the arachnoid seen on all surfaces of the brain?   Yes / No

Select an area of the brain's surface where you can position the tip of a probe or dissecting needle just beneath the arachnoid. Gently tear the arachnoid in this area to expose the surface of the brain which is covered by the deepest of the meninges, the pia mater. Does the pia appear to be an obvious, thick and strong covering?   Yes / No
Is the pia easily separable from the brain's surface?   Yes / No

In order to view the pia more clearly, your instructor may instruct you in how to make a preparation that can be viewed under a dissecting microscope.

Surface Features:
3. Notice that the dorsal surface of the cerebrum is organized into a series of ridges separated from each other by grooves, some of them shallow and not easily demonstrated and others less numerous but deep and obvious.

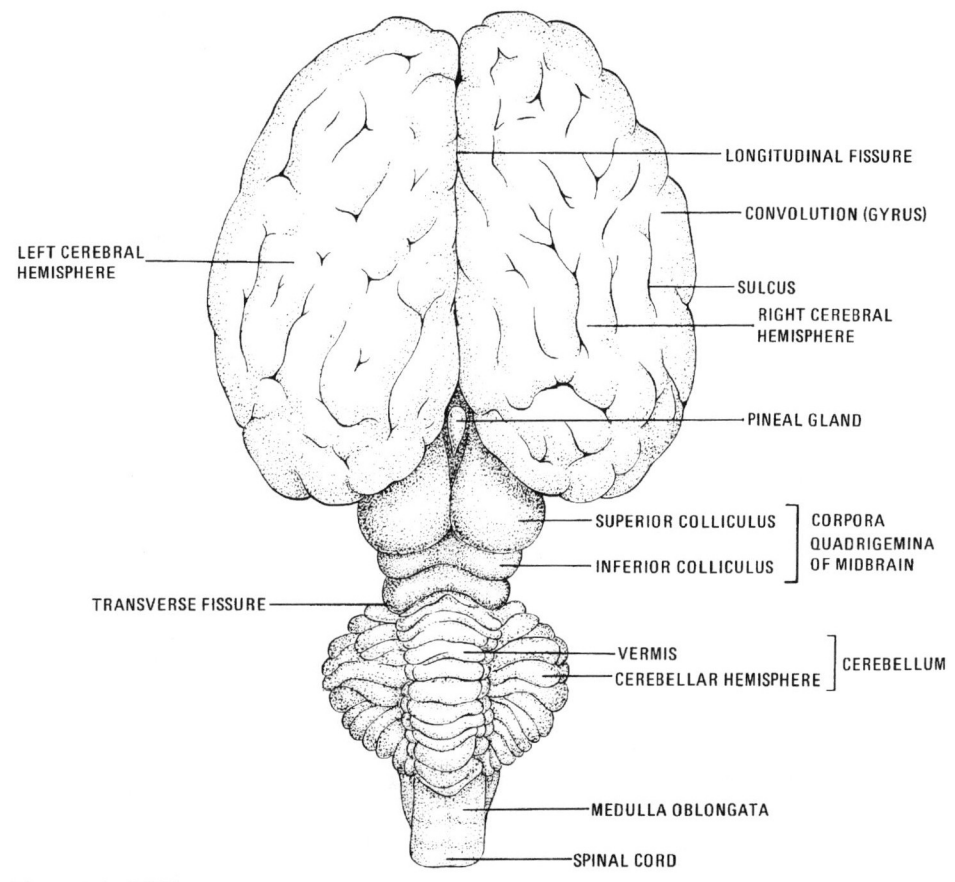

Locate and identify sulci (singular is sulcus), gyri (singular is gyrus), and fissures. Based on your inspection, how can sulci be distinguished from fissures?

_____

What do you think is the functional advantage of this "ridge and groove" architecture over a brain surface that is uniformly smooth and unbroken.

_____

_____

Be prepared to demonstrate these structures to your instructor.

4. With a sharp knife or a scalpel, carefully remove the most superficial portion of one cerebral hemisphere as follows. With the tip of the blade anteriorly, its flat side held parallel to the table surface, and the sharp edge facing medially (that is, toward the longitudinal fissure), carefully slice of the most dorsal ¼ inch of one cerebral hemisphere. As depicted in the accompanying illustration, flip this section up and examine the cut surface. Observe the change in appearance of the nerve tissue from superficial to deep.

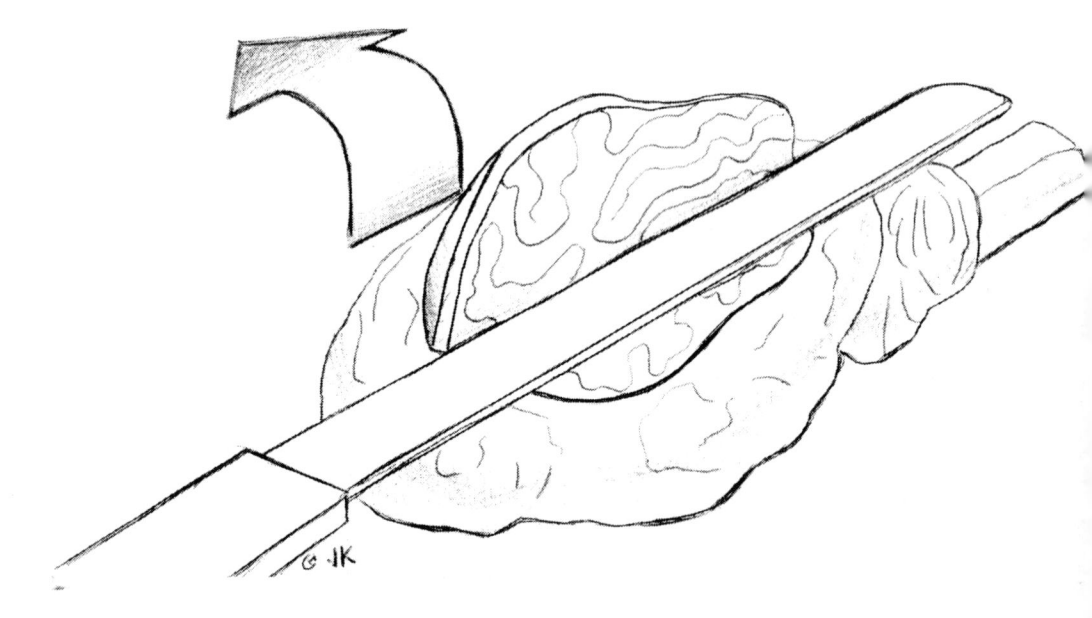

Are you able to distinguish the gray matter from the white matter?   Yes / No
Which is the deeper layer?   ___ white matter   ___ gray matter
On average, how thick is the cerebral cortex (the layer of gray matter)? _____ mm
Is the thickness of the cerebral cortex constant wherever you measure?   Yes / No

Be prepared to demonstrate this to your instructor.

5. Another obvious brain structure is the cerebellum.
   Are there gyri and sulci associated with the cerebellum?   Yes / No
   If yes, be prepared to demonstrate them to your instructor.

6. Working from the dorsal side, expose the dorsal surface of the brain stem by carefully and gently pulling the cerebellum in a posterior direction (as depicted in the illustration which follows), thereby separating the cerebrum and cerebellum. Be gentle with this maneuver. Pulling the cerebellum too far will tear portions of the brain stem which you have yet to examine.

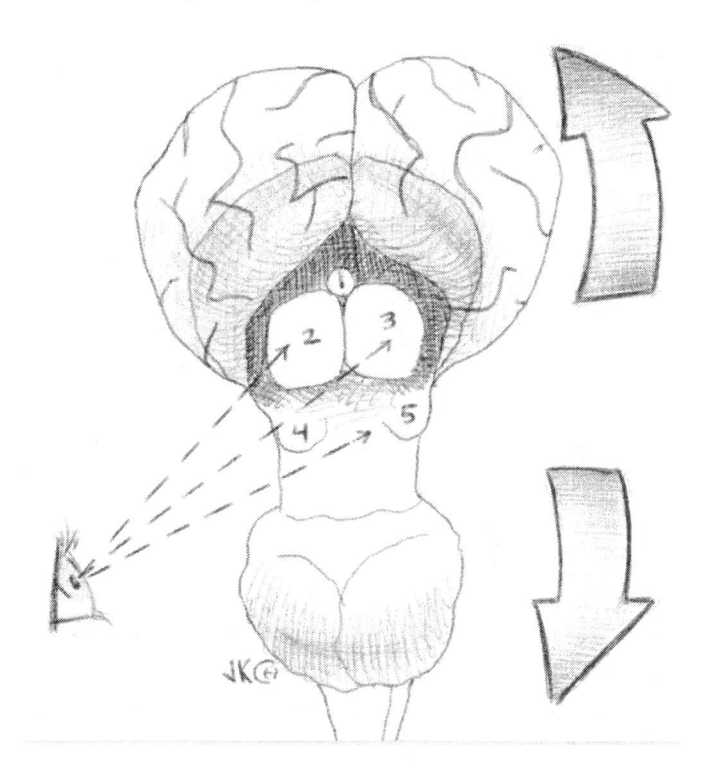

   Does this separation that exists between cerebrum and cerebellum run along a longitudinal or a transverse plane?

   ___ longitudinal plane   ___ transverse plane

   Based on an earlier answer, is this separation an example of a sulcus or a fissure?

   ___ sulcus   ___ fissure

   The dorsal surface of the midbrain should now be visible. If not, you may find it necessary to gently tear some arachnoid mater from the area. Doing this should yield good exposure of the midbrain and its associated structures. You should be able to see four paired eminences or bumps. These comprise the corpora quadrigemina. The corpora quadrigemina includes the paired superior and inferior colliculi. In addition, you should be able to see a fifth midline nodular structure (pineal body) slightly anterior and superior to the superior colliculi.

143

Visualizing the pineal body may require you to also gently separate the posterior portions of the two cerebral hemispheres.

Be prepared to demonstrate these structures to your instructor.

Refer to an available reference and determine the result of damaging or destroying the superior colliculi. Note: This can be done outside of lab time.

Deficit resulting from a damaged superior colliculus: _____

_____

Refer to an available reference and determine the result of damaging or destroying the inferior colliculi. Note: This also can also be done outside of lab time.

Deficit resulting from a damaged inferior colliculus: _____

_____

7. Viewing the brain from the lateral view, you should be able to see a band of tissue connecting the cerebellum laterally to the brain stem. This is the middle cerebellar peduncle, one of three pairs of cerebellar peduncles. Based on your inspection, would you consider them examples of gray or white matter?
    ____ gray matter   ____ white matter

   To what part of brain stem does it connect? _____

   There are actually three pairs of cerebellar peduncles, one pair for each of the three elements of the brain stem. The other two pairs are best viewed after the brain has been sectioned along a sagittal plane which comes later in this exercise. Be prepared to demonstrate the middle cerebellar peduncles to your instructor.

8. Move to the ventral surface of the cerebrum. Find the olfactory tracts and the olfactory bulbs. Measure the width of the <u>bulbs</u> for later comparison with those of the human. Be prepared to demonstrate these structures to your instructor.

   Width in millimeters: Right _____   Left _____

9. Examine the ventral surface of the brain, starting at the most anterior end and progressing caudally. Find each of the following structures. Use the labeled illustrations provided in this exercise to create your own study guide for these structures.

   Be prepared to demonstrate each structure to your instructor.

Briefly describe each in the spaces provided.

optic nerves _____

_____

optic chiasma _____

_____

optic tracts _____

_____

infundibulum _____

_____

pituitary or hypophysis (if present) _____

_____

mammillary body _____

_____

cerebral peduncles _____

_____

pons _____

_____

medulla _____

_____

From the above list of structures:
Select two whose functions are purely sensory.

_____   _____

Select one structure from the list whose function is totally motor.

_____

Select a structure from this list that is a part of the hypothalamus.

_____

Select a structure from this list which is a part of the midbrain.

_____

Also, pay special attention to the structure (design) of the mammillary body and to the sizes of the pons and medulla in the sheep brain. You will soon be comparing these structures in the human to determine if the same design and size relationships exist.

Mammillary body: _____

Which is bigger in the sheep?   Pons   Medulla

11. Now with the sheep brain positioned so that the ventral surface is facing down, section your specimen in the <u>midsagittal</u> plane. This is best done with a long bladed knife after the cerebral hemispheres have been bluntly separated. What fissure did you section <u>along</u> to do this?

_____

What fissure did you section <u>across</u> to do this?

_____

Have you separated the cerebral hemispheres by your sectioning?   Yes / No

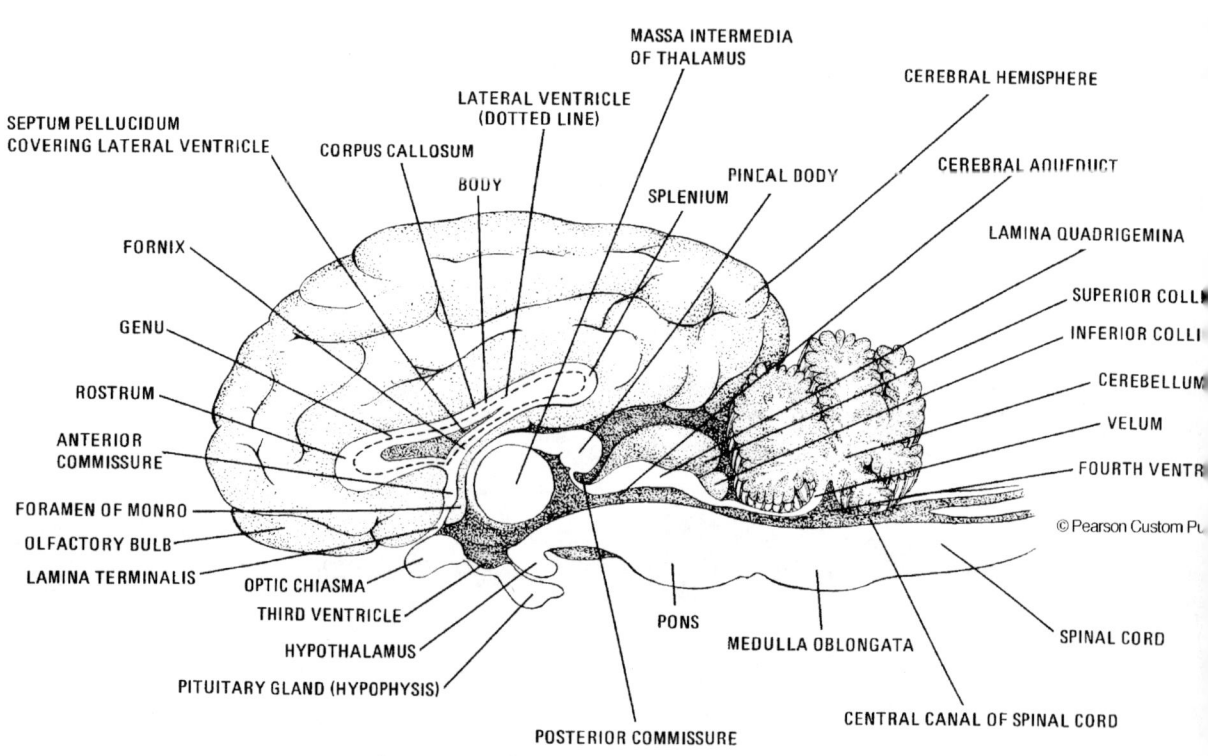

Consider the following list of structures. Which are now visible on the medial surface of the sectioned brain? Which of these structures were also visible on the ventral surface of the intact brain? Some of these are newly exposed structures not previously visible in the ventral view. Others are new views of structures already seen in the ventral view. Determine the visibility of these structures in both views.

Be prepared to support your findings for your instructor.

	Visible ventrally	Visible medially
Optic Nerve	Yes / No	Yes / No
Optic chiasma	Yes / No	Yes / No
Optic tract	Yes / No	Yes / No
Infundibulum	Yes / No	Yes / No
Cerebral peduncles	Yes / No	Yes / No
Mammillary body	Yes / No	Yes / No
Pons	Yes / No	Yes / No
Medulla	Yes / No	Yes / No

12. Refer to your midsagittal section. Is a lateral ventricle visible?   Yes / No
    If yes, be prepared to demonstrate it for your instructor.

    Within what major brain structure are the lateral ventricles located?

    _____

    What structure forms the roof of the lateral ventricles?

    _____

    What structure separates one lateral ventricle from the other?

    _____

    Is this structure visible on both halves of your specimen?   Yes / No
    If not, why?
    _____

    Be prepared to demonstrate all these structures for your instructor.

13. Use a doubled over pipe cleaner (or other soft, flexible probe) to <u>carefully</u> explore one lateral ventricle. Try not to tear the delicate cerebral tissue as you do so.

    Based on this gentle exploration, try to visualize the lateral ventricle and then draw its shape in the box that follows.

147

After you have done so, compare your conception of the lateral ventricles to the plastic casts of the ventricles which are available in the lab. Discard this pipe cleaner with <u>soiled waste</u> when you have completed your exploration.

Are the lateral ventricles more or less extensive than you envisioned on initial examination?

     ___ More extensive   ___ Less extensive

Describe an approach, method, or technique that an investigator could use to demonstrate the entire size, extent, and shape of a lateral ventricle.

_____

_____

Do you see any brownish material or what may appear to be debris within the ventricle of your specimen. Yes / No
If yes, this material is choroid plexus, a specialized capillary bed that is involved in the production of cerebrospinal fluid.
Based on your observation, do the lateral ventricles produce CSF? Yes / No

14. Sitting atop the midbrain but still inferior to the cerebrum is the region of the brain called the diencephalon. Functionally it links the brainstem to the higher brain centers of the cerebrum. External structures of the diencephalon include the optic chiasma, infundibulum and the mammillary bodies. The principal components of the diencephalon are the thalamus and the hypothalamus. The sagittal view of the brain is the best way to appreciate these elements. Locate the thalamus and the hypothalamus? The thalamus is composed of gray matter and is vaguely shaped like a yo-yo, with one half of the yo-yo on each side of the brain. The two halves of the thalamus are connected by the intermediate mass which is analogous to the peg that holds the yo-yo together. The hypothalamus is

immediately inferior to the thalamus. While its internal structure is unremarkable, you should be able to point it out if asked. Briefly describe the functions of the thalamus and hypothalamus. Note: This can be done outside of lab.

Thalamus _____

_____

_____

Hypothalamus _____

_____

_____

Does the diencephalon contain or contribute to any brain ventricles?   Yes / No
If yes, name it/them.
_____

Be prepared to demonstrate these structures for your instructor.

15. Observe the midbrain in midsagittal view.
Does the it contain or contribute to a brain ventricle? Yes / No
If yes, name it.
_____

Does the midbrain possess a passage through which CSF flows?   Yes / No
If yes, name it.
_____

Be prepared to demonstrate these structures for your instructor.

16. Move now to the hindbrain which houses the remaining brain ventricle.
Find and name this ventricle.
_____

Note: Because of earlier exploration involving the cerebellum, the margins (walls) of this chamber may no longer be intact. Nevertheless, be prepared to demonstrate its location for your instructor.

Compare the cut surface of the cerebellum with that of the cerebrum.
Do they show the same distribution pattern of gray and white matter?   Yes / No
Can you identify a cerebellar cortex?   Yes / No
If yes, how does the thickness of the cerebellar cortex compare to that of the cerebrum?   ___ cerebral cortex is thicker   ___ cerebellar cortex is thicker

Be prepared to demonstrate these to your instructor.

The cerebellum has an interesting pattern of white matter which is clearly visible in midsagittal section. Describe this pattern.

_____

Refer to your text to determine what this pattern is called.

_____

Be prepared to demonstrate it for your instructor.

17. Note: <u>Before beginning with this next activity, check with your instructor to see if you should proceed.</u> Working from the medial surface of the sectioned brain, locate the two remaining fiber tracts between the cerebellum and the brainstem. Be very gentle as you try to complete this. These are the superior cerebellar peduncle and the inferior cerebellar peduncle. To what specific portion of the brainstem does each connect?

Superior cerebellar peduncle: connects to _____

Inferior cerebellar peduncle: connects to _____

18. Lastly, section <u>another brain</u> through the infundibulum in the frontal plane. Note: To save time and facilitate your activity, your instructor may provide already sectioned specimens to support this last activity of the exercise.

Are any of the brain ventricles visible in a frontal section.   Yes / No
If yes, in the space which follows on the next page, draw a simple labeled diagram that illustrates each.

Is/are the thalamus and/or hypothalamus visible in the frontal section?   Yes / No
If yes, add them to the illustration below with appropriate labels.
Be prepared to demonstrate these structures for your instructor.

Are there any other structures which you identified in the midsagittal section which you can also see in this frontal view?   Yes / No
If yes, list them.

_____

_____

_____

_____

_____

_____

Be prepared to demonstrate any such structures to your instructor.

Part B: The Human Brain

1.   Meninges:
    With the ventral surface of the brain facing downward, examine the meninges covering the cerebrum.
    Is there any dura visible on your human brain specimen?   Yes / No
    If yes, how does it compare in thickness to that which you may have seen on the sheep brains?

    ____ Thicker than sheep   ____ Thinner than sheep

    Be prepared to demonstrate this membrane to your instructor.

    Look at all surfaces of your specimen. Find the arachnoid mater.
    Does the arachnoid cover the entire surface of the brain?   Yes / No
    Compare it with the arachnoid seen on the sheep brain.

    It is: ____ Thicker than sheep   ____ Thinner than sheep
              ____ Stronger than sheep   ____ Weaker than sheep
              ____ More vascular   ____ Less vascular

    Be prepared to demonstrate this meninge for your instructor.

    If some portion of the surface of the cerebrum is not already exposed to view, select an area of the brain's surface where you can position the tip of a probe just beneath the arachnoid. Gently lift the arachnoid in this area to expose the surface of the brain which is covered by the deepest of the meninges, the pia mater.

    Does the pia appear to be a thick, obvious, tough covering?   Yes / No
    Is the pia easily separable from the brain's surface?   Yes / No
    Is it significantly different from what you observed in the sheep?   Yes / No

    If you've had some difficulty with these observations, your instructor may prepare a section of human brain tissue that can be viewed under a dissecting microscope. That should more clearly demonstrate the pia and the arachnoid.

2.   Surface features:
    Compare the surface anatomy of the exposed cerebral hemispheres of the human brain with that of the sheep.

    Do they both exhibit a convoluted system of gyri and sulci?   Yes / No
    Do they both possess a longitudinal fissure?   Yes / No
    Do they both contribute to a transverse fissure?   Yes / No

    Since there are a number of human brain specimens that have already been sectioned to expose the cortex, it is not necessary for you to remove a thin superficial portion of one cerebral hemisphere as you did in the sheep. As in the sheep, observe the change in appearance of the nerve tissue from superficial to deep.

Can you distinguish the gray matter from the white matter?   Yes / No
Which is the deeper layer?   ____ Gray matter   ____ White matter
On average, how thick is the cerebral cortex (the layer of gray matter)? ____mm
Does the thickness of the cerebral cortex appear to be the same everywhere you measure?   Yes / No

Each hemisphere is divided into lobes. These lobes are named for the corresponding skull bones which overlie them. Refer to one of the human skulls available in the lab. Without using a reference other than the skull and based on your knowledge of the bones comprising the brain case, assign a name to the most anterior, the most posterior, the most superior, and the most lateral regions of the cerebral hemispheres.

    Anterior lobes _____

    Posterior lobes _____

    Superior lobes _____

    Lateral lobes _____

These lobes are separated by sulci. Try to distinguish the lobes by finding/identifying the sulci that separate them. Do the right and left lobes of the same brain exhibit <u>perfect</u> bilateral symmetry?   Yes / No

The central sulcus separates the anterior _____ lobes from the

more superior _____ lobes. Find it on each side of the brain.

Is the sulcus identical from one side to the other?   Yes / No
Is the sulcus identical from one specimen to another?   Yes / No

The ridge (gyrus) of tissue immediately anterior to the central sulcus is called the precentral gyrus. The gyrus immediately posterior to the sulcus is the postcentral gyrus. Find them and be prepared to demonstrate them to your instructor.

Are they identical from side to side?   Yes / No
Are they identical from specimen to specimen?   Yes / No

The sulcus which separates the parietal lobes from the occipital lobes is the parieto-occipital sulcus. It is generally <u>not</u> visible from a dorsal or posterior view. To best visualize it, you must examine a sagittally sectioned brain or gently spread open the posterior portion of the longitudinal fissure of an unsectioned brain and view the cerebral hemispheres from their medial aspects. Try to find this sulcus and be prepared to demonstrate it to your instructor.

Is it identical from side to side?   Yes / No
Is it identical from specimen to specimen? Yes / No

On each side of the brain, there is one deep lobe that is not visible from the surface. It is called the insula (Island of Reil). In order to visualize it, the lateral sulcus which separates the parietal and temporal lobes must be gently spread apart or a portion of a temporal lobe must be carefully removed. Refer first to one of the brain models available in the lab. These allow easy removal of the covering portion of the cerebrum and provide the needed exposure. Now that you have a clearer understanding of what you are looking for, carefully separate the parietal and temporal lobes and try to visualize the insula on an actual specimen. For this, your instructor may point out one or two specific specimens which have been specially prepared to expose the insula. Be prepared to demonstrate these structures for your instructor.

3. Observe the cerebrum from an inferior perspective. This corresponds to a ventral view of the sheep brain.

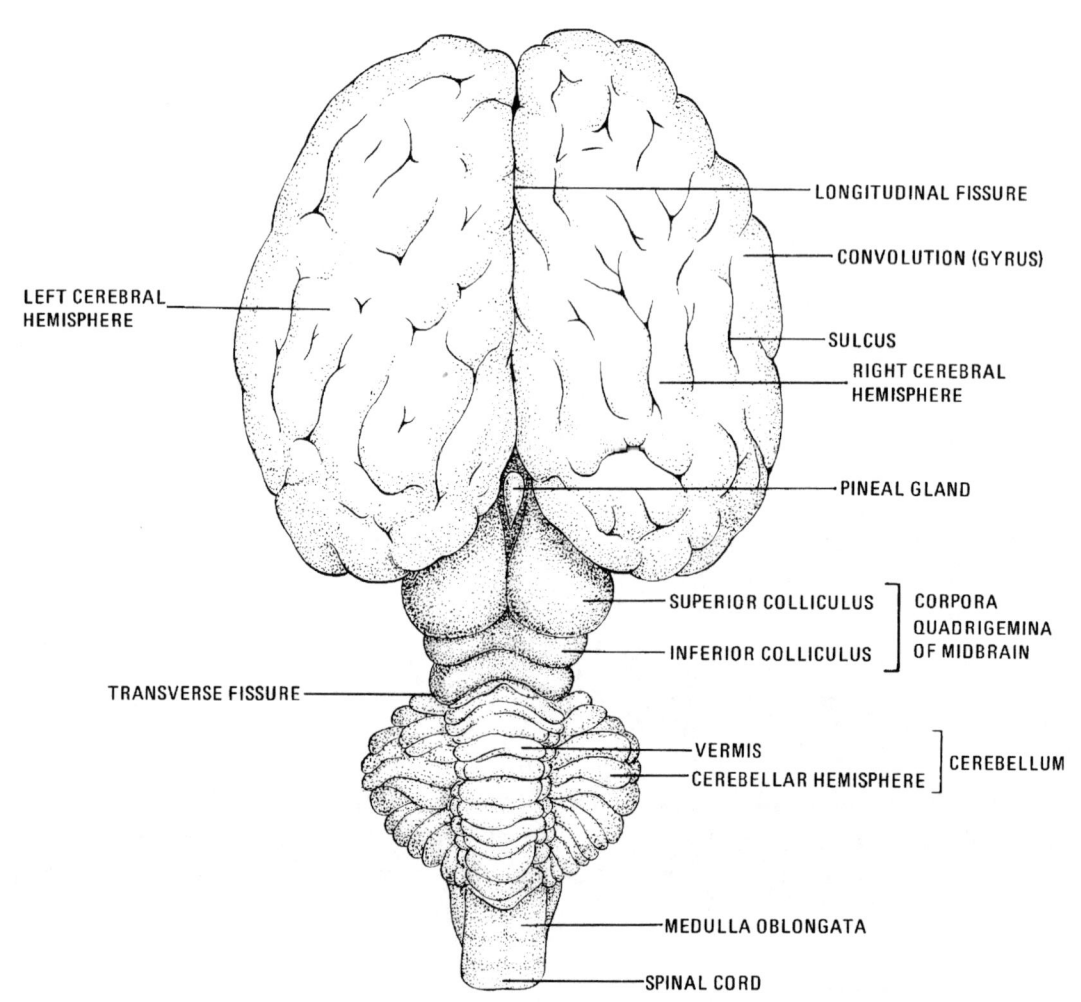

Find the olfactory tracts and bulbs. Compare the width of the olfactory bulbs with the width seen in the sheep brain.

    ____ Wider in human brain
    ____ Wider in sheep brain

Be prepared to demonstrate these structures for your instructor.

What might this indicate about the sense of smell in sheep as compared to humans?
_____

4. Compare the cerebellum of the human with that of the sheep.

Obvious gyrus/sulcus architecture:	sheep	human	both	neither
Obvious longitudinal division:	sheep	human	both	neither
Contributes to transverse fissure:	sheep	human	both	neither

5. Now, if you have not already done so, move to a sagittal section of a human brain.

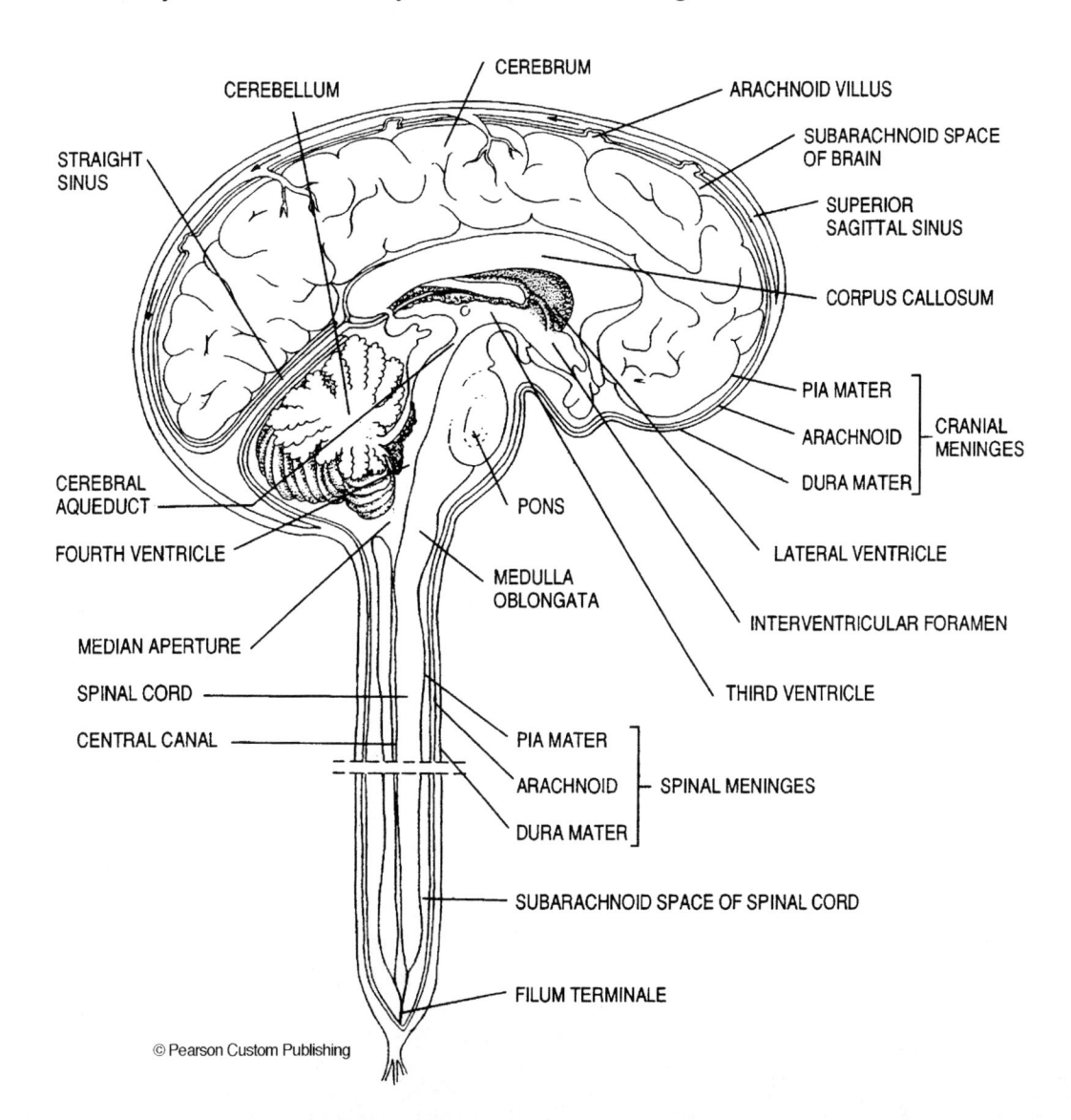

155

Refer to one of the human brain/brain stem/diencephalon models available in the lab and identify the cerebellar peduncles. Then try to <u>very gently</u> expose and identify the cerebellar peduncles in the human brain. Remember that in the sheep brain, the middle cerebellar peduncle was best viewed from the lateral perspective while the inferior and superior cerebellar peduncles were better seen by looking at a sagittal section from the medial aspect. To what portion of the brainstem does each cerebellar peduncle connect?

Superior _____

Middle   _____

Inferior _____

6. Observe and identify the structures of the dorsal midbrain as you did with the sheep brain. Can you locate the corpora quadrigemina?
From the dorsal perspective, which appears larger?   Superior / Inferior
Is this the same as was seen in the sheep brain?   Yes / No

Note any structural differences from sheep to human. _____
_____

Be prepared to demonstrate these structures and any differences for your instructor.

7. Observe the brain stem from the ventral view as you did with the sheep. Identify the same structures and be prepared to demonstrate them to your instructor.
 ____ optic nerves   ____ optic chiasma
 ____ optic tracts   ____ infundibulum
 ____ pituitary or hypophysis (if present)
 ____ mammillary body   ____ cerebral peduncles
 ____ pons   ____ medulla

Pay special attention to the relative prominence of the cerebral (not cerebellar) peduncles. Are they more prominent (that is, do they stand out more) in the sheep brain or in the human brain? You may find that you have the clearest view of the cerebral peduncles on the various human brain models available in lab.

 ___ More prominent in humans   ___ More prominent in sheep

Notice also the sizes of the pons and medulla.
In the human, which of the two is the larger?   ____ Pons   ____ Medulla
Was this also the case when you examined the sheep brain?   Yes / No
Describe any difference you notice.

Refer to an available reference and determine the function(s) of the cerebral peduncles.

_____

_____

Now, with their function in mind, do the differences in the structure/prominence of the cerebral peduncles you observed in the sheep and human brains make sense?   Yes / No
Please explain. _____

_____

8. On the ventral surface of the diencephalon, locate and identify the mammillary bodies. Compare them to the corresponding structure of the sheep. How are they different?

_____

_____

Be prepared to demonstrate these structures for your instructor.

Is the pituitary gland (hypophysis) present/intact in this specimen? Present / Absent
If present, be prepared to demonstrate it.

Identify the structure (or whatever remains of the structure) which connects the pituitary to the ventral surface of the diencephalon. _____

Be prepared to demonstrate this structure for your instructor.

9. Continue to work with a sagittal section of the human brain. As you did with the sheep brain, identify and determine the visibility in both the medial and ventral views of each of the following. Be prepared to demonstrate these structures for your instructor.

	Visible ventrally	Visible medially
Optic Nerve	Yes / No	Yes / No
Optic chiasma	Yes / No	Yes / No
Optic tract	Yes / No	Yes / No
Infundibulum	Yes / No	Yes / No
Cerebral peduncles	Yes / No	Yes / No
Mammillary body	Yes / No	Yes / No
Pons	Yes / No	Yes / No
Medulla	Yes / No	Yes / No

10. Study the plastic cast of the human brain ventricles. Find the interventricular foramen of Monroe. What <u>chambers</u> within the brain are joined by this passage?

___

Return to the sagittal section of the human brain and find an interventricular foramen of Monroe. Be very gentle and careful as you do this. The frontal section of the plastinated brain also shows the interventricular foramen quite nicely. Be prepared to demonstrate it to your instructor.

Go back to the brain ventricle casting. Now find a representation of a choroid plexus. Return to the sagittal section of the human brain and find an actual choroid plexus. What is the function of the choroid plexus?

___

Be prepared to demonstrate it to your instructor.

On the plastic casting, also notice the small hole in the third ventricle. In the intact brain, this hole is occupied by brain tissue. What structure of the diencephalon passes through this hole?

___

Compare the diameter of this structure in the human with that seen in the sheep brain.

___ Larger in sheep   ___ Larger in human

Be prepared to demonstrate it to your instructor.

11. Lastly, study a frontal section of the human brain. From the list provided below, identify those structures which are visible in this section. Be prepared to demonstrate these structures to your instructor.

___ lateral ventricles   ___ third ventricle
___ fourth ventricle   ___ thalamus
___ hypothalamus   ___ cerebral cortex
___ optic chiasm   ___ cerebellum

Are you able to identify any brain nuclei (defined areas of gray matter) in the frontal section?   Yes / No
If yes, be prepared to demonstrate examples to your instructor.

Exercise A-11

Gross Anatomy of the Central Nervous System - 2
The Spinal Cord

This portion of the central nervous system exercise involves the examination and study of a number of human specimens and models, including the spinal cord in situ, a wet preserved spinal cord, plastinated portions of spinal cord, and several models showing the spinal cord in cross section. Be sure that you work through this exercise systematically using a cadaver that has at least some of the spinal cord exposed by way of a mid-dorsal approach.

When working with the nervous system materials in general and the spinal cord in particular, you must exercise especial care because some of the structures are extremely delicate and fragile. Such structures are not at all forgiving of rough or careless technique. So…

Think before you explore these specimens.

Think while you explore these specimens.

Be very gentle and deliberate in handling these specimens.

Restore these specimens to their original condition when finished.

1. View the exposed spinal cord in the cadaver. First, what regions of the spinal cord (cervical, thoracic, lumbar) have been exposed on your cadaver?
    ___ cervical   ___ thoracic   ___ lumbar

    Next, in order to accomplish this exposure, specific posterior portions of individual vertebrae were removed. Carefully examine your specimen and then examine one of the skeletons. What specific parts of vertebrae were removed?
    _____

2. You already examined the dura mater during your study of the brain. Now find the dura around the cord. Be prepared to demonstrate it to your instructor.

    Examine the relationship between the dura mater and the surrounding bone. Demonstrate a space that exists between the dura and each vertebra.
    Is this space deep to or superficial to the dura?   Deep   Superficial
    Based on its location, what is this space called?
    _____

Use any available reference material to determine the nature of a clinical procedure to provide analgesia (elimination of pain) called an epidural nerve block. Be prepared to briefly describe and explain it to your instructor.

_____

_____

_____

3. The arachnoid mater is much more delicate and difficult to visualize on the spinal cord than was the case in the brain. Can you find this layer?   Yes / No
You may need to seek help from your instructor.

4. The delicate pia mater directly covers and is attached to the surface of the spinal cord. The surface of the pia mater is laced with tiny blood vessels which may or may not be visible (especially without magnification). Be prepared to demonstrate the pia mater (and, if visible, its vessels) to your instructor.

Carefully, and without tearing any structures, reflect the dura laterally. Extending in an outward direction are thin, delicate extensions called denticulate ligaments. These structures taper from the surface of the cord to a point where they attaché to the dura. In this way, they act to stabilize the position of the spinal cord within the dural sac. Carefully examine any denticulate ligaments that are still intact on your specimen. Draw them as viewed from behind in the space below and be prepared to demonstrate them to your instructor.

5. Look for a sulcus on the posterior surface of the spinal cord. Does it run along a transverse, coronal, or sagittal plane?
    ___ transverse   ___ coronal   ___ sagittal

Based on its orientation, what is the most appropriate name for this sulcus?

_____

Be prepared to demonstrate it to your instructor.

Now use a wet preserved and/or plastinated cord segment to examine the anterior surface of the spinal cord. Is there a discernible groove or crease on the anterior surface similar to the midline depression you examined on the posterior surface of the cord above?   Yes / No
If yes, be prepared to demonstrate it to your instructor. Be sure you know its name.

_____

6. Spinal nerves emerge from the cord by two sets of roots. Note that these roots are themselves formed by the coalescence of several even smaller nerve rootlets. Rootlets are the individual threads. They bundle together to form the root. The root is often hidden by the bone of the intervertebral foramen. Carefully find these rootlets and be prepared to demonstrate them to your instructor.

   Then find the individual nerve roots which merge to form a single spinal nerve. These nerve roots are referred to as dorsal and ventral. Notice that the extensions of the pia mater which you previously identified (denticulate ligaments) lie between the two nerve roots which combine to form one spinal nerve.

   As you progress laterally along the dorsal or posterior nerve root, you should notice a tiny bulbous enlargement. This structure is the spinal or dorsal root ganglion. Be prepared to demonstrate it to your instructor.

   What type of impairment, sensory or motor, would result from severing just the ventral nerve root?

   ___ sensory   ___ motor   ___ both

   Likewise, what type of impairment, sensory or motor, would result from severing the just dorsal nerve root?

   ___ sensory   ___ motor   ___ both

   Lastly, what type of impairment, sensory or motor or both, would result from severing an entire spinal nerve?

   ___ sensory   ___ motor   ___ both

7. Follow the spinal cord inferiorly. Notice that it tapers very obviously at its inferior end, a structure called the conus medularis. Find this structure and be prepared to demonstrate it to your instructor. Use the available human skeletons to determine at what vertebral level this structure lies, indicating the termination of the spinal cord. Note: Be sure to use proper vertebral notation.

   _____

8. Associated with the inferior portion of the spinal cord is a mass of nerve fibers called the cauda equina. Examine this structure carefully and closely. Is the cauda equina composed of spinal nerves or spinal nerve roots?

   _____

Try to envision the development of the spinal cord and that of the vertebral column. Since they begin development being equal in length, what must happen to their rates of growth to yield the arrangement of fibers that you are now examining?

9. Try to find the filum terminale. It is actually an extension of the pia mater. Be prepared to demonstrate this structure to your instructor. Even though it may not be fully exposed on these cadavers, try to determine how far inferiorly it extends?

10. Use a model and an appropriate reference to study the cord in cross section. If there is a section of preserved spinal cord available, it will be best viewed under a dissecting microscope. Draw and label a diagram that demonstrates the following structures or regions: gray matter, white matter, dorsal horn, ventral horn, lateral horn, posterior column, anterior column, lateral column, posterior median sulcus, anterior median fissure, posterior or dorsal roots, anterior or ventral roots, dorsal root ganglion, spinal nerve.

Notice that there is both white matter and gray matter visible in the cross section of the spinal cord. Which is the more superficial tissue.

How does this arrangement of white and gray matter in the spinal cord compare with what you have already observed in the brain?

From the above list of structures, indicate all which are visible in the cadaver.

Exercise A-12

Gross Anatomy of the
Peripheral Nervous System 1:
The Cranial Floor and the Cranial Nerves

This exercise involves the examination and study of the cranial floor with its associated dura mater and the distal segments of cranial nerves. Also involved in this exercise is the examination of the proximal portions of the cranial nerves as observable on the forebrain and the ventral brain stem.

Part A: Floor of the Cranium

In completing this portion of the exercise, the human cadavers will be your primary specimens. On each, the calvarium has been removed, clearly exposing the cranial floor. In addition, you should use the "empty head" models and the human skulls to aid you in your study. When using the human skulls, remember to handle them carefully and always <u>with two clean hands from underneath</u>.

1. Find the dura mater on the cranial floor. It is composed of two layers: a periosteal layer that strongly adheres to the cranial floor and a deeper meningeal layer actually closer to the brain). Over most of the dura these layers are inseparable and therefore not easily observed. The two layers are most visible wherever the dura splits to form dural sinuses which serve as passages for venous blood draining from the brain.

2. The meningeal layer of the dura extends inward from the inner cranial surface to form three different partitions which serve to anchor the brain. Two of these are oriented in a mid-sagittal plane and the third is a transverse partition.
    The most superior and most extensive partition anchors the cerebral hemispheres sagittally. Look first at the "empty head" models available in lab and then at the cadaver craniums and separate brains to identify this structure.

    What is its name? _____

    A much less prominent partition anchors the cerebellum sagitally in exactly the same fashion. Try to locate it on both models and specimens.

    What is its name? _____

    Lastly, locate and identify the transverse partition that separates and stabilizes the cerebrum and cerebellum.

    What is its name? _____

2. Find examples of dural sinuses. Wherever you identify a dural sinus, you should be able to appreciate that its formation results from the separation of the dura into its meningeal and periosteal layers. Be prepared to demonstrate both dural layers for your instructor if asked.

Two specific sinuses which are visible on all specimens are the superior sagittal sinus and the transverse sinus. Each of these is associated with one of the dural partitions that you have already identified. Given that, their respective names should help you greatly in locating each. In the space below, link each of these sinuses to the dural partition with which it is closely associated. Be prepared to demonstrate each to your instructor.

Sinus	Dural Partition
Superior sagittal sinus	
Transverse sinus	

Part B: Cranial Nerves

Your study of cranial nerves begins with identifying each and then mastering essential information about each of the twelve pairs of nerves. Following this is further observation and a more extensive investigation of selected cranial nerves.

1. For each of the 12 pairs of cranial nerves, you need to be able to demonstrate the following:
    a. the proximal portion of the nerve on the human brain.
    b. the distal portion of the nerve on the floor of the cranium.
    c. the opening used by the nerve to exit the cranium (either as visible on the cadaver or on a separate skull).

2. For each of the 12 pairs of cranial nerves, you should be able to provide the following functional information:
    a. whether it is sensory, mixed, or motor with proprioception (mostly motor).
    b. as applicable, the organs receiving motor input by a specific nerve.
    c. as applicable, the source of sensory input carried by a specific nerve.

Use your textbook or the following illustrations to complete the outline which follows for each of the 12 pairs of cranial nerves.

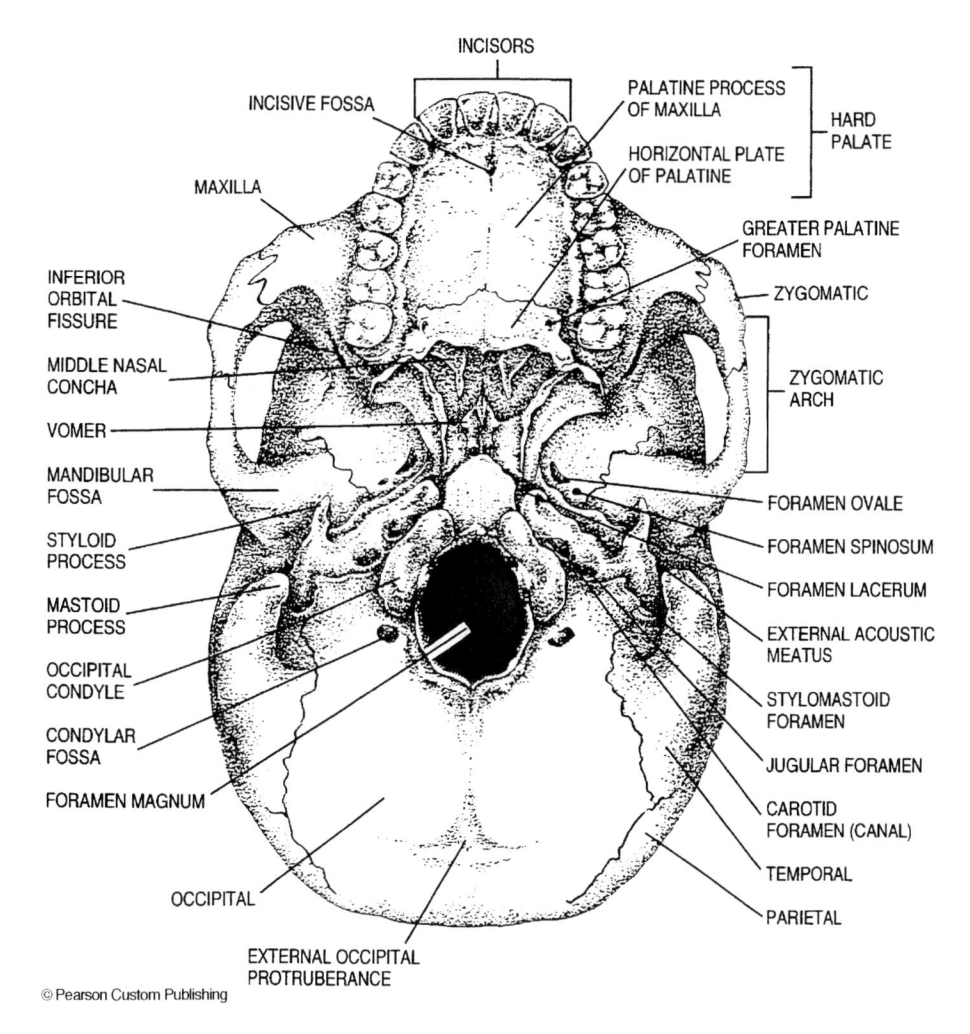

HUMAN, SKULL, INFERIOR VIEW

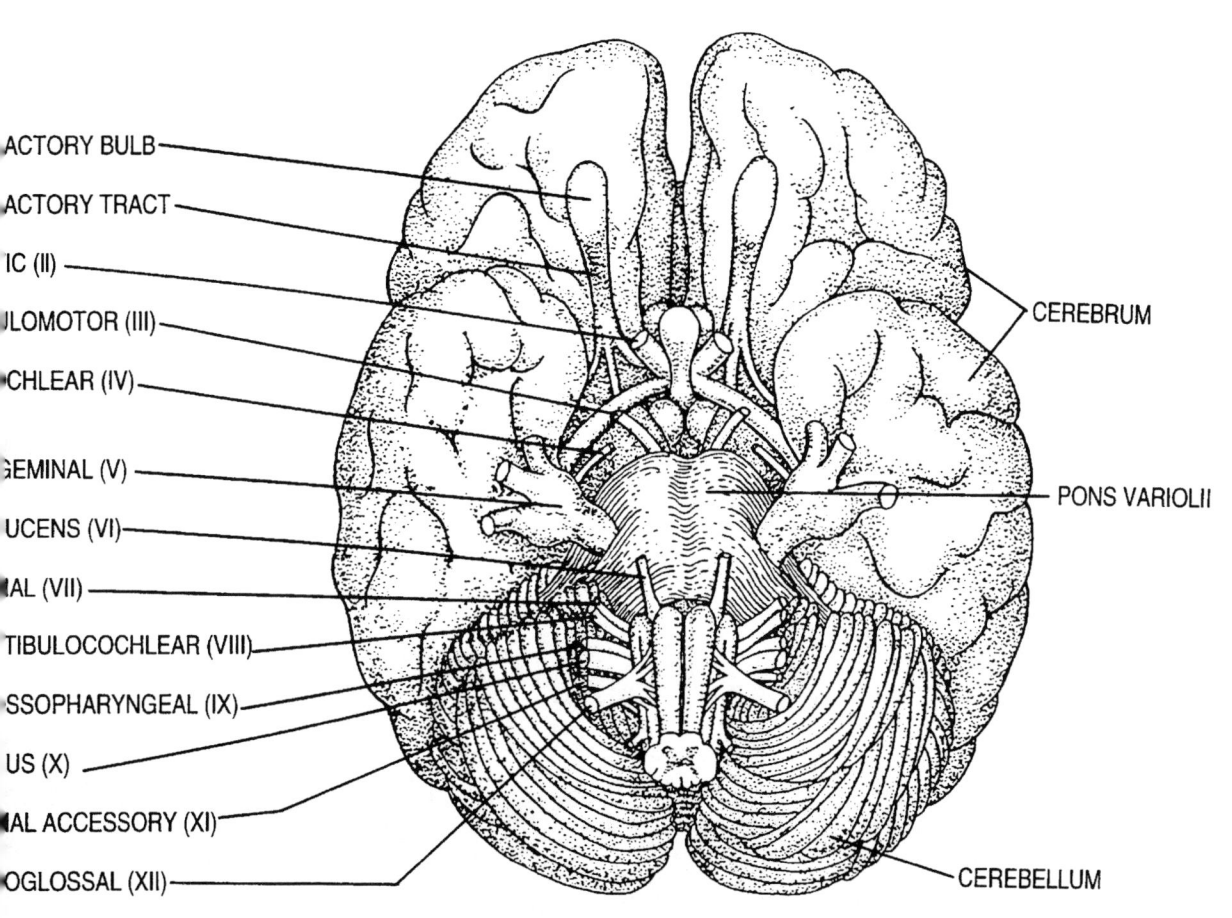

I Name: _____ Sensory / Motor / Mixed

Exit foramen: _____

Sensory source: _____ or

Motor target(s) _____

Representative function(s) _____

_____

_____

II Name: _____ Sensory / Motor / Mixed

Exit foramen: _____

Sensory source: _____ or

Motor target(s) _____

Representative function(s) _____

_____

_____

III Name: _____ Sensory / Motor / Mixed

Exit foramen: _____

Sensory source: _____ or

Motor target(s) _____

Representative function(s) _____

_____

_____

IV   Name: _____   Sensory / Motor / Mixed

   Exit foramen: _____

   Sensory source: _____ or

   Motor target(s) _____

   Representative function(s) _____

   _____

   _____

V   Name: _____   Sensory / Motor / Mixed

   Exit foramen: _____

   Sensory source: _____ or

   Motor target(s) _____

   Representative function(s) _____

   _____

   _____

VI   Name: _____   Sensory / Motor / Mixed

   Exit foramen: _____

   Sensory source: _____ or

   Motor target(s) _____

   Representative function(s) _____

   _____

   _____

VII Name: _____ Sensory / Motor / Mixed

Exit foramen: _____

Sensory source: _____ or

Motor target(s) _____

Representative function(s) _____

_____

_____

VIII Name: _____ Sensory / Motor / Mixed

Exit foramen: _____

Sensory source: _____ or

Motor target(s) _____

Representative function(s) _____

_____

_____

IX Name: _____ Sensory / Motor / Mixed

Exit foramen: _____

Sensory source: _____ or

Motor target(s) _____

Representative function(s) _____

_____

X   Name: _____   Sensory / Motor / Mixed

        Exit foramen: _____

        Sensory source: _____ or

        Motor target(s) _____

        Representative function(s) _____

        _____

        _____

XI   Name: _____   Sensory / Motor / Mixed

        Exit foramen: _____

        Sensory source: _____ or

        Motor target(s) _____

        Representative function(s) _____

        _____

        _____

XII   Name: _____   Sensory / Motor / Mixed

        Exit foramen: _____

        Sensory source: _____ or

        Motor target(s) _____

        Representative function(s) _____

        _____

        _____

3. Only one cranial nerve extends beyond the head and neck. Name it.

_____

This nerve is visible in the neck on either side running between the common carotid artery and the internal jugular vein. Be prepared to demonstrate this nerve to your instructor as it travels into and within the mediastinum.

4. One cranial nerve, the facial (VII), splits into 5 motor branches which control the muscles of facial expression. Name its five branches.

_____   _____

_____   _____

_____

Be prepared to demonstrate the approximate locations of these branches on yourself. If a specimen has been appropriately dissected, you should identify the branches of the facial nerve there as well.

5. Use reference material to find the hypoglossal nerve within the carotid triangle. Note, the carotid triangle is an area of the neck bordered by the sternocleidomastoid muscle, the posterior belly of the digastricus muscles and the superior belly of the omohyoid muscle. If it has been exposed on your cadaver, be prepared to demonstrate the carotid triangle and the hypoglossal nerve within this triangle.

6. Only one cranial nerve (XI) originates partly from the spinal cord. In its course, it therefore both enters and exits the skull. Name this nerve.

Name _____

    Entry foramen _____

    Exit foramen _____

Be prepared to demonstrate the nerve and its entry and exit passages for your instructor.

7. The largest cranial nerve is the trigeminal. The main trunk enters a large ganglion in the epidural space before exiting the skull. It then splits into three main branches. Try to identify the trigeminal (Gasserian) ganglion and the three nerve branches which arise from it.

The names of the branches refer to the regions innervated. Briefly summarize the areas innervated by each branch.

Opthalmic   _____

Maxillary   _____

Mandibular   _____

If the dura has been opened to allow it, follow the branches distally to the cranial exit ports for each. Be prepared to demonstrate these to your instructor.

Exercise A-13

**Gross Anatomy of the
Peripheral Nervous System 2:
Peripheral Nerves**

This exercise involves the examination and study of one nerve plexus and a limited selection of peripheral nerves. Specific structures have been selected for this exercise because of their visibility and/or their clinical or practical relevance. Depending on the dissection exposures used on some specimens, it is possible that other nerve plexi and/or peripheral nerves may be exposed. Your instructor will call these to your attention if such are available.

A nerve plexus is a network of spinal nerves in which fibers originating at one level of the cord intermingle with fibers from one or more other nearby levels to form peripheral nerves. The result is the formation of peripheral nerves containing fibers from different cord levels. Such a design makes it less likely that a localized injury to a particular nerve's origin or to the spinal cord will completely eliminate the function served by that spinal nerve.

Today you will examine the brachial plexus which is one of four such plexi. In addition, a number of peripheral nerves have been selected for your observation. These are associated with the thorax, the upper extremity, and the lower extremity.

1. The brachial plexus has been exposed in at least one of the specimens. Examine the plexus and verify that there is a progression of intermingling of fibers starting from the nerve roots which originate at the spinal cord through trunks, divisions, cords and finally terminal nerves. The diagram below depicts this design for the brachial plexus. Refer to a reference to indicate the roots, trunks, divisions, cords, and terminal nerves.

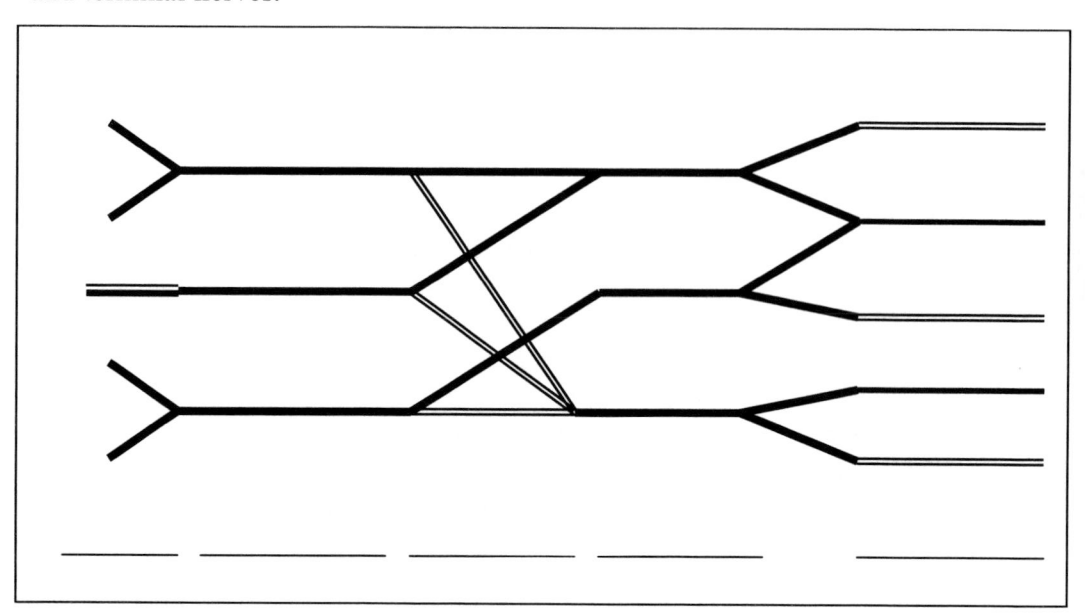

   There are a number of peripheral nerves which arise from the brachial plexus but only five of them are considered major nerves. Two of these, the axillary supplying the deltoid muscle and the musculocutaneous supplying the biceps brachii and brachialis muscles remain in the proximal portion of the upper extremity. Try to locate and identify these nerves?

   Three major nerves extend to the most distal portions of the upper extremity. These are the median, radial, and ulnar nerves. Try to locate and identify these three nerves.

   If the ulnar nerve was damaged, which portion of the hand do you think would lose sensation?
   ____ Lateral fingers   ____ Medial fingers

   If the median nerve was damaged, which portion of the hand do you think would lose sensation?
   ____ Lateral fingers   ____ Medial fingers

   Identify and trace the radial nerve distally. If it was damaged, which function would more likely be lost?
   ____ Finger flexion   ____ Finger extension

   Be prepared to demonstrate these nerves to your instructor.

2. The most important nerve arising from the cervical plexus (often not easily viewed) is the phrenic nerve. It supplies the diaphragm. Try to locate the phrenic nerve in the thorax. If successful, trace it as far as you can in a superior direction. In the neck, it runs parallel to and lateral to the internal jugular vein. At what vertebral level does it appear to arise? (Depending on the exposure in your cadaver, you may not be able to make an accurate determination.)

    _____   ___ Can't tell

    Based on its peripheral innervation, what would be the outcome if the spinal cord were severed such that the phrenic nerve was no longer connected to the brain?

    _____

    Be prepared to demonstrate this nerve to your instructor.

3. Also in the thorax running from superior to inferior along the vertebral bodies is the sympathetic chain of paravertebral ganglia. These ganglia are visible beneath the parietal pleura which lines the chest cavity. They will appear as slightly widened portions of a continuous band of nerve fibers along the inner thoracic wall very close to or only slightly lateral to the vertebral bodies of the thoracic spine. Try to locate the chain and any individual ganglia.

    Chain visible: Yes / No

    Individual ganglia visible: Yes / No

    There are also sympathetic nerves (actually preganglionic fibers) which originate between T5 and T12 and pass through the chain ganglia without synapsing on their way to the abdomen. These are the greater, lesser, and least splanchnic nerves and should be visible extending obliquely and inferiorly toward the diaphragm. Once in the abdomen, these nerves contribute to the large autonomic ganglia of the abdomen. Locate one or more of these splanchnic nerves within the thorax and try to trace it/them toward or into the abdomen.

    Splanchnic nerves:
        Greater splanchnic nerve: Visible: Yes / No

        Lesser splanchnic nerve: Visible: Yes / No

        Least splanchnic nerve: Visible: Yes / No

4. Two major nerves supplying structures of the lower extremity are the femoral nerve and the sciatic nerve. Only one is easily visible from an anterior approach. Which one?

    _____

Find it and describe its location relative to the large blood vessels with which it is associated.

___ Medial to both   ___ Intermediate to vessels   ___ Lateral to both

Be prepared to demonstrate this nerve to your instructor.

Find the sciatic nerve. Based on its location and the path of branches which arise from it, what major muscle group of the thigh is likely supplied by this nerve?

_____

When an individual suffers from sciatica, where do you think the pain is felt?

_____

Be prepared to demonstrate this nerve to your instructor.

Exercise A-14

Special Sensory Structures:
The Eye and the Ear

Introduction:
In contrast to the general cutaneous senses, the four senses of smell, taste, sight and hearing are given the designation "special senses" because they have receptor organs which are highly complex. The special senses of smell and taste will be studied physiologically later in the semester. In this exercise, we will concentrate on the anatomy of the eye and ear.

Part A: The Eye
Your study of the anatomy of the eye will involve the dissection of a cow eye and the examination of the extrinsic muscles of the eye on one of the human cadavers. In addition, there are various models and museum mounted specimens to facilitate your study. While there are numerous reference texts available in the lab, probably the best source of information for you is your course textbook. Information, illustrations, and photos of eye and ear anatomy can be found in the chapter on special senses. You should bring your text to lab for this exercise.

Cow Eye Dissection:
1. One member of your group will gather up the dissection tools (scalpel, scissors, blunt probe, dissecting needle) while another member obtains a specimen from your instructor.

2. With the scissors, trim away most of the soft tissue and muscle that surrounds the eyeball. You should be able to identify the large optic nerve stump extending from the posterior surface of the eyeball. What is its diameter in millimeters? Cut it and the associated soft tissue transversely so that the back portion of the specimen is flat and the eye will rest in your tray facing upwards.

3. There are two primary chambers within the eye; a large posterior vitreous chamber and a smaller anterior aqueous chamber. You will first open and examine the aqueous chamber. Using the point of the scalpel, scratch back and forth until you are through the cornea just inside its outermost edge.

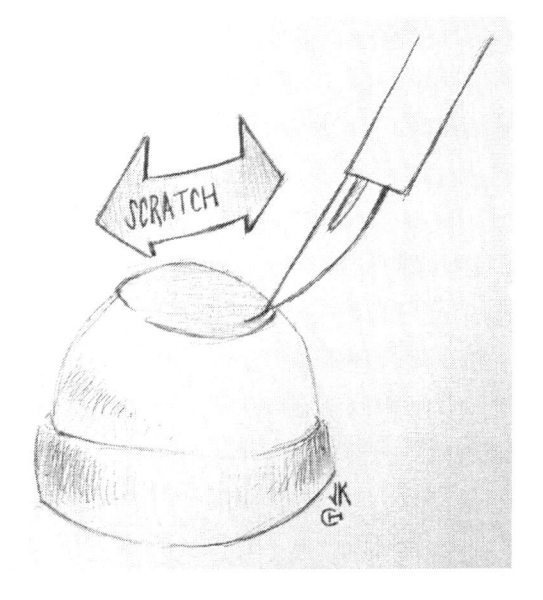

Is the shape of the cow cornea the same as the human cornea? Yes / No
Is there any observable feature of the preserved cornea that is not consistent with the appearance of this structure in the <u>living</u> organism?   Yes / No
If yes, explain.

_____

_____

When you are successful in scratching completely through the full thickness of the cornea, some clear fluid will likely be expressed. Now take a scissors and gently snip <u>just inside</u> the outer rim of the cornea.

You may either remove it completely or leave it attached by a small hinge of tissue. Is the cornea thicker or thinner than you expected?
       ___ Thicker   ___ Thinner

You should now easily be able to visualize and inspect the lens and the iris which controls the size of the pupil. Is the iris thick or thin?
       ___ Thick   ___ Thin

The lens should be held firmly in place. Press it <u>gently</u>. Is it?   Yes / No

Describe its appearance. _____

_____

Is its appearance consistent with the lens of a living individual?   Yes / No

Explain _____

_____

4. Next open the vitreous chamber. Do so by again using the <u>point</u> of your scalpel to scratch back and forth creating a small slit through the wall of the sclera approximately 1/4 inch from the outer edge of the cornea.

See the illustration to the right for clarification.

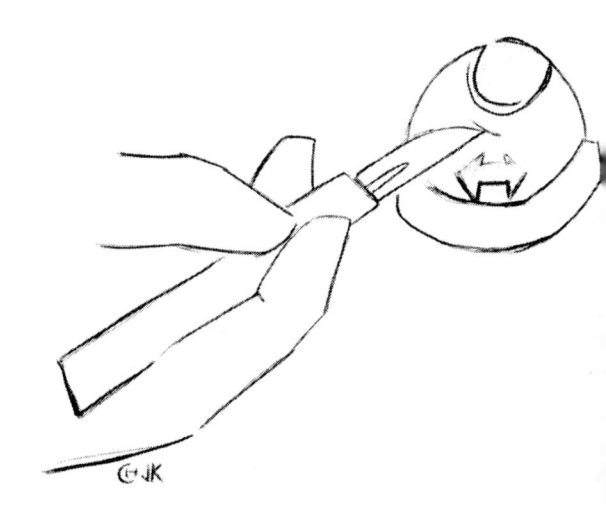

Once completely through the sclera (the tip of the scalpel blade should extend at least 1/2 inch into the vitreous chamber), use your scissors to extend the cut completely around the eyeball.

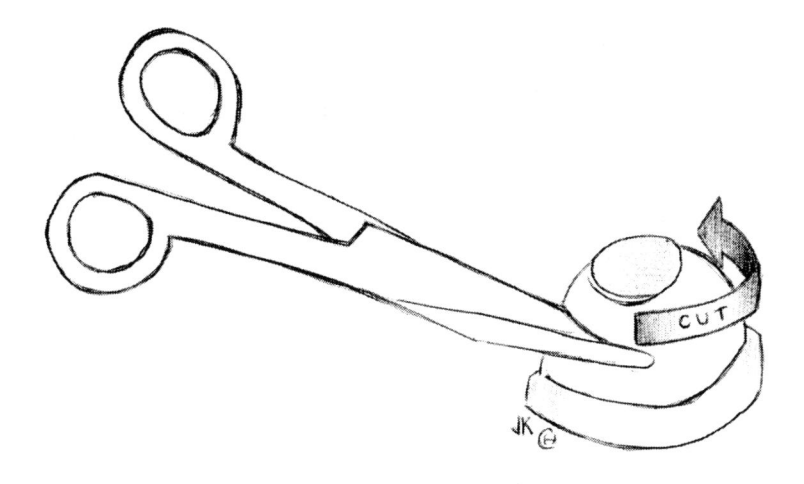

Very important: Do <u>not</u> try to lift or remove the anterior portion of the eyeball yet.

Before proceeding further, make a prediction regarding the color and light-transmitting nature of the vitreous body.

Once the cut through the sclera is completed, insert the scissors through the cut that you've made and completely sever all connection between the anterior and posterior portions of the specimen. It will seem as if you are not cutting anything. In reality, you are cutting through the gel that is the vitreous and which connects the delicate retina to the lens. **Again, do not try to lift the anterior piece until all connection between the vitreous and the lens has been severed.** If you are confused as to how to proceed, consult your instructor before proceeding further. Once this cut has been accomplished, gently lift the anterior piece to expose the vitreous chamber and the delicate internal structure of the eye.

Refer to the diagram of the eye which follows on the next page. Although the plane of the diagram is different than the perspective you obtain with your dissection, the drawing should prove helpful in your examination of the eye.

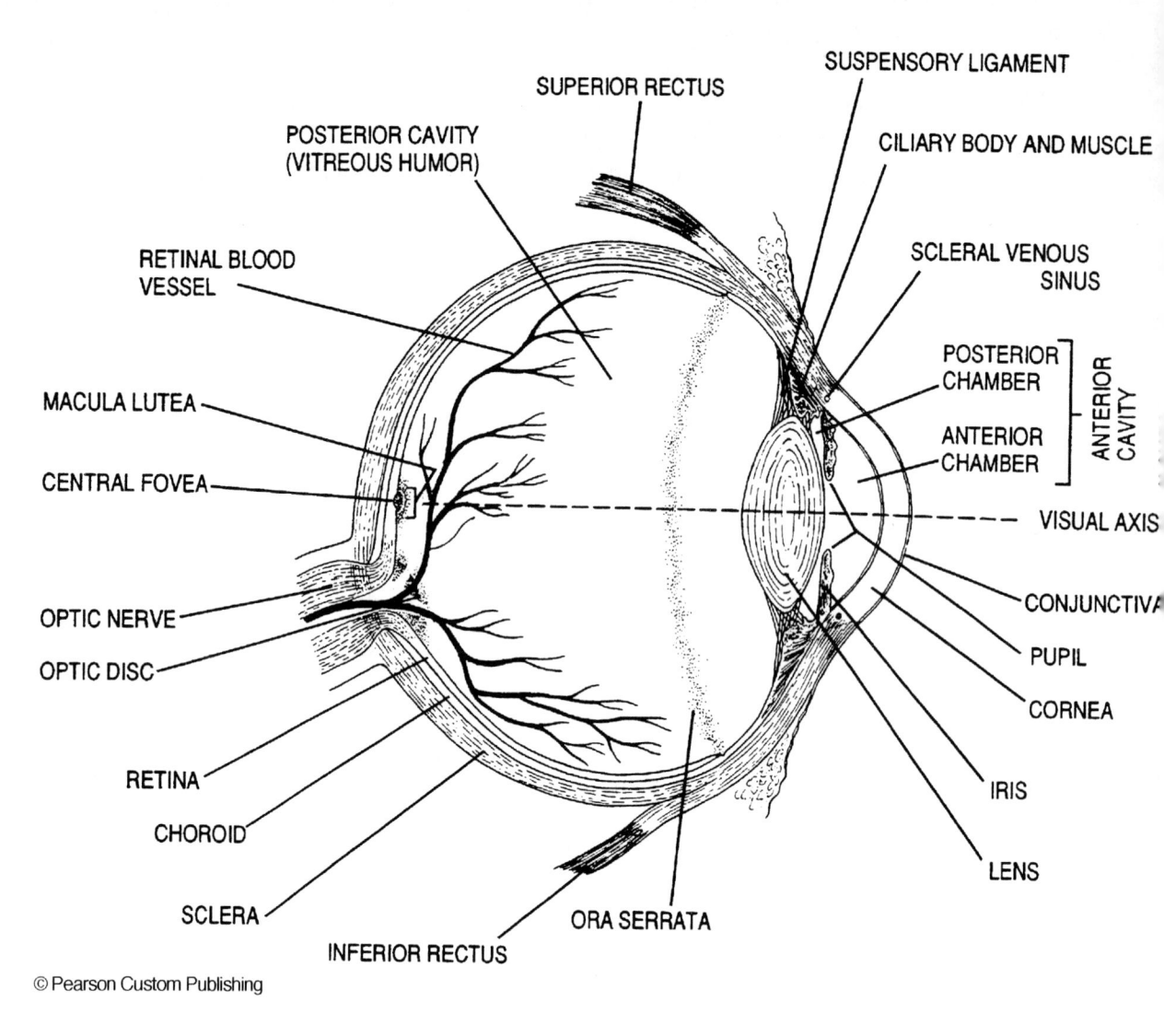

You should now be able to visualize and inspect the three layers or tunics which form the wall of the eye, namely the retina, choroid, and sclera or fibrous tunic. Use the diagram above to list them from superficial to deep.

Superficial _____

Middle _____

Deep _____

Gently roll the eyeball to one side and then the other.
Is the retina attached to the vitreous?   Yes / No

Describe the color and consistency of the vitreous body. _____

_____

How does appearance of the vitreous compare to your earlier prediction?

_____

Next, locate the optic disc (blind spot), the fovea, and the macula lutea. The optic disc is formed by the convergence of all the nerve fibers which originate in the photoreceptors of the retina. On inspection, it is usually visible as the site in the retina where all blood vessels appear to be converging.
Is it visible in your specimen?   Yes / No

The fovea is a small pit located near the optic disc.
Is it visible in your specimen?   Yes / No
What is the approximate distance between these two structures? _____ mm
Examine these structures on the specimens of your fellow students. Based on this, is the distance between fovea and optic disc constant or is it variable from specimen to specimen.
          ___ constant   ___ variable

If you have a well preserved specimen, the macula lutea will appear as a pale yellow ring around the fovea. In many specimens the macula is not distinct or clearly defined.
Is it visible in your specimen?   Yes / No

Be prepared to demonstrate these structures to your instructor.

An examination of the internal surface of the anterior portion of the vitreous chamber (which includes the posterior surface of the lens) will demonstrate the ciliary body. It is a thickened extension of the vascular coat of the eye and contains the ciliary muscles. In the box provided below, draw the ciliary body (muscles) and the lens as they appear from the perspective of your dissection.

The ciliary muscles function in altering the tension applied to the perimeter of the lens and thereby act to change the shape of the lens.

With gentle care it is possible to visualize the suspensory ligaments (zonule) which connect the ciliary body to the lens. Hold the anterior section of the eye facing downward. With a finger, apply gentle upward pressure on the lens. As you do so, the suspensory ligaments are stressed and can be seen from the interior side as fine, colorless, radiating lines extending outward from the lens. Be prepared to demonstrate these structures for your instructor and to briefly describe their functions.

Refer to your text and try to determine how the ciliary muscles and the suspensory ligaments cooperate to change the shape of the lens for near and distant vision. Use a reference to complete the following statements.

a. When the ciliary muscles contract, how does the tension on the suspensory ligaments change?

___ increase ___ decrease

How is the shape of the lens affected?

___ flatter ___ rounder

b. When the ciliary muscles relax, how does the tension on the suspensory ligaments change?

___ increase ___ decrease

How is the shape of the lens affected?

___ flatter ___ rounder

Cadaver Exploration - Extrinsic Eye Muscles:

1. Two different approaches are possible to provide exposure of the extrinsic eye muscles. One involves cutting through the portion of the frontal bone which forms the roof of the orbit. This is done from inside the brain case. With the exception of the inferior rectus muscle, this approach allows excellent visualization of the rectus muscles, the levator palpebrae superioris, and the belly of the superior oblique. It also provides the best access to the nerves which innervate these muscles and to the optic nerve.

   The other approach is a frontal one. By carefully cutting through the upper and lower conjunctiva, all six extrinsic muscles can be well exposed.

   It is likely that both approaches will be represented on the cadavers you are studying. You should explore the orbit using access gained by both approaches.

Carefully probe the orbit to locate and identify the six extrinsic muscles which act to move the eyeball. Four of these six muscles are named "rectus". Based on your observation, can you explain why? A table or list of word roots should prove helpful here.

_____

_____

The remaining two are named "oblique". Based on your observation, attempt to explain why?

_____

_____

You should also locate and identify the levator palpebrae superioris muscle which moves the upper eyelid. Based on your observation, does this muscle move the eyelid up or down?

        ___ moves it up   ___ moves it down

Although you can (and should) look up the actions of the six extrinsic eye muscles for verification, we recommend you first try to deduce (without the assistance of any reference material) how each moves the eye when contracting. Some find it helpful to use a ball as the eye and a piece of tape as an individual muscle. Pulling the tape in the same direction as would the muscle will allow the ball to mimic the resulting movement of the eye. The movements of the rectus muscles are straightforward and easily determined. Those of the two obliques are more subtle and require more concentration and insight. In the spaces below, briefly summarize the eye movements caused by contraction of the six extrinsic eye muscles.

Superior rectus _____

Medial rectus _____

Inferior rectus _____

Lateral rectus _____

Superior oblique _____

Inferior oblique _____

2. As you continue to examine the orbit from within, try to locate and identify the lacrimal glands. They are small and located external to the superior and lateral portion of the eyeball. If you are successful, indicate whether these glands share

the characteristic texture you have previously observed in other glandular structures.

                     ___ characteristic texture   ___ not typical texture

Be prepared to demonstrate this to your instructor.

Use one of the skeletons or a skull to locate the bony passage through which the nasolacrimal duct passes. Be prepared to demonstrate this to your instructor. If there is a sagittal head section available, the opening of the nasolacrimal duct into the nasal passage will be visible as a small hole just inferior to the inferior nasal concha.

Part B: The Ear:
Your study of the ear will largely center on the identification of structures using anatomical models and the few bony specimens (ossicles in plexiglass, opened temporal bone) that are available in lab. However, if we are successful in exposing the structures of the middle and inner ear on one of the human specimens (technically a very difficult dissection), students may have the opportunity to view the auditory ossicles and other related structures *in situ*. Unless directed otherwise by your instructor, limit your investigation to the level of detail visible on the anatomical models. The most available references for this work are the illustrations which follow and your textbook. Other general and specialized references are available in the lab for your use if needed.

Use the ear models and the ear ossicles in plexiglass to find the structures listed below. With the exception of the auditory tube and the vestibulocochlear nerve, you should be able to categorize each structure as belonging to either the inner (internal) ear, middle ear, or outer (external) ear.

Auricle	___ inner ear	___ middle ear	___ outer ear
External auditory canal	___ inner ear	___ middle ear	___ outer ear
Tympanic membrane	___ inner ear	___ middle ear	___ outer ear
Malleus	___ inner ear	___ middle ear	___ outer ear
Incus	___ inner ear	___ middle ear	___ outer ear
Stapes	___ inner ear	___ middle ear	___ outer ear
Oval window	___ inner ear	___ middle ear	___ outer ear
Round window	___ inner ear	___ middle ear	___ outer ear
Vestibule	___ inner ear	___ middle ear	___ outer ear
Cochlea	___ inner ear	___ middle ear	___ outer ear
Semicircular canals	___ inner ear	___ middle ear	___ outer ear
Vestibulocochlear nerve (including the vestibular and cochlear branches)	___ inner ear	___ middle ear	___ outer ear
Eustachian tube (auditory tube or pharyngotympanic tube)	___ inner ear	___ middle ear	___ outer ear

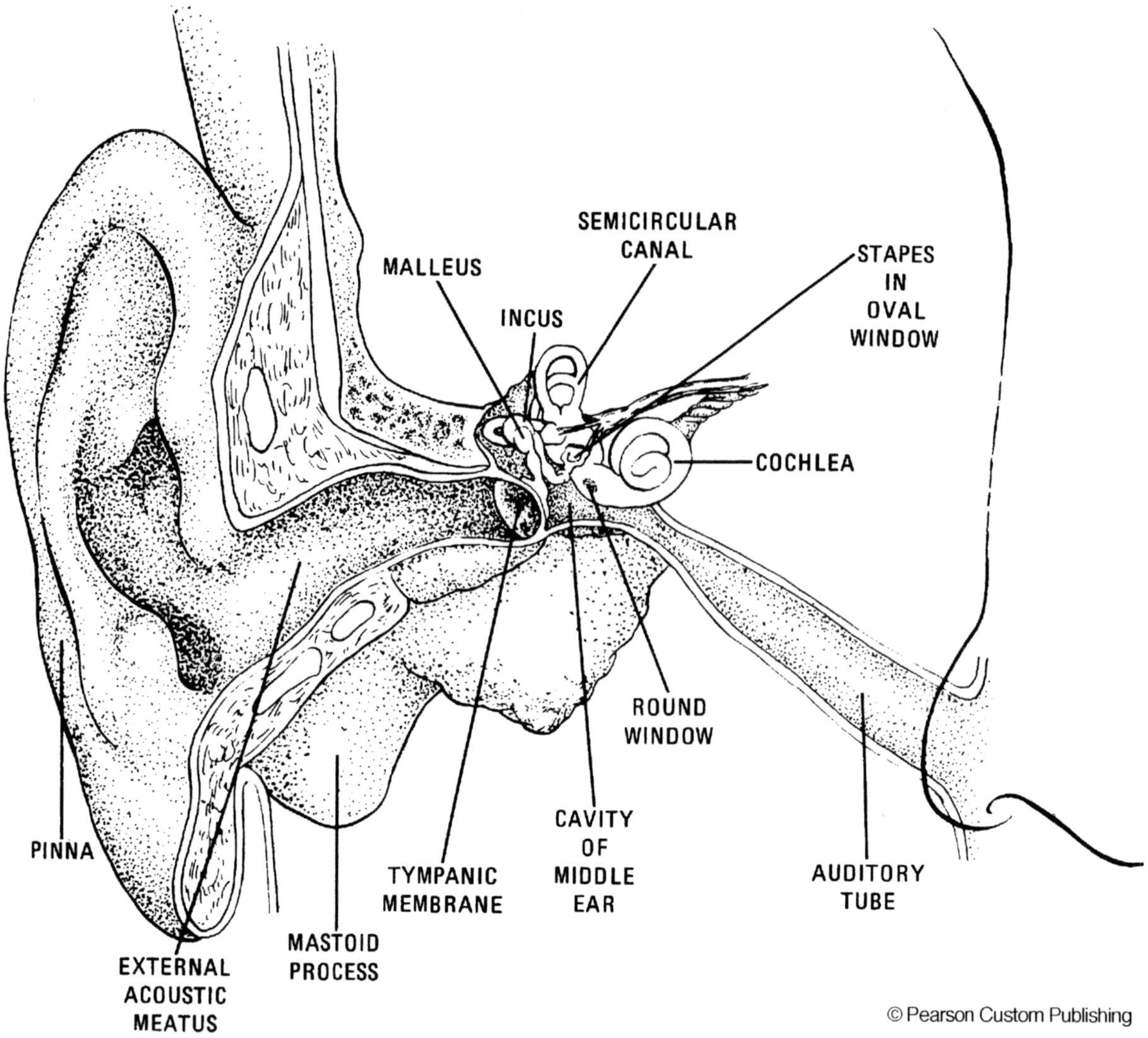
SEMICIRCULAR CANAL
MALLEUS
STAPES IN OVAL WINDOW
INCUS
COCHLEA
ROUND WINDOW
CAVITY OF MIDDLE EAR
PINNA
TYMPANIC MEMBRANE
AUDITORY TUBE
MASTOID PROCESS
EXTERNAL ACOUSTIC MEATUS

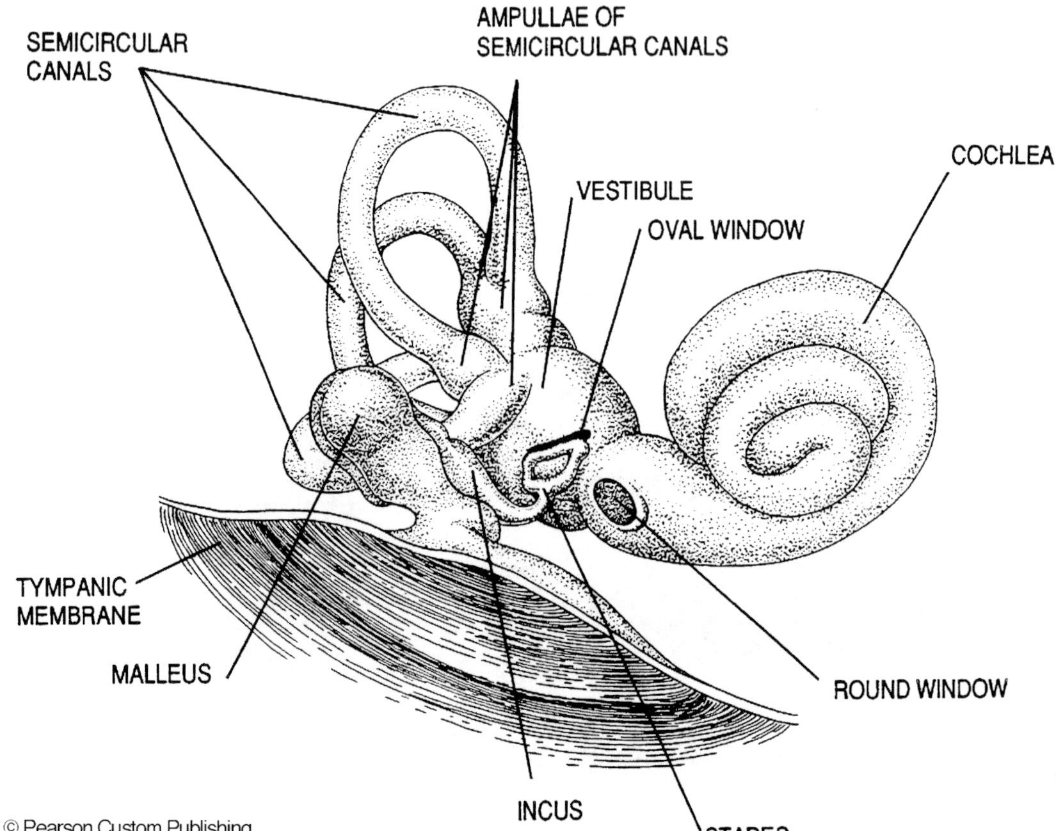
AMPULLAE OF SEMICIRCULAR CANALS
SEMICIRCULAR CANALS
COCHLEA
VESTIBULE
OVAL WINDOW
TYMPANIC MEMBRANE
MALLEUS
ROUND WINDOW
INCUS
STAPES

Exercise A-15

Gross Anatomy of the Heart

This exercise involves the examination and study of the heart. The first step in this process is the dissection and study of the sheep heart. Occasionally a fresh cow heart specimen is available as well. Once that portion of the exercise is completed, you will move to the examination and study of the actual human specimens that are available in the lab. As always, treat the human materials and the cadavers with respect and care.

Part A: Examination and Dissection of the Sheep Heart
During this initial exercise, you will work in groups of two or three. One member of the group should obtain a sheep heart from the instructor. Another member of the group should gather up the necessary dissection tools (blunt scissors, fine and coarse probes, forceps). Actually the most versatile probe is a closed pair of blunt scissors.

Orientation and External Exploration of the Sheep Heart:
1. Examine the heart carefully. Most of the mass of the heart is concentrated in the very muscular pumping chambers, the ventricles. Notice that the end of the ventricles is somewhat pointed. This is referred to as the apex. The other end of the heart from which a number of blood vessels emerge is called the base.

2. Orient the heart as you think it sits in the chest. You may refer to the torso models in lab as you consider this. Verify this positioning before you proceed any further. Using 3 or 4 lines, in the box below create and label a simple illustration that depicts the sheep heart as viewed from an anterior perspective. You will add some detail to this drawing as the exercise proceeds.

3. Slowly rotate the heart, always keeping the apex facing down. As you do so, press the wall of the ventricles with your thumb. At some point you should notice that the wall of the ventricles feels softer, or less solid. This is the outer wall of the right ventricle. Verify this with your instructor. Now that you have accurately located the right ventricle, you must remember one important fact…

   No matter how you turn or position or orient the specimen, this chamber will always be the <u>right</u> ventricle… the <u>right side</u> of the heart. Whether this chamber is oriented toward <u>your</u> right or toward <u>your</u> left does not matter… it remains the right side of the heart.

   The remainder of the ventricular muscle mass which feels more dense and solid is therefore the wall of the left ventricle. The same rules apply for this chamber and the entire left side of the heart. **Any reference to the right or left in these directions refers specifically to the right or left sides <u>of the heart.</u>**

4. Position the heart in your hand so that the apex faces down and the right ventricle faces you. You should notice a line of adipose running along a diagonal from the apex to the base and separating the right ventricle from the left ventricle. This adipose covers a groove called the interventricular sulcus, the point where the right and left ventricular walls meet. Add this to the illustration you have just completed (if it is not already included). If you follow the sulcus all the way to the base, you should see a large vessel that extends from the right ventricle along roughly the same plane as the sulcus. This is the pulmonary trunk, the large artery that carries blood from the right ventricle. Add this to the illustration. Examine its wall.
   Is it thick or thin?   ___ Thick   ___ Thin
   When compressed and released, does it exhibit elasticity?   Yes / No

   Verify your findings with your instructor before you continue further.

5. Notice that at the base of the heart there are two flattened structures that vaguely resemble ears (some say they look more like mushrooms). These are the auricles, outward extensions of the right and left atria. These are the holding chambers of the heart and they direct blood into the ventricles. One is associated with the right ventricle and is therefore a portion of the right atrium. Palpate it gently.
   How does the thickness of its wall compare to that of the right ventricle?
   ___ Thicker than ventricle   ___ Thinner than ventricle

   Is there any noticeable difference between the right and left auricles?   Yes / No
   If yes, describe the difference(s).

   _____

   _____

   _____

6. Using your blunt scissors, create a small hole in the middle of the superior surface of the right auricle. Take a fine probe (a closed blunt scissors works best for this) and carefully and gently pass it through the hole into the right atrium. Carefully advance the probe so that it enters the right ventricle. Continue to advance the probe until its tip can be felt near the apex through the ventricular wall. Repeat this procedure once or twice more so that you can clearly visualize the direction and extent of the first cut you will make.

7. Now that you have visualized and palpated the pathway from atrium to ventricular apex, insert one blade of the scissors in the hole and proceed to cut through the atrial and then ventricular wall until you reach the apical end of the right ventricle. Be careful not to cut into or through the interventricular septum which separates the two ventricular chambers. Once the cut is completed, you can open the right side of the heart (atrium and ventricle) like a book. Do so and examine the internal structure of both chambers. Describe the inner surface first of the atrium and then of the ventricle.

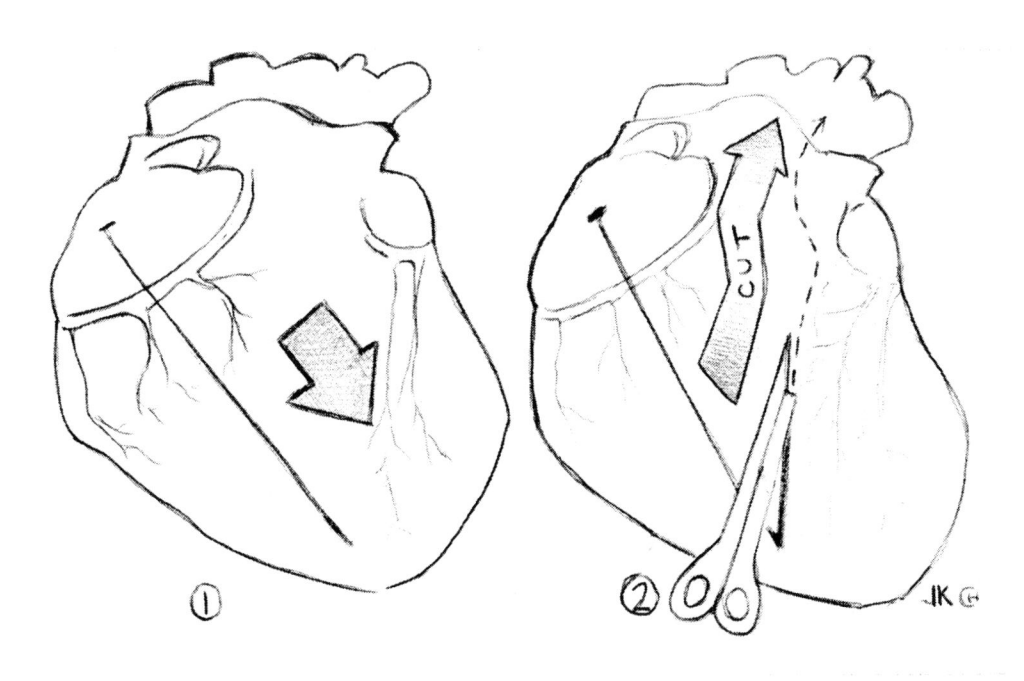

Inner surface of right atrium _____

_____

Inner surface of right ventricle _____

_____

You should see that the two chambers are separated by a valve, one of the two atrioventricular (a-v) valves. Describe the structural features of this valve. Try to be thorough in your observations because they will be your basis for comparison when you expose and examine the corresponding valve on the left side.

Structural features of the right atrioventricular valve _____

_____

_____

Notice that in the right ventricle there is a thick cord of tissue that extends from the outer ventricular wall to the ventricular septum. This band is called the moderator band. It houses the right bundle branch which is a portion of the electrical conduction system of the heart.
Can you identify a moderator band in your specimen?   Yes / No

8. Starting at the apical end of the first cut, begin a second cut through the wall of the right ventricle. This second cut is depicted in the previous illustration and will run parallel and close to (1/4 inch) the interventricular sulcus you identified earlier. Do this carefully so that your cut does not inadvertently drift across the sulcus or into the left ventricle. As you approach the base, angle the scissors so that they enter the pulmonary trunk (also identified earlier). Extend the cut so that you open the entire length of the pulmonary trunk. When you are done, you should now be able to open the right ventricle and the pulmonary artery for visualization of their interiors. At the junction of the ventricle and the artery, you should see a second valve. It is one of the semilunar valves. Examine it carefully and gently.
Does it share the same structure as the a-v valve you examined earlier?   Yes / No

Structural features of this semilunar valve _____

_____

_____

9. Now turn your attention to the left auricle and proceed to enter it in exactly the same manner as you did the right auricle. Again, gently pass a closed blunt scissors through the atrium into the left ventricle. Use your scissors to open the left side of the heart from atrium to apex. When the cut is completed, open the left side of the heart as you did the right side (like a book) and inspect its internal structure. Describe the inner surfaces of the left atrium and ventricle.

Inner surface of left atrium _____

Inner surface of left ventricle _____

Examine and describe the structure of the a-v valve that should be clearly visible.

_____

_____

_____

10. The outflow pathway from the left ventricle is behind the a-v valve cusp that remains intact. Gently pass a probe (blunt scissors is best) from the ventricle through this channel. Notice the vessel from which the probe emerges. Describe the wall of this vessel.

   _____

   Do you think this vessel is an artery or a vein?   Artery   Vein

   Why? _____

   _____

   _____

11. Now that you can visualize the outflow tract from the ventricle, you can determine how to cut through the remaining valve cusp to open and expose the pathway out of the left ventricle. When you have completed that cut, you should be able to examine the second of the semilunar valves. As on the right side, it will be located at the origin of the artery that carries blood from the ventricle.

   Structural features of this semilunar valve _____

   _____

   _____

12. Since you have by now thoroughly examined both sides of the heart, indicate in the space provided <u>structural</u> features the two sides share (similarities).

   _____

   _____

   _____

13. Do likewise for <u>structural</u> differences from one side to the other. Record them in the space provided on the next page.

Right side	Left side
_____	_____
_____	_____
_____	_____
_____	_____
_____	_____
_____	_____
_____	_____
_____	_____

Venture a guess as to the functional significance of these differences.

_____

_____

14. Complete your exploration and examination of the sheep heart by inspecting and identifying the great vessels that are visible at the base of the heart. Distinguish the arteries from the veins and list them as you identify them.

    Arteries: _____ _____

    Veins: _____

    _____

    _____

    What is the structural basis for your choices?

    _____

    _____

15. Inspect the atria from within. In which atrium is the inner surface smoother?

    ____ Right atrium   ____ Left atrium

How many inlets do you see into the right atrium?   1   2   3   4
Name each one.

_____

_____

How many inlets do you see into the left atrium?   1   2   3   4
Name them.

_____

Next examine the atrial septum. During fetal development there exists an opening in the septum between the right side and the left that directs blood away from the fetal lungs which are non-functional *in utero*. Can you see any remnant of this communication in the septum of the specimen you are examining?   Yes / No
(Note: If visible, it will appear as a circle of thin tissue in the atrial septum.)

What is this passageway called during uterine development? _____

What is the remnant that remains now called? _____

16. While the coronary circulation (and its venous drainage) in the sheep are similar to that seen in the human, do not spend time now trying to identify any of the coronary arteries or cardiac veins in the sheep hearts. For that, the actual human hearts and human heart models will be used.

Part B: Exploration of the Human Heart:
You will begin your exploration of human cardiac anatomy by examining the heart *in situ*. Once the "in place" observations are completed, the hearts may be removed from the cadavers for additional study (if they have been dissected to allow that). More likely, additional separate heart specimens will then be made available for your study. When you are finished, return any hearts removed from a cadaver to the matching body. All hearts should be returned to the proper anatomical position within the thorax. All separate hearts must be returned to similarly numbered container.

1. Before beginning your study of the heart, <u>use your textbook and other reference materials</u> to complete the accompanying table to indicate the typical surface landmarks that a clinician might use to localize the heart and related structures.

Structure	Actual Landmark (per reference)
Base of Heart	
Arch of Aorta (superior extent)	
Apex of Heart	

2. Examine the heart and great vessels on your cadaver. How does the <u>actual</u> location of the regions and structures listed above in item 1 compare with the locations listed in your chart? To answer this question, complete the following chart with the actual locations of the indicated structures based on your careful observations.
Does your cadaver match the accepted standard from a reference? Yes / No.

Structure	Actual Landmark (per observation)
Base of Heart	
Arch of Aorta (superior extent)	
Apex of Heart	

3. Observe the pericardium in your cadaver. Note: the pericardium may not be fully intact in any of the specimens. Distinguish between the fibrous pericardium and the parietal pericardium.

   _____

   _____

Which of these is part of the <u>serous</u> pericardium?	Fibrous	Parietal
Is the visceral pericardium a serous membrane?	Yes / No	
Is the visceral pericardium visible or palpable?	Yes / No	

   Be prepared to demonstrate these components to your instructor.

4. Find in the human heart specimens all the heart chambers, landmarks, and great vessels previously studied on the sheep. In studying the great vessels, be sure to view both the proximal portions of the great vessels attached to the heart and whatever distal continuations of these vessels may remain in the mediastinum of each cadaver from which the heart was removed. Be prepared to demonstrate these structures to your instructor.

   Check off as found.

	On separate heart	In chest
Apex & Base	_____	_____
Right atria	_____	_____
Left atria	_____	_____
Right ventricle	_____	_____
Left ventricle	_____	_____
Superior vena cava	_____	_____
Inferior vena cava	_____	_____
Pulmonary veins	_____	_____
Pulmonary trunk	_____	_____
Aorta	_____	_____
Anterior interventricular sulcus	_____	_____

5. As you did in exploring the sheep heart, examine the internal structure of the right and left chambers of the heart. Indicate which of the listed structures you were able to locate and identify.

____ right atrium	____ left atrium
____ opening for coronary sinus	____ moderator band
____ right ventricle	____ left ventricle
____ bicuspid valve	____ tricuspid valve
____ aortic valve	____ pulmonic valve
____ opening for right coronary artery	____ opening for left coronary artery

6. As you did in exploring the sheep heart, examine the atrial septum to determine if the fossa ovalis (the remnant of the foramen ovale) is evident.
Is the fossa ovalis visible on your specimen?   Yes / No

7. During uterine development, a bypass between the aorta and the pulmonary trunk develops to shunt blood away from the immature, nonfunctional fetal lungs. This bypass vessel is called the ductus arteriosus. After birth, the walls of the vessel constrict. This transforms the vessel into a solid ligament called the ligamentum arteriosum. The ligamentum has been exposed on several of the separate human heart specimens. Be sure to find it on at least one such specimen.
Were you able to locate and identify a ligamentum arteriosum?   Yes / No

8. Study the coronary arterial circulation. This branch of the circulatory system provides oxygenated blood to the muscle of the heart. Find the following arteries. Indicate those that you are successful in finding.
   ____ left coronary artery
   ____ right coronary artery;
   ____ left anterior interventricular artery (referred to clinically as the left anterior descending artery);
   ____ posterior interventricular artery (referred to clinically as the right posterior descending artery);
   ____ circumflex artery;
   ____ marginal arteries.
   Be prepared to demonstrate these vessels to your instructor.

9. There is a system of cardiac veins which accompany most of the coronary arteries and carry the deoxygenated blood of the coronary circulation to the right atrium. Be sure you can distinguish them from their corresponding arteries. These veins return blood to a large vein called the coronary sinus, located in the posterior atrioventricular sulcus. Trace the path of blood in these veins.
Where does it go?
_____

Find the following veins. Indicate those that you are successful in finding.
   ____ great cardiac vein   ____ coronary sinus
   ____ middle cardiac vein

10. Heart dominance is determined by which main coronary artery gives rise to the posterior interventricular artery. A majority of hearts (60+%) in the general population are right-dominant, A smaller percentage (<30%) are left-dominant and a very small percentage are neither. Since the posterior interventricular artery supplies the ventricular septum and some of the posterior wall of the left ventricle, a blockage of the circumflex artery in a left-dominant heart carries a poorer prognosis than the same blockage in a right-dominant heart. Determine if the heart you are studying is right-dominant or left-dominant. Be prepared to demonstrate heart dominance to your instructor.

Exercise A-16

Gross Anatomy of Systemic Circulation

This exercise involves the examination and study of some of the vessels which make up the human systemic circulation. As always, treat the cadavers with respect and care. For our study, the vessels will be divided into four categories: superior arteries, superior veins, inferior arteries, and inferior veins. Vessels above the diaphragm are considered superior vessels and those below the diaphragm are considered inferior vessels. For any particular vessel or vascular region, exposure may be better in one cadaver than in another. Therefore, if you are having difficulty locating a specific vascular structure, do not hesitate to visit one of the other cadavers. Be particularly mindful that vessels which lie within mesenteries are often damaged or destroyed due to the stress the membranes experience as structures are moved during organ exploration.

Lastly, as you explore the systemic circulatory system, be conscious of the fact that in individuals who have reached their later years, there are often structural changes that will not be visible in younger human or animal specimens. Therefore, in each specimen be observant for evidence of sclerotic changes and/or calcification in any opened vessels that you examine. Also, often older specimens possess bulging areas of weakness in the walls of larger arteries. These bulges are called aneurysms. If any of the specimens you examine possess any of these, or other, anomalies, describe it/them and be prepared to demonstrate it/them to your instructor.

Part A - Arteries Superior to the Diaphragm

1. Start at the heart and identify the arch of the aorta. The arch of aorta in the human gives rise to three branches. Find them and be sure you can name them.

   _____

   _____

   _____

   Be prepared to demonstrate these vessels to your instructor.

2. Find and follow the common carotid to its bifurcation into an external and an internal carotid artery. One of these branches gives rise to many smaller branches in the neck and face area.
   Which branch does this? _____

   The internal carotid artery enters the cranium through the carotid canal? By examining the cranial floor, you should be able to visualize its continuation within the skull. Be prepared to demonstrate these vessels to your instructor.

3. Find the left subclavian artery and follow it. The first large branch of the subclavian which emerges medially (and proceeds dorsally) is the vertebral artery. Find this artery and try to determine its destination and then its function.

   Destination _____

   Function _____

   Another branch of the subclavian artery is the internal thoracic artery (sometimes referred to as the internal mammary artery). Starting near the origin of the subclavian, it briefly extends anteriorly and superiorly before bending inferiorly to supply the anterior wall of the thorax. It is clearly visible on the internal surface of each chest plate along both sternal margins. Examine and trace it. It is a vessel that is used in coronary bypass surgery. Venture a guess as to how this vessel can be used as a bypass graft.

   _____

   _____

   Find the section of the subclavian artery that lies between the clavicle and the first rib. Distal to this, the subclavian changes its name to the axillary artery.
   Be prepared to demonstrate this vessel to your instructor.

4. Find the brachial artery. Describe the location of this vessel relative to the humerus.

   _____

   Be prepared to demonstrate this vessel to your instructor.

5. Distal to the antecubital fossa, the brachial artery divides into two major branches. Find and identify these two vessels. They are named for the bones they "follow".

   _____   _____

   Be prepared to demonstrate these vessels to your instructor.

6. Many areas of the body receive blood carrying oxygen and nutrients from more than one artery. Such additional blood supplies are referred to as collateral channels. Collateral circulation protects an organ or structure or area in the event that the primary blood supply is cut off.

   In the hand there are two arterial loops, the superficial palmar arch and the deep palmar arch, each with two arterial sources. Names these two arteries.

   _____   _____

   The blood supply to the individual fingers originates from these two loops. In our specimens, it is most likely that only the superficial palmar arches are exposed. Examine those hands which have been dissected. Find and demonstrate whichever arterial arch(es) are exposed. The palmar arches are the first examples of collateral circulation that you have encountered. Depending on the individual, the palmar arches may be complete or incomplete.

   Determine whether the arches that are exposed are complete or incomplete.

Cadaver # _____	Arm:	Right / Left	Complete / Incomplete.
Cadaver # _____	Arm:	Right / Left	Complete / Incomplete.
Specimen # _____	Arm:	Right / Left	Complete / Incomplete.

   Select one such palmar arch and
   Draw it in the box at the right.
   Label the radial and ulnar arteries.

How would circulation to the digits be affected if the ulnar artery was blocked in an individual with a <u>complete</u> palmar arch system?
____ compromised to medial aspect of hand
____ compromised to lateral aspect of hand
____ compromised to entire hand
____ no circulatory compromise

How would circulation to the digits be affected if the ulnar artery was blocked in an individual with a <u>incomplete</u> palmar arch system?
____ compromised to medial aspect of hand
____ compromised to lateral aspect of hand
____ compromised to entire hand
____ no circulatory compromise

A simple technique called the Allen Test is used to assess the status of the palmar arches in a living individual? Follow these directions to perform the Allen Test on a partner.
- Use your thumbs to compress both the radial and ulnar arteries at the wrist simultaneously.
- Have the subject clench and release his/her fist until the palm blanches.
- Then release <u>only</u> the ulnar artery.

If color returns to the hand within 2-3 seconds, the arches are complete and there is adequate collateral circulation. Remove your gloves and perform the Allen Test on the other members of your group. Record the results below.

Allen Test: Results from lab partners: Delayed filling = + result.

Student _____ Result: Right + / -
                                                      Left + / -
Student _____ Result: Right + / -
                                                      Left + / -
Student _____ Result: Right + / -
                                                      Left + / -

7. Based on your observations, is the following statement true?
The upper limb is supplied entirely by the branches of the subclavian artery.
____ True   ____ False

8. Follow the thoracic aorta inferiorly and find the posterior branches of the intercostal arteries. Describe the <u>precise</u> position of these vessels within the intercostal space. In doing so, refer to a specific bony landmark on the rib.

_____

Be prepared to demonstrate these vessels to your instructor.

9. Examine the arterial circuit which has been exposed on the ventral surface of the human brain that is available for your examination. This is called the arterial circle of Willis. As you can see, there are four vessels (2 pairs) by which blood can enter this circuit, each of which you have already identified. Name them.

_____   _____

Trace the path of flow through the circle from any one of these four entry points.
Are you satisfied that this arrangement of vessels constitutes a circle. Yes / No
Is it a complete circle?   Yes / No
Is the circle of Willis an example of collateral circulation? Yes / No

Go to one of the cadavers and inspect the cranial floor. You should be able to recognize and identify the four supply vessels to the circle of Willis. Be prepared to demonstrate them to your instructor.

Previously you have considered the concept of collateral circulation.
Does a complete circle of Willis provide collateral pathways for blood flow to the brain?   Yes / No
Be prepared to defend/explain your answer to your instructor.

In the box below, draw and identify the following vessels of the circle of Willis as they appear <u>on the specimen that you have examined</u>.

     basilar artery
     posterior cerebral arteries
     posterior communicating arteries
     anterior cerebral arteries
     anterior communicating artery

Part B - Arteries Inferior to the Diaphragm

1. Follow the aorta into the abdomen. The abdominal aorta gives rise to three major unpaired branches all arising from its anterior surface:
   - the celiac trunk
   - the superior mesenteric artery
   - the inferior mesenteric artery

   Be sure you can identify these three major branches from the abdominal aorta. Which of these three vessels gives rise to the common hepatic, splenic, and left gastric arteries?

   _____

   Be prepared to demonstrate these vessels to your instructor.

2. Find the splenic artery. Examine it carefully. What structural feature makes it easy to distinguish this vessel from many others you have seen thus far in your explorations?

   _____

   What advantage might be associated with this feature of the splenic artery?

   _____

   _____

3. Examine the blood supply to the stomach very carefully. Does the stomach have one arterial supply or more than one? ____ one   ____ more than one
   Is there any advantage to this design?   Yes / No
   Explain.

   _____

   _____

   Be prepared to demonstrate these vessels to your instructor.

4. Find the inferior mesentery artery. At what vertebral level does it arise? _____
   Follow the branches of the inferior mesenteric artery and determine the portions of the digestive tube that it supplies.

   _____

   _____

   _____

   Be prepared to demonstrate this vessel and its branches to your instructor.

5. Find the following paired arteries which arise from the abdominal aorta:
    - renal arteries
    - gonadal arteries
    - common iliac arteries

    Are the renal arteries of equal length?   Yes / No
    If not, which is longer?   ___ Right   ___ Left

    Be sure you observe the gonadal arteries in both the male and female. In which sex are the gonadal arteries longer?   ___ Male   ___ Female

    Be prepared to demonstrate these vessels to your instructor.

6. Find the common iliac arteries. At what vertebral level do they arise? _____
    Examine more than one specimen. Is the bifurcation site consistent?   Yes / No
    Is the length of the common iliac artery consistent from side to side?   Yes / No
    Is the length of the common iliac artery consistent
    from specimen to specimen?   Yes / No

    Follow the common iliac artery to the point where it splits into an external iliac artery and an internal iliac artery. Based on your observation, which of these branches supplies the pelvis?   ____ internal iliac   ____ external iliac

    Which branch of the common iliac artery continues into the leg?
    ____ internal iliac   ____ external iliac

    Be prepared to demonstrate these vessels to your instructor.

7. Find the femoral artery. Describe its course within the leg?

    _____

    _____

    A very early and large branch off the femoral artery is the deep femoral artery. Based on your observation of its course through the thigh, what muscle group is most likely supplied by this vessel?

    _____

    Find and probe with your finger the adductor hiatus through which the femoral artery passes. At this point, what happens to the femoral artery?

    _____

    Be prepared to demonstrate this passage and this vessel to your instructor.

8. Find the anterior and posterior tibial arteries. Which of these vessels gives rise to

the dorsalis pedis artery? _____

Which of these vessels provides a pulse point on the <u>medial</u> aspect of the ankle.
_____

Which of these two vessels provides the most distal pulse point?
_____

Be prepared to demonstrate these vessels to your instructor.

9. Now that you have completed your survey of the systemic arterial system, describe any pathology you may have noticed in any of the specimens studied.

Specimen	Abnormality/Anomoly
_____	_____
_____	_____
_____	_____

Part C - Veins Superior to the Diaphragm

1. Find the internal and external jugular veins in the neck region.
   Which of these vessels is larger? ___ internal jugular ___ external jugular
   Are these vessels consistent from side to side?   Yes / No
   In the box below, draw and label the jugular vessels as viewed on your specimen.

Which of these vessels receives blood from the dural sinuses?
                       ____ internal jugular   ____ external jugular

Do either or both of these vessels empty into the subclavian vein? Yes / No
If yes, which?   ____ internal jugular   ____ external jugular

Do either or both of these vessels empty into the brachiocephalic vein? Yes / No
If yes, which?   ____ internal jugular   ____ external jugular

Is the arrangement and course of the jugular veins consistent from specimen to specimen? Yes / No
If there are differences, describe them. _____

_____

Be prepared to demonstrate these vessels to your instructor.

2. Demonstrate the subclavian and brachiocephalic veins. At a point close to the heart, the two brachiocephalic veins merge to form a larger vessel. What vessel is formed?
_____

Be prepared to demonstrate these vessels to your instructor.

3. Distal to the clavicle and the first rib, the subclavian vein changes its name. What vein does it become?
_____

Be prepared to demonstrate this vessel to your instructor.

4. Find the cephalic vein. Describe its course in the arm. _____

_____

What is the likely basis for its name? _____

Into what vein does the cephalic vein drain? _____

Find the basilic vein. Describe its course in the arm. _____

_____

Into what vein does the basilic vein drain? _____

Notice that the cephalic and basilic veins interconnect in the antecubital area. In the box below, draw a simple line diagram which depicts the course of these vessels on the arm.

```
┌─────────────────────────────────┐
│           Proximal              │
│                                 │
│                                 │
│                                 │
│                                 │
│                                 │
│                                 │
│                                 │
│                                 │
│                                 │
│            Distal               │
└─────────────────────────────────┘
```

For what purpose are these interconnecting veins clinically useful? _____

_____

Is the arrangement of these superficial veins consistent from specimen to specimen?   Yes / No
If there are differences, describe them. _____

_____

Do you think such differences that you may observe are physiologically significant?   Yes / No
Explain. _____

_____

Be prepared to demonstrate these vessels and any differences you may have found to your instructor.

5. Two veins merge to form the axillary vein. These are the basilic vein and the

brachial vein. This generally occurs proximal to the midshaft point of the humerus. Find these veins and the point at which they unite.
Is the site of this merger consistent from side to side in your specimen? Yes / No
Be prepared to demonstrate these vessels to your instructor.

6. Emptying into the superior vena cava very close to the heart is the azygos vein. The azygos vein is the main branch of a venous drainage system which bears the same name. Depending on the extent of dissection in the chest, the entire system may be viewable or just the junction at the vena cava. The azygos system exhibits considerable variability from one individual to another. In fact, it is likely that each specimen you will examine in this exercise will have an azygos system that is in some way different from each of the others. Find the azygos vein very close to the dorsal midline in the right side of the thorax.

If exposed in the left hemithorax, find the hemiazygos and accessory hemiazygos veins. In the box provided below, draw the azygos system as it appears in your specimen and label what you consider to be the azygos, hemiazygos, and accessory hemiazygos veins. Include the vertebral column in your drawing.

Trace the origin of these veins. Is their drainage solely thoracic or is there evidence that these vessels carry abdominal blood? ____ solely thoracic   ____ also abdominal
Based on your observations, summarize the function of the azygos system in one sentence.

_____

_____

Be prepared to demonstrate the vessels of the azygos system to your instructor.

Part D - Veins Inferior to the Diaphragm

1. Find the inferior vena cava (IVC) in the thorax. How is it positioned relative to the thoracic aorta?
   _____

   Compare the size of its lumen and the thickness of its wall with those of the aorta.
   Larger diameter   ____ IVC   ____ Aorta
   Thicker wall   ____ IVC   ____ Aorta

   Trace the IVC in an inferior direction.
   Does it extend beyond the diaphragm?   Yes / No
   Be prepared to demonstrate this vessel to your instructor.

2. Examine one of the separate liver specimens. First, emerging from its superior surface, find the hepatic veins which carry blood from the liver. How many hepatic veins are there?   1   2   >3
   Into what vessel do they drain?
   _____

   Next, find the hepatic portal vein which delivers blood to the liver. Find its point of entry on the inferior surface of the liver. If the structures of the lesser omentum are reasonably intact in your specimen, you may be able to view the entire length of the hepatic portal vein. Realizing that some of the vessels that contribute blood to the hepatic portal vein may be cut or not exposed (or both), trace some of these vessels distally. Based on this observation, from what organs does the blood that enters the hepatic portal vein generally seem to originate?
   _____
   _____

   Be prepared to demonstrate the hepatic veins, the hepatic portal vein, and some of these unnamed vessels to your instructor.

3. Try to find venous drainage from the kidneys and the gonads. If you find venous drainage from these organs, determine if it is consistent from one side of the body to the other.
   Length   ____ Longer on right   ____ Longer on left   ____ Equal R&L

   Number of vessels   ____ > on right   ____ > on left   Equal R&L

   Is it consistent from specimen to specimen? Yes / No
   Be prepared to demonstrate these channels to your instructor.

4. Follow the inferior vena cava to its origin from the common iliac veins. What

two vessels unite to form each common iliac vein?

_____   _____

Be prepared to demonstrate these vessels to your instructor.

5. Locate and identify the femoral vein. Into what vein does it empty?

_____

Be prepared to demonstrate these vessels to your instructor.

6. Locate the greater saphenous vein. The word saphenous comes from a Greek word meaning manifest or obvious. Having examined this vessel, does this name make sense?   Yes / No   Why?
_____

_____

Describe its course. _____

Into what vein does it empty? _____

This vessel has historically been used as the bypass graft in coronary bypass surgery. Is this surprising in any way?   Yes / No
Explain.
_____

_____

Be prepared to demonstrate this vessel to your instructor.

Exercise A-17

Gross Anatomy of the Respiratory System

This exercise involves the examination and study of the major non-muscular structures of the respiratory system. As always, treat the cadavers with respect and care. For our study, structures of the respiratory system will be divided into three categories. We will begin our study by examining and tracing the extent of the membranes associated with the lungs and chest wall. Next, we will examine the lungs themselves, both *in situ* and as separate, excised organs. Finally, we will study the major cartilaginous structures and airways as they appear within the posterior mediastinum.

Part A - The Pleura and the Pleural Cavity

1. Distinguish the serous membranes associated with the chest and lungs, namely the parietal pleura and the visceral pleura. Be prepared to demonstrate these to your instructor. The parietal pleura is divided into different regions based upon the parts of the chest cavity which it covers. These regions are the costal, the mediastinal, and the diaphragmatic. Locate each of these regions (portions of the parietal pleura) and be prepared to demonstrate each to your instructor.

    The space between the two pleurae defines the pleural cavity, often referred to as the intrapleural space. Since both the parietal and visceral pleurae are serous membranes, would you expect the two pleurae to rub against each other during regular breathing? If this is the case, how is this abrasive stress handled? Hint: Recalling the specific type of epithelium that contributes to the pleurae and its particular functional characteristics should help with this.

    _____

    _____

2. Explore the most inferior (deepest) extent of the pleural cavity.
    Is it in the anterior, medial posterior, or lateral posterior thorax?

    _____ anterior   _____ medial posterior   _____ lateral posterior

    As you explore the extent of the parietal pleura, you should notice that there are several places areas where the membrane folds back on itself to form a space or a recess. Find such an area in the posterior thorax. Explore it with your gloved hand. This is the costodiaphragmatic recess. Might the depth and extent of this space change with breathing patterns?   Yes / No
    If yes, during what part of the breathing cycle is it deeper?

    _____ inspiration   _____ expiration

Support or refute this statement. The extent of the pleural cavity actually occupied by the lungs changes during different phases of the breathing cycle. Share your ideas with your instructor.

_____
_____
_____
_____

This space has clinical significance. Can you determine what the significance is? Hint: Consider this space as it exists in an upright individual. Then keep it in mind that it is possible for fluid to accumulate between the pleurae as a result of different disorders or injuries. Where is this accumulation most likely to be?

_____

Part B - The Lungs
1. Observe the lungs *in situ*. Use external anatomical landmarks to locate and describe the uppermost extent of the apex of the lungs.

   _____
   _____

   The subclavian vein crosses transversely in close proximity to the apex of the lung. This vessel is a common entry point for intravenous infusions. What might be the respiratory consequence of poor technique during insertion of a needle into the subclavian vein?

   _____
   _____

   Be prepared to demonstrate this vessel to your instructor.

2. Find the base of the lung. Be prepared to demonstrate this region to your instructor. How does the base of the lung relate to the diaphragm?

   _____

   Is the base on the right side at the same level as the base on the left? Yes / No
   If not, describe the difference.

   _____

3. To whatever extent is possible in your specimen, carefully remove the lungs from the cadaver. Examine the lungs from your specimen carefully. Do so visually and by thorough palpation. Compare the right and left lungs in your specimen. Normal lungs are light yet firm, consistently elastic, and should show only a moderate dark or mottled appearance. Consider in your observations the color and size of the right and left lungs, their density when deflated and when inflated, and the number and completeness of any fissures. Record your observations in the space provided below.

        Right lung   Left lung

_____   _____

_____   _____

_____   _____

_____   _____

_____   _____

Note: Depending on how the lungs of the different specimens were exposed and dissected, it may be possible to inflate some of them. There is available for your use a self-inflating resuscitation bag and a number of endotracheal tubes of varying sizes for this purpose. Ask your instructor for assistance in this. If you are able to inflate any of the specimens, you should also observe carefully the ease with which the lung tissue inflates <u>and</u> the speed with which it deflates. Include these observations in your comparisons.

4. Next compare the lungs from different cadavers and from whatever separate specimens are available. Again, do so visually and by palpation. Be thorough in your comparative observations. Record these observations in the space provided on the facing page. Be prepared to demonstrate any differences you discover to your instructor. When you are finished with this comparison, gently and carefully return all lungs to the proper cadaver(s).

_____   _____

_____   _____

_____   _____

_____   _____

_____   _____

5. Lungs have three surfaces: costal, mediastinal, and diaphragmatic. Be prepared to point these out to your instructor on both the right and left lungs.

6. The distinction between the hilum of the lung and the root of the lung is a subtle one. The structures that enter and exit the lung comprise the root while the hilum is the area of the lung through which these structures pass.
On what surface of the lung are the root and hilum found?
_____ costal   _____ mediastinal   _____ diaphragmatic

Describe and identify the structures of the root that are exposed.

_____

_____

Be prepared to demonstrate them for your instructor if asked.

What characteristics allow you to distinguish between arteries, veins, and airways?

Arteries   _____

            _____

Airways   _____

            _____

Veins   _____

            _____

7. The lung has two arterial supplies, one is pulmonary and the other is systemic. The gas exchange structures of the lungs are supplied by the pulmonary (deoxygenated blood) arteries and the tissues that comprise the airway walls are supplied by systemic (oxygenated blood) arteries. The systemic vessels are called bronchial arteries and they tend to be very small in diameter. By contrast, the pulmonary vessels are considerably larger. In the hilar area, locate and identify vessels of each system. Be prepared to demonstrate these to your instructor.

8. List at least three identifying features of the right lung that distinguish it from the left lung. Likewise, list at least three identifying features of the left lung that distinguish it from the right lung.

      Right Lung   Left Lung

_____   _____

_____   _____

_____   _____

_____   _____

What is the lingula of the lung? _____

In what lung is it found? _____

Note: the term is derived from the Latin word meaning "little tongue". Based on your observations, does this make sense? Yes / No

Explain. _____

Is the lingula of different specimens of consistent size and shape? Yes / No

Be prepared to demonstrate the lingula to your instructor.

Part C – Larynx and Major Airways

1. Direct your attention to the anterior neck where you will see the larynx. It is composed of a number of separate cartilages, some individual, some paired. Carefully palpate the anterior larynx.
   How many separate cartilages can you feel?   1   2   3   4
   Next, palpate the larynx bilaterally in a superior direction. Based on this, does the larynx possess any bony support?   Yes / No
   If yes, identify this supporting structure. _____
   Be prepared to demonstrate your finding to your instructor.

2. A transverse incision may have been performed in one of the specimens to separate the larynx from the more superior pharynx. If this is the case, it allows the larynx to be reflected anteriorly. This exposes the air passage through the larynx into the lungs and the passage to the stomach. From this superior perspective, the position of the esophagus relative to the larynx is clearly visible.

   Describe it. _____

3. Again working from this superior perspective, gently push a large flaplike cartilage in an anterior direction. This in exposes the air passage through the larynx into the trachea. Identify this cartilage.

   _____

Is it stiff or does it bend easily?   ____ stiff   ____ bends easily
Is it elastic?   Yes / No
How did you determine this? _____

You should now see that the lateral inner wall of the larynx houses two sets of tissue folds, the superior and more lateral ventricular folds (false vocal cords) and the inferior and more medial true vocal folds (true vocal cords). These folds extend medially and are separated by a horizontal crease in the lateral wall called the ventricle. Use a probe to gently locate this crease. From the superior perspective, you must look past (between) the false cords to see the true cords and the opening between them. The opening between the true cords is called the rima glottidis (often simply referred to as the glottis). Notice that the opening is not of uniform width. Generally the posterior portion of the glottis is wider.

Now that you have examined the larynx in some detail, which of the structures you have identified can play a role in preventing fluids and/or other foreign substances from entering the trachea?

_____

Be prepared to demonstrate all these laryngeal structures for your instructor.

A common surgical procedure performed to improve a person's breathing is called a tracheotomy. This operation is commonly done inferior to the isthmus of the thyroid by cutting an opening in the wall of the trachea in the area of the third or fourth cartilaginous tracheal rings. The most inferior cartilage of the larynx, the cricoid cartilage, is a substantial ringlike structure. Immediately inferior to the cricoid is the start of the trachea. Find the cricoid and then precisely indicate the position of the isthmus by referring to specific tracheal cartilages (by number).

_____

If asked, demonstrate for your instructor precisely where a tracheotomy would typically be performed.

4. Trace the trachea distally. The point at which it divides (bifurcates) into the two primary bronchi is called the carina. Your instructor will provide a frontal chest X-ray and demonstrate the carina on it and how to count ribs and vertebrae. At what vertebral level does the trachea divide?

_____

Be prepared to demonstrate this to your instructor. Compare the diameter and vertical orientation of the right and left primary (mainstem) bronchi.

Which has the larger diameter?   ____ Right bronchus   ____ Left bronchus
Which is more vertical?   ____ Right bronchus   ____ Left bronchus

Verify ____ or refute ____ this statement solely on the basis of the airway anatomy.
If a supine person vomits and inhales (aspirates) some of this material, the right lung is less likely to be affected than the left.

Defend your answer. _____

_____

_____

5. Observe the lungs for evidence of secondary and tertiary bronchi. Note: this may be difficult (particularly in the case of tertiary bronchi) depending on how your specimen has been dissected.
Do these airways ($2°$ and $3°$) contain cartilage in their walls?   Yes / No
Be prepared to demonstrate any that you locate.

Lab Exercise 18

Gross Anatomy of the Urinary System

The anatomy of the urinary system involves the examination and study of some of the organs that make up the excretory system. As always, treat the cadavers with respect and care. Our study has three major areas of emphasis. We will begin by studying the kidneys *in situ*. Next we will study the kidneys in longitudinal (frontal) section. Finally, we will observe and study some of the non-renal organs of the excretory system.

Before we begin our study of the excretory system, it will be helpful if you will recall the close relationship between pelvic reproductive anatomy and certain excretory structures. It will also serve you well if you will remember the relationship between the kidneys and other excretory organs (e.g. ureter) with the parietal peritoneum. Lastly, remember that the extent of the dissections done in the different cadavers will surely vary as will your access to the different organs that are the focus of this exercise.

Part A – Kidneys *in Situ*

1. In your cadaver and others, observe (or palpate) the kidneys in place against the dorsal body wall.
   Are they readily and equally visible on both sides of your specimen?   Yes / No
   If not, why not?

   _____

   Are they readily and equally visible in all cadavers?   Yes / No
   If not, why not?

   _____

   Are both kidneys positioned at the same level within the ventral body cavity of the same specimen?   Yes / No
   If not, explain any difference on a purely anatomic basis. _____

   _____

   Using proper vertebral references, determine and describe the extent of each kidney (from the superior pole to the inferior pole). That is, for each kidney, indicate the vertebral level at which the superior and inferior poles can be found. You may find it helpful to use one of the available skeletons to assist you in completing this task.

	Vertebral level
Right kidney	
       Superior pole   _____
       Inferior pole   _____
   Left kidney
       Superior pole   _____
       Inferior pole   _____

2. Recall the use of the term "ectopic" from the previous analysis of electrocardiogram tracings. An ectopic heart beat is one which originates in a location other than the usual. There is also a condition referred to as an "ectopic" kidney. Based on the use of the term in relation to cardiac function, how might you define an ectopic kidney?

_____

From a purely anatomic basis, why would an ectopic kidney be a fairly common complication of chronic malnutrition or starvation? Hint: Carefully consider the "packaging" of the kidney as observed in your cadaver.

_____

_____

3. Recall that in your exploration of the respiratory system you identified the hilum as the area of the lung where blood vessels and airways entered and exited. A specific area of the kidney is also referred by the same term. Find the hilum of the kidney.
Is the hilum located on the medial or lateral surface of the kidney?
    ____ Medial surface   ____ Lateral surface

You should be able to locate and identify three different types of structures which enter and exit the kidney at the hilum.   List them below.

_____   _____

_____

Indicate with a check mark which of the above structures you have not previously studied? Be prepared to demonstrate these structures to your instructor.

Part B – Longitudinal Kidney Section

1. Now observe a kidney in longitudinal (frontal) section. Identify these three regions: the capsule, cortex, and medulla. Within the medulla, find the pyramids. In a sectioned kidney, the pyramids are often triangular structures which taper to a point as they extend more deeply into the medulla. In three dimensions, they more resemble a cone with the tip (apex) farthest from and pointing away from the cortex. In each pyramid, the apex forms a renal papilla. The papillae project into a space defined by a funnel-shaped structure called a renal calyx which is not always (or easily) apparent in a dissected specimen. Given its design, what is the likely purpose of a calyx?

_____

_____

Note: Your ability to recognize and appreciate the renal calyx network in a freshly dissected kidney or a sectioned, plastinated specimen can be greatly aided by careful examination of one of the anatomical models available in the lab.

2. Find the renal pelvis. What structures converge to form the renal pelvis?

_____

_____

What is the relationship of the renal pelvis to the ureter?

_____

Be prepared to demonstrate these structures to your instructor.

Part C – Ureters and Bladder

1. Start by following the ureters from the kidneys to the urinary bladder. Describe the position of the ureters relative to the parietal peritoneum.

_____

What major artery does each ureter cross before entering the urinary bladder?

_____

Be prepared to demonstrate this to your instructor.

2. Next, explore the urinary bladder that has been opened to allow examination of its internal structure. Notice its position relative to the positions of adjacent digestive and reproductive structures. If the bladder is open, explore its interior surface. Recall the internal structure of the stomach. What structural similarity do the stomach and urinary bladder share?

_____

What is the functional capability does this design impart to the bladder?

_____

Locate the trigone. Identify the three elements which define the extent of the trigone. Be prepared to point out these elements to your instructor.

One final note - We are not studying the urethra as a urinary structure although it certainly has standing within the urinary system. The reason the urethra is not being considered at this time is because it was already considered when you studied the anatomy of the reproductive system in both the male and female specimens.

PART 2

Exercises in Histology

Exercise H-1

An Introduction to Tissues

Introduction

Organs are made up of tissues. A tissue is an assembly of similar cells and intercellular material which share the task of carrying out a rather distinct function. Although there are many different kinds of tissues in the body, each one is classified into one of four major groups. Classification of tissues depends on the arrangement and appearance of its cells and the nature and appearance of the intercellular material. Tissue cells possess a specialized structure for better performance of their particular function. There are four basic tissue types in the human body. They are epithelial tissue, connective tissue, muscle tissue, and nervous tissue. Each of these tissue types is specialized for one or more specific roles in the body.

1. **Epithelium**: Epithelial tissue is characterized by the presence of uniform sheets of cells. These cells are closely packed with only very little matrix or ground substance in between. Matrix is the material between cells. Epithelium generally has an exposed surface (typically referred to as the free or apical surface). This surface is the most superficial aspect of the epithelium and it is adjacent to a space, a cavity, or a lumen. All epithelia also possess an anchored surface (typically referred to as the bound or basal surface) and a basement membrane which serves to attach the epithelium to the underlying connective tissue. The basal layer is the deepest aspect of an epithelium. It is continuous with the basement membrane which anchors the basal surface of the epithelium to the connective tissue underneath. A complete absence of vascularity (blood vessels) is another important distinguishing feature of epithelial tissue. It is important to remember that the lack of blood vessels in epithelia does not mean that epithelial cells do not need the oxygen carried in blood. Rather the oxygen they require must diffuse from the tiny blood vessels supported in the connective tissue which anchors epithelia.

    The cells that comprise an epithelium may be categorized in different ways. First they can be distinguished by their shape. Thin, flat cells are referred to as squamous cells. Blocky cells (that is, those whose height, width and length are roughly the same) are referred to as cuboidal. Lastly, cells that are taller than they are wide are called columnar cells. Epithelial cells may also be categorized by how they are layered or organized. A single-layered epithelium is a simple epithelium. An epithelium composed of several or multiple layers is said to be stratified. A third organizational scheme involves a single-layered epithelium that appears to be multilayered because there are nuclei visible at different levels. In reality, all the cells of this epithelium are anchored to the basement membrane but many do not extend all the way to the free surface of the epithelium. This epithelium is referred to as pseudostratified. When an epithelium is named, it typically takes both shape and organization into consideration. The result is epithelia with such names as simple squamous, stratified squamous, pseudostratified columnar, etc.

Epithelial tissue is found on all surfaces of the body: the external surface of the skin, the internal surface of the digestive, respiratory, the genitourinary tracts, the closed serous cavities, the inner surfaces of vessels, the ducts of all glands, the ventricles of the brain, and the central canal of the spinal cord. Epithelial tissue also constitutes the major functional tissue (parenchyma) of all glands of the body. The function of the epithelial tissue is varied, forming in some cases a protective layer from trauma, abrasion, dehydration, or stretching while in others acting as an agent of exchange, secretion, filtration, excretion or absorption.

Different roles place different demands on cells and require different shapes and cellular arrangements. Some processes such as simple diffusion of gases or the filtration of solutes are best accomplished by cells that are flat and arranged in a single layer. Recall that filtration is a process in which water and dissolved solutes are forced through a thin membrane by a hydrostatic pressure. In instances such as these, the cell layer is largely passive, merely providing the shortest possible diffusion distance to be traversed. In other roles such as secretion and absorption, the task is much more demanding metabolically. It requires a cell of sufficient size and volume to accommodate the increased number of varied organelles required of a more involved and energy expensive process. Some epithelia must withstand mechanical forces and still maintain an effective barrier protecting underlying tissue. Such epithelia are typically multilayered, better insuring that underlying tissue remains protected. Lastly some epithelia possess specialized structures or modifications at the free (apical) surface to better accomplish their specific tasks. Cilia are microscopic hairs that extend from the free surface and move in unison to move material along the epithelial free surface. Microvilli on the other hand are tiny fingerlike projections of cell membrane that are often too fine to observe individually even under high magnification. Since the core of a microvillus is continuous with the interior of the cell, these structures provide a significant increase in the apical surface area of the cells.

2. **Connective tissue**: Connective tissue makes up most of the framework of the organs in the body. Connective tissue is found throughout the body and serves primarily to support the body and bind or connect its parts. It also provides a framework for movement and acts to store minerals. The primary characteristics of connective tissue are production by its cells of extensive deposits of extracellular (intercellular) matrix material. This matrix is composed of a nonliving, amorphous ground substance, several different types of protein fibers, and a number of different cell types. In general, connective tissue is characterized by the presence of more than one cell type, varying amounts of intercellular matrix containing different arrays of protein fibers, and the presence of capillaries in variable numbers.

We can state therefore that connective tissues are made basically of three substances: ground substance, fibers and cells. The ground substance is usually material made from proteins, carbohydrates, or both. Depending on the specific category of connective tissue, it varies from a fluid to a semisolid gel to a calcified solid state.

Fibers comprise the second element of connective tissue matrix. There are basically three kinds of fibers present in connective tissue. Two of them are made of collagen. Collagen is a protein which provides high tensile strength (very strong and able to resist stretch and tearing when stretched). The two types of collagenous fibers are reticular fibers and collagenous fibers. Collagenous fibers appear in connective tissue as long, slightly wavy, non- elastic bands whereas reticular fibers are short, very thin, branching threads. Particularly in the case of reticular fibers, special stains are often needed to visualize them clearly. Very few, if any, of the slides you will view have been stained to demonstrate these fibers. The result is that they are virtually invisible in most of the specimens you will be examining. The other fiber type found in connective tissue is composed of the protein elastin. Elastic fibers are generally long, thin, wavy, wirelike threads that may branch to form a network or may appear somewhat like a coiled spring or corkscrew. The use of special stains can make these fibers show up very clearly and distinctly. Some specimens you will view have been treated with these special stains. In those specimens not so treated, elastic fibers will be identifiable to varying degrees.

The third major category of connective tissue structure is the connective tissue cell. There are three predominant types of connective tissue cells: the fibroblast, the macrophage, and the mast cell. Technically, a "blast" cell is a young, active cell which is involved in the synthesis of matrix material. Therefore a fibroblast gives origin to both the ground substance and the fibers found in connective tissue. These cells are found within the matrix of adult connective tissue in areas where collections of fibers are located. They're not motile but rather are fixed in place. When a "blast" cell matures and is no longer actively synthesizing matrix, it is referred to as a "cyte". Fibroblasts (and the other corresponding connective tissue cells) are important for two reasons. First, they are responsible for the synthesis of ground substance. Second, they are responsible for the synthesis of the three types of connective tissue fibers already mentioned. Fibroblasts are known by different names in different types of connective tissue. For instance, in cartilage tissue fibroblasts are known as chondroblasts (chondrocytes) while in bone they are called osteoblasts (osteocytes). The second major cell type found in connective tissue is the macrophage cell. These cells may be round or oval in shape and are often quite large. Macrophage cells generally have small, dark nuclei and their cytoplasm often contains ingested matter. They are related to a type of circulating white blood cell called a monocyte. The primary function of this cell type is to ingest and destroy debris found within connective tissue. As is the case with many cells within connective tissue, the cytoplasm and outlines of the entire cell are often not easily visualized with the instruments and stains at our disposal. As a result, you will largely be observing their nuclei and letting the size and shape of the nuclei tell you something about the size and shape of the whole cell. The third major cell type noted in connective tissue is the mast cell.

Mast cells are tissue-bound relatives of another circulating white blood cell, the basophil. These cells produce histamine (and other chemical mediator substances) in response to a localized injury or infection. Histamine causes changes in circulatory supply to the injured area which serves to prevent the spread of the injury or infective agent. These cells are circular and show numerous dark cytoplasmic granules.

Connective tissue actually encompasses a very broad range of specific and very different tissue types. What lumps these different tissues together as connective tissues is their common origin from an embryonic precursor tissue called mesenchyme. Different references will utilize different classification schemes to group the various specific types. Your text divides connective tissue into embryonic CT (mesenchyme), connective tissue proper (which includes the fibrous CTs and adipose), cartilage, bone, and blood. In the exercise which follows, we have simplified the scheme to include just fibrous CTs, adipose, cartilage, and bone. The fibrous connective tissues are categorized by the dominant protein fiber type (collagenous, elastic, or reticular), the packing of the fibers (dense or loose), and the orientation of the fibers (oriented along one plane - regular or oriented along several planes - irregular). Adipose is characterized by large cells occupied mostly by a single, fat-filled vacuole. Cartilage and bone possess matrix with the greatest density. Because of this, blast cells (chondroblasts and osteoblasts) gradually become completely surrounded and isolated within a small cavity or space as they synthesize matrix around themselves. This transforms a chondroblast into a chondrocyte or an osteoblast into an osteocyte. These cavities are referred to as lacunae (singular: lacuna) and cells contained within lacunae are a hallmark of cartilage and bone.

3. **Muscle tissue**: Muscle tissue is the contractile tissue of the body. Although the cells are generally elongated, they are capable of shortening which gives this tissue the ability to do mechanical work. The three types of muscle tissue found in the body are skeletal muscle, smooth muscle, and cardiac muscle. Skeletal muscle tissue is made up of a collection of muscle fibers. A typical skeletal muscle fiber is a giant (long), multi-nucleated, cylindrical cell which may reach a diameter of 100 micrometers and a length of 8 centimeters. Skeletal muscle fibers exhibit characteristic crossbands or striations which are seen as alternating light and dark stained regions when a muscle fiber is viewed longitudinally under the microscope. Skeletal muscle is attached to bones via tendons or sheets of connective tissue called aponeuroses and moves bones through the movable joints of the body. Smooth muscle cells are not as long as skeletal muscle cells and are much more narrow. They are tapered at each end and often described as being spindle-shaped. Smooth muscle is also called "visceral muscle" because it is the muscle of the internal organs of the body. It is referred to as "smooth" because it lacks the striations which are so prominent in skeletal muscle. Cardiac muscle is composed of short branching fibers that form a complex network. Because these cells branch, they are characterized by specialized end to end connections with one cell attaching to several other cells. As with skeletal muscle, cardiac muscle

exhibits cross striations, although they may not be as distinct or dark as those found in skeletal muscle. Cardiac muscle is found in only one place in the body, the heart.

4. **Nerve tissue**: Nerve tissue consists of cells called neurons that possess elongated cytoplasmic processes. The neuron is the basic anatomical and functional unit of the nervous system. It is the most complex and specialized cell of the body. These cells have a nucleus contained within a cell body which also contains many dark stating granules, slender filaments called neurofibrils, mitochondria, and various other organelles. Emerging from the cell body are cytoplasmic extensions (processes) containing neurofibrils. These processes or are of two types, axons and dendrites. An axon is a single process which emerges from one point (the hillock) on the cell body. An axon generally does not branch until it reaches its termination where it may then divide many times into a spray of tiny fibers. Dendrites are short, highly branched processes. A typical cell body gives rise to many dendrites. Although both axons and dendrites may be called nerve fibers, we generally associate the term "nerve fiber" with the axon.

Preparation

Although preparation for lab is an ongoing part of your anatomy and physiology laboratory experience, your preparation for this lab is absolutely essential to your success in the mastery of anatomy at the microscopic level. A sound knowledge of the four basic types of tissue is the key to your ability to identify and understand the microscopic structure of the organs of the human body. In order to successfully complete this lab exercise, you must come to lab clearly prepared for what you are going to encounter. Carefully read over this exercise before lab. You must come to lab with a basic familiarity of the four major types of tissue found within the body and a working knowledge of the terminology used to discuss these four types of tissue. In order to achieve this objective, you must spend time reading and studying the chapter on tissues in your textbook. Use the chapter to reinforce and clarify any of the concepts and specialized terms presented within this lab exercise. Also use it to address the items of specific responsibility presented at the end of this lab exercise. Although you may not be able to completely address all such items until you actually work through the exercise in lab, you should nevertheless be able to gather a great deal of information relevant to your particular responsibilities prior to lab. Histology images that support all elements of this exercise are included in the *Exploring A&P* CD that accompanies this manual. As part of your preparation for the microscopic anatomy portion of your lab experience, there is a prelab quiz that you must complete. Details about this are included below.

Prelab Quiz - An Introduction to Tissues

Complete the prelab quiz prior to arriving for lab.
This quiz is available on the accompanying *Exploring A&P* CD in color.
Use your textbook and on-line histology references to help complete this quiz.
Part of your lab check-off will be based on the content of this quiz.
Attached at the end of this exercise is the answer sheet.
Bring your completed answer sheet to lab.

Part 1: The Four Types of Tissue
In this exercise you will be provided with **six** (6) slides. For each of these slides, use the preceding descriptive information to determine whether the slide is an example of epithelial tissue, muscle tissue, connective tissue, or nerve tissue. Base this determination on the tissue type which is the most notable and abundant on the slide. You should observe the slides first using the scanning objective and then under the low power objective. For this assignment it is probably not necessary to view the specimens under the high power objective but you may do so if you think it will be helpful. Scan the slides thoroughly before making your determination. Circle your choices.

Slide #	Primary Tissue Type
T1-1	epithelium / connective / muscle / nerve
T1-2	epithelium / connective / muscle / nerve
T1-3	epithelium / connective / muscle / nerve
T1-4	epithelium / connective / muscle / nerve
T1-5	epithelium / connective / muscle / nerve
T1-6	epithelium / connective / muscle / nerve

Part 2: Epithelium

In this exercise, you will be provided with **four** (4) slides. Each slide contains an example of a type of epithelium. Locate the epithelium on the slide and observe it under both low power and high power. Based on these observations, answer the following questions about each of the epithelia presented.

Location. Is the epithelium lining a passage/cavity or covering a surface, or is the epithelium a major component of the mass of the organ?

Organization. Is the epithelium organized into a single layer, or is it organized in multiple layers?

Classification. Classify the epithelium you are observing on this slide into one of the following categories: simple squamous, stratified squamous, simple columnar, ciliated columnar with goblet cells, simple cuboidal, or transitional (akin to stratified cuboidal).

Specializations of the free surface. Does the free surface of the epithelium display cilia or microvilli creating a brush border?

Where appropriate, circle your choices below. For classification, write in the specific epithelial name (of those provided) that best describes what you have observed.

Slide #	Location	Organization	Classification	Free Surface
1	lining or covering / mass of the organ	single layer / multiple layers	_____	cilia / microvilli
2	lining or covering / mass of the organ	single layer / multiple layers	_____	cilia / microvilli
3	lining or covering / mass of the organ	single layer / multiple layers	_____	cilia / microvilli
4	lining or covering / mass of the organ	single layer / multiple layers	_____	cilia / microvilli

Part 3: Connective Tissue.
In this exercise you will be presented with **five** (5) slides that show examples of different types of connective tissue. From this collection, provide the numbers of all the slides that demonstrate each of the following characteristics:

Number(s) of slide(s) which contain more than one major type of connective tissue. (Note: The types are fibrous CT, adipose, cartilage, and bone.)

T3-1   T3-2   T3-3   T3-4   T3-5

Number(s) of slide(s) which contain fibrous connective tissue.

T3-1   T3-2   T3-3   T3-4   T3-5

Number(s) of slide(s) which contain cartilage.

T3-1   T3-2   T3-3   T3-4   T3-5

Number(s) of slide(s) which contain bone.

T3-1   T3-2   T3-3   T3-4   T3-5

Number(s) of slide(s) which contain dense, regular fibrous connective tissue.

T3-1   T3-2   T3-3   T3-4   T3-5

Number(s) of slide(s) which contain dense, irregular fibrous connective tissue.

T3-1   T3-2   T3-3   T3-4   T3-5

Number(s) of slide(s) which contain loose connective tissue.

T3-1   T3-2   T3-3   T3-4   T3-5

Number(s) of slide(s) which contain adipose tissue.

T3-1   T3-2   T3-3   T3-4   T3-5

Part 4: Muscle Tissue

In this exercise you are presented with a collection of **four** (4) slides that demonstrate the different types of muscle tissue. Besides illustrating the three types of muscle tissue, these slides also demonstrate various muscle tissue arrangements or perspectives from which muscle tissue may be viewed. From this collection of slides, provide numbers of all the slides that demonstrate each of the following characteristics:

Number(s) of slide(s) which contain muscle cut <u>longitudinally</u>:	T4-1	T4-2	T4-3	T4-4
Number(s) of slide(s) which contain muscle tissue cut <u>transversely</u>:	T4-1	T4-2	T4-3	T4-4
Slide(s) which contain muscle fibers with <u>visible</u> striations:	T4-1	T4-2	T4-3	T4-4
Slide(s) which contain branching muscle fibers:	T4-1	T4-2	T4-3	T4-4
Slide(s) which contain muscle fibers arranged in bundles or fascicles:	T4-1	T4-2	T4-3	T4-4
Slide(s) which contain tapering muscle fibers:	T4-1	T4-2	T4-3	T4-4
Slide(s) which contain two muscle layers arranged at 90 degrees to each other:	T4-1	T4-2	T4-3	T4-4
Slide(s) which contain smooth muscle:	T4-1	T4-2	T4-3	T4-4
Slide(s) which contain cardiac muscle:	T4-1	T4-2	T4-3	T4-4
Slide(s) which contain skeletal muscle:	T4-1	T4-2	T4-3	T4-4

Part 5: Nerve Tissue
Nerve tissue is a highly specialized and very complicated tissue type. The detailed study of nerve tissue is not appropriate for an introductory course in Anatomy & Physiology. However as an introduction to nerve tissue, do the following: Using the nerve tissue slide provided (T5), find an area which clearly demonstrates the two cellular components from which nerve tissue is constructed, namely neurons and neuroglia (support cells). Draw this area showing a neuron and any structures of the neuron you can recognize. Also include any neuroglia that are visible on this area of the slide. Make your drawing as accurate as possible and be sure to label all of the elements that are visible in your drawing.

Part 6: Microscopic and Macroscopic Structure

This exercise is designed to illustrate the principle that the macroscopic structure of an organ is a reflection of the histological makeup of that organ. This exercise involves two activities. In each, you will be required to examine the same 4 slides (T6-1, T6-2, T6-3, and T6-4) of different tissues.

Activity 1: Observe the macroscopic structure of the quadriceps tendon. This large tendon transfers the force of contraction of the quadriceps group of muscle to the lower leg when the leg is straightened at the knee joint. At least one example of this tendon will be presented in cross section. After inspecting the gross anatomy of the tendon, select from a collection of four numbered slides the single slide which exhibits this same type of structure (a major tendon). Support your choice by providing the reasons you rejected each slide you believe to be incorrect and the reason(s) for selecting the slide you identified as the tendon.

Tendon slide # _____ :
Reasons: _____

_____

_____

_____

Incorrect slides:
    # _____
    Reasons: _____

_____

_____

    # _____
    Reasons: _____

_____

_____

    # _____
    Reasons: _____

_____

_____

Part 6 (continued)

Activity 2: Observe the macroscopic structure of a gland. After inspecting the gross anatomy of a selection of representative glands from a specimens provided by your instructor, select from a collection of four numbered slides <u>the single slide</u> which exhibits this same type of structure (consistent with a major gland). Support your choice by providing the reasons you rejected each slide you believe to be incorrect and the reason(s) for selecting the slide you identified as the gland.

Gland slide # _____ :
Reasons: _____

_____

_____

_____

Incorrect slides:
    # _____
    Reasons: _____

_____

_____

    # _____
    Reasons: _____

_____

_____

    # _____
    Reasons: _____

_____

_____

Part 7: Functional Correlations - Epithelium:
Now that you are familiar with the different epithelial tissues, you must consider the capabilities or functional ramifications of the very different structural arrangements which you have observed. Consider each of the questions posed and select the best answer choice.

1. Cell shape that provides the most cell volume per cell surface area:
   squamous   cuboidal   columnar

2. Cell shape that provides most cell surface area per cell volume:
   squamous   cuboidal   columnar

3. Cell arrangement best suited to deal with surface friction:
   simple   stratified   pseudostratified

4. Free surface structure intended to increase the free surface area for absorption:
   cilia   microvilli (brush border)

5. Free surface structure intended to move material along the free surface:
   cilia   microvilli (brush border)

6. Cell shape best suited for filtration:
   squamous   cuboidal   columnar

7. Free surface structure intended to enhance absorption ability:
   cilia   microvilli (brush border)

8. Cell arrangement best suited to allow the easy passage of substances:
   simple   stratified   pseudostratified

9. Cell arrangement best suited to withstand stretching forces:
   simple   stratified   pseudostratified

10. Two cell shapes suited to a role in secretion:
    squamous   cuboidal   columnar

11. Two cell shapes suited to a role in absorption:
    squamous   cuboidal   columnar

12. Epithelium best suited to secreting a product and moving it along a free surface:
    stratified squamous   cuboidal with microvilli   columnar with cilia

Part 8: Functional Correlations - Connective Tissue:
Now that you are familiar with the different connective tissues, you must consider the capabilities or functional ramifications of the very different structural arrangements which you have observed. Consider each question and select the best answer choice.

1. Type of fiber packing that is stronger: dense   loose

2. Type of fiber arrangement that can cope with multidirectional stress:
    regular   irregular

3. Type of fibrous CT that has the more strength:
    mostly collagenous   mostly elastic

4. Two CT types that can maintain shape and bear weight:
    fibrous   adipose   cartilage   bone

5. Two CT types with the richest blood supply:
    fibrous   adipose   cartilage   bone

6. CT type with the greater ability to heal quickly?   fibrous   bone

7. CT type with the greater ability to heal quickly?   fibrous   cartilage

8. Ligaments hold bone to bone and must be strong and able to stretch and recoil. Which CT is best suited for that?
    dense, irregular, collagenous   dense, regular, collagenous
    dense, regular, elastic   loose, irregular

9. Tendons hold muscle to bone and must be very strong and not stretch very much. Which CT is best suited for that?
    dense, irregular, collagenous   dense, regular, collagenous
    dense, regular, elastic   loose, irregular

10. Skin is held in place by a fibrous CT that must have some strength and be able to stretch in many directions and recoil. Which CT is best suited for that?
    dense, irregular, collagenous   dense, regular, collagenous
    dense, regular, elastic   loose, irregular

11. Which CT type can maintain shape and still be quite flexible?
    fibrous   adipose   cartilage   bone

12. Which CT type prevents the windpipe from collapsing?
    fibrous   adipose   cartilage   bone

13. Which CT type can probably best stabilize and cushion internal organs?
    fibrous   adipose   cartilage   bone

Learning Outcomes: An Introduction to Tissue

Once you have done the preparation and completed the exercises dealing with the four primary tissue types, you should be able to:

General Histological Knowledge:
1. Define histology.
2. Indicate where tissue fits into the levels of structural complexity hierarchy.
3. List the four fundamental tissue types found in the human body and provide descriptions and distinguishing features of each.
4. List specific examples of the four primary tissue types found in the human body.
5. Illustrate by example the principle that the macroscopic appearance of an organ and functional characteristics of an organ are often reflected and more completely understood on the basis of the types of tissue which make up that organ.

Epithelium:
1. For each of the epithelial slides studied, classify (name) the epithelium.
2. For each of the epithelial slides studied, describe the specific epithelium which you are viewing. This descriptive ability should include the following: cell shape; cell arrangement; the location of the free surface; the location of the basal area of the epithelium; the ability to identify a basement membrane, if visible; the ability to point out free surface specializations such as cilia and brush borders; and the ability to identify specialized epithelial cell types such as basal cells or goblet cells.
3. For each of the epithelia studied, specify the functional significance of that particular epithelium. This includes indicating the special role or job that sets this epithelium apart from other epithelia found within the body.
4. Provide a number of examples of where any particular epithelium you have studied is found within the body

Connective Tissue:
1. For each of the connective tissue slides studied, recognize that particular connective tissue by name.
2. For each of the connective tissue slides studied, classify that connective tissue as bone, cartilage, fibrous CT, or adipose.
3. For each of the connective tissue slides studied, indicate whether the cells of that connective tissue are found in lacunae.
4. For each of the fibrous connective tissue slides studied, describe the specific fiber arrangement and types present.
5. For each of the connective tissues studied, specify the special role or job performed by that connective tissue within the body.
6. Provide a number of examples of where any particular connective tissue which we have studied is found within the body.

Muscle Tissue:
1. For each of the muscle tissue slides studied, recognize that particular muscle tissue by name.
2. For each of the muscle tissue slides studied, describe the muscle tissue which you are viewing. This descriptive ability should include the following: muscle cell shape; muscle cell arrangement; muscle cell orientation in multiple-layered muscle tissue examples; the location of the nucleus/nuclei within a muscle cell; the presence of striations in those muscle cell types which exhibit striations; and the ability to identify the three investing connective tissue layers associated with skeletal muscle tissue. These layers are epimysium, perimysium and endomysium.
3. For each of the muscle tissues studied, specify the special role or job that sets one particular muscle tissue apart from other muscle tissues found within the body.
4. Indicate for each muscle tissue where in the body that particular muscle tissue is found.

Nerve Tissue:
1. Distinguish neurons from supporting cells (neuroglia) structurally and functionally.
2. For the nerve tissue slide studied, distinguish neurons from neuroglia.
3. On a slide that exhibits a typical multipolar neuron, distinguish the nerve cell body (with nucleus and nucleolus) from neuronal processes.
4. List various structures within the body that are composed of nerve tissue.

An Introduction to Tissues: Prelab Quiz   Name: _____

Complete this brief quiz prior to lab. Your instructor may collect this at the start of lab.

Question I
Supply the correct letter from the Prelab Quiz Question I slide/figure.

1. _____   Stratified Epithelium

2. _____   Squamous Cell

3. _____   Simple Epithelium

4. _____   Free Surface

5. _____   Basal Layer

Question II
Supply the correct letter from the Prelab Quiz Question II slide/figure.

1. _____   Matrix   2. _____   Protein Fiber

3. _____   Fibroblast   4. _____   Fat Cell

Question III
Supply the correct letter from the Prelab Quiz Question III slide/figure.

1. _____   Neuron Fiber   2. _____   Nerve Cell Body

3. _____   Neuroglia

Question IV
Supply the correct letter from the Prelab Quiz Question IV slide/figure.

1. _____   Nucleus of Muscle Cell

2. _____   Muscle Cell

Question V
Supply the correct letter from the Prelab Quiz Question V slide/figure.

1. _____   Epithelial Tissue   2. _____   Connective Tissue

3. _____   Muscle Tissue   4. _____   Nerve Tissue

Exercise H-2
Histology of the Integument

Introduction
The integument, or skin, is the organ-system that provides the external barrier between the outside environment and the internal environment. It is composed of two very different layers which contribute different functional capabilities to the skin. The outer layer of the skin, or the epidermis, is an epithelial layer and consists of stratified epithelial cells. Because the epidermis is exposed to the air, its exposed surface is dry and somewhat hardened. Deep to this superficial epithelial layer is the fibrous connective tissue layer, the dermis. The dermis is the layer from which leather is derived which should tell you something about its strength and durability. This layer also contains many elements that are actually derived from the superficial epithelial layer. These epithelial structures extend from the epidermal surface into the underlying connective tissue area where they can be seen.

Although all skin is fundamentally the same and composed of the same two major layers, the skin in different regions of the body does demonstrate marked structural differences. Because of this, skin can be broadly divided into two categories, thick skin and thin skin. In this exercise, you will be comparing the skin from two different regions of the body. One specimen is of thick skin. It is actually plantar skin which is found on the palms of the hand and on the soles of the feet. It has a structure that is suitable for the very significant wear and tear (mechanical stress) that these areas of the body surface experience. The example of thin skin that we will examine is the scalp. Although not subject to the same mechanical stresses and strain as plantar skin, the scalp does show a number of adaptations which are consistent with its role as the covering for the most superior portion of the body.

Consult your textbook for a more thorough description of the structure of the skin. Master the names and descriptions of each of the layers or regions of the epidermis and the dermis. Be comfortable with the distinguishing features and structural characteristics of each layer. Learn about the appendages of the integument derived from the epidermis. Focus on the basic structure of these appendages and how they are distributed in different regions of the body.

Histology images that support all elements of this exercise are included in the *Exploring A&P* CD that accompanies this manual.

Prelab Quiz - Histology of the Integumentary System
    Complete the prelab quiz prior to arriving for lab.
    This quiz is available on the accompanying *Exploring A&P* CD in color.
    Use your textbook and on-line histology references to help complete this quiz.
    Part of your lab check-off will be based on the content of this quiz.
    Attached at the end of this exercise is the answer sheet.
    Bring your completed answer sheet to lab.

Part 1: The Epidermis

In this exercise you will be working with a slide of plantar skin. Find the outer epithelial layer (epidermis) of plantar skin.

1. Based on the classification system that characterizes epithelium by cell arrangement or layering (simple, stratified, pseudostratified), how would you classify the epithelium of this epidermis?

    ___ simple   ___ stratified   ___ pseudostratified

2. By counting the number of cells in a band running from basal surface to free surface, try to estimate the thickness of the epidermis. For this, select an area where the epidermis is thickest. Is it 1 cell, 5 cells, ~~10 cells,~~ or more than ~~10~~ 5 cells in thickness?

    1   5   >5

    Does the thickness of the epidermis appear to be consistent? Yes / No

    Does the concentration (number of cells per unit of area) of epithelial cells seem consistent throughout the thickness of the epidermis? Yes / No
    Please describe what you observe.

    _____

    _____

    _____

3. Do the cells throughout the thickness of the epidermis appear to be of the same size?   Yes / No
    Please describe what you observe. _____

    _____

    _____

    Do the cells throughout the thickness of the epidermis appear to be of the same shape?   Yes / No
    Please describe what you observe. _____

    _____

    Based on the classification system that characterizes epithelium by cell shape at the surface (squamous, cuboidal, columnar), how would you classify the epithelium of this epidermis?

    ___ squamous   ___ cuboidal   ___ columnar

4. Is the epithelium which makes up the epidermis observable as a single uniform sheet or thickness of cells? In other words, based on your careful examination of the full thickness of the epidermis, does it appear to be composed of different divisions, regions, or sublayers?   Yes / No

    If you believe that the epidermis is made up of more than one sublayer or region, how many layers do you observe?

                                        2   3   4   5   6

    If you believe that the epidermis is made up of more than one layer or region, Provide a simple labeled drawing in the space provided might to illustrate the structural details of these layers epidermis.

    Free surface

    Basal surface

5. Direct your attention to the border between the epithelial epidermis and the underlying connective tissue layer, the dermis. In the space below, draw the <u>line</u> that results when you trace this border <u>across</u> the full low-power field of view.

    Epidermis

    Start your line here →

    Dermis

    Once you have determined the shape of this junction between dermis and epidermis by drawing your line, speculate on the functional significance of this particular design. In what way is it helpful?

Part 2: The Dermis
Now direct your attention to the dermis. It was already mentioned that the dermis is largely made up of connective tissue. Based on your previous work with connective tissues, what would be the best description of the connective tissue framework of the dermis? Be careful not to be distracted by the subcutaneous (hypodermal) tissue that may be visible in your field of view. Circle your choice.

___ fibrous   ___ adipose   ___ cartilaginous   ___ bony

1. Based on fiber arrangement (regular or irregular) and fiber packing (dense or loose), classify the connective tissue of the dermis.

   dense regular   dense irregular   loose regular   loose irregular

2. Make your best assessment of the degree of vascularity of the dermis. In doing this, it is important to keep in mind that blood flows through vessels which are tubular in nature. Try to visualize how vessels will appear when sectioned along different planes. In the space below, draw how a tube will appear when sectioned:

   longitudinally   transversely   obliquely

   Now, based on what you are observing, which statement best characterizes the blood supply of the dermis? Circle your choice.

   ___ avascular   ___ vascular

3. With the scanning or low-power objective in place, scan your entire slide and try to find adipose tissue. Which statement best describes the predominate location of the adipose tissue you observe in this slide?

   ___ There is an abundance of adipose tissue in the epidermis.
   ___ There is an abundance of adipose tissue scattered evenly throughout the full thickness of the dermis.
   ___ There is an abundance of adipose tissue, but only in the more superficial portion of the dermis.
   ___ Most adipose is found deep to the dermis in the subcutaneous tissue.

Part 3: Comparing Plantar Skin and Scalp
In this exercise, you will be comparing the structure of thick skin (plantar skin) with the structure of thin skin (scalp). For each of the indicated descriptions, indicate if the description applies to plantar skin alone, to the scalp alone, or to both plantar skin and the scalp.

Note: In each instance, **base your answer on what you can actually observe** on the slides with which you are working. **DO NOT** base your answer on text information that you read or on pictures in a reference. However, **DO** use your textbook to enable you to identify the different specific structures which are listed and which you cannot be expected to know or recognize without the aid of some sort of reference material.

Type of skin with the thickest epidermis.	plantar	scalp	no difference
Type of skin with the thickest dermis.	plantar	scalp	no difference
Type of skin with the largest dermal papillae	plantar	scalp	no difference
Type of skin with a wavy junction between dermis and epidermis.	plantar	scalp	both
Type of skin with a vascular dermis.	plantar	scalp	both
Type of skin adapted to withstand friction at the free surface.	plantar	scalp	both
Type of skin adapted to withstand multidirectional stress.	plantar	scalp	both
Type of skin which contains sweat glands.	plantar	scalp	both
Type of skin which contains hair follicles.	plantar	scalp	both
Type of skin which contains sebaceous glands.	plantar	scalp	both
Type of skin which contains arrector pili muscle.	plantar	scalp	both
Type of skin which contains adipose tissue.	plantar	scalp	both

Part 4: Model of the Integument
Using one of the models of the integument available in the laboratory, you must be able to identify, describe, and discuss the functional significance of each of the structural components listed below. Use your text to help.

1. Function of selected layers of the epidermis:
    Stratum corneum _____

    _____

    Stratum spinosum _____

    _____

    Stratum basale _____

    _____

2. Function of each layer of the dermis
    Reticular dermis _____

    _____

    Papillary dermis _____

    _____

3. Function of the hypodermis (subcutaneous tissue or superficial fascia)

    _____

4. Function of eccrine (merocrine) sweat glands

    _____

5. Function of apocrine sweat glands

    _____

6. Function of sebaceous glands

    _____

7. Function of hair follicles and arrector pili muscles

    _____

Learning Outcomes: Integument
Once you have done the preparation and completed the exercises dealing with the integument, you should be able to:

General Knowledge of the Integument
1. Define the integumentary system.
2. Distinguish between the structure of thick and thin skin.
3. List the organs that constitute the integumentary system.
4. List the major layers and sub-layers of the integument.
5. List the function of each major layer and sub-layer of the integument.

Scalp:
1. Recognize a slide as scalp.
2. Correctly categorize this slide as an example of thin skin.
3. Describe the scalp and its component structures in terms of the fundamental tissue types contained within it.
4. Identify the following layers in the epidermis of thin skin - stratum corneum, stratum spinosum, and stratum basale;
5. Identify the following layers in the dermis of thin skin - papillary and reticular layers.
6. Identify the following integumentary organs on this slide: hair follicles, sebaceous glands, arrector pili muscles, and eccrine sweat glands.

Plantar Skin:
1. Identify a slide as plantar skin.
2. Correctly categorize this slide as an example of thick skin.
3. Describe plantar skin and its component structures in terms of the fundamental tissue types contained within it.
4. Distinguish the following layers in the epidermis of plantar skin - stratum corneum, stratum lucidum (if present), stratum granulosum, stratum spinosum, and stratum basale;
5. Distinguish the following layers in the dermis of plantar skin - papillary layer and reticular layer.
6. Identify the following plantar skin organs: eccrine sweat glands and Pacinian corpuscles (if present).

Scalp/Plantar Skin Comparison:
1. List the common features found on both thin skin and thick skin.
2. List elements of contrast (differences) between thin skin and thick skin, that is, ways in which they are structurally different.
3. Discuss the functions of thin skin and thick skin.
4. Specify locations in the body where each type of skin can be found.

Model of Integument:
1. Identify and describe the functions of the layers and accessory structures of thick and thin skin listed above.

Histology of the Integument: Prelab Quiz   Name: _____

Complete this brief quiz prior to lab. Your instructor may collect this at the start of lab.

Question I
Supply the correct letter from the Prelab Quiz Question I slide/figure.

1. _____ Epidermis

2. _____ Dermis

3. _____ Border between Dermis and Epidermis

4. _____ Gland

5. _____ Sensory Structure

6. _____ Hair Shaft

7. _____ Subcutaneous Tissue

Question II
Supply the correct letter from the Prelab Quiz Question II slide/figure.

1. _____ Dermis

2. _____ Deepest Layer of Epidermis

3. _____ Granular Layer of Epidermis

4. _____ Surface of Epidermis

Question III
Supply the correct letter from the Prelab Quiz Question III slide/figure.

1. _____ Connective Tissue in Dermis

2. _____ Glandular Structure of Dermis

3. _____ Non-Glandular Structure of Dermis

Exercise H-3
Histology of the Digestive System

Introduction

The organs of the digestive system can be divided into three basic categories, solid organs made up primarily of epithelium, solid organs made up largely of muscle, and hollow (saclike or tubular) organs. Solid organs made up primarily of epithelia are glandular in nature and include the major salivary glands, the pancreas, and the liver. There is only one solid, predominately muscular organ that is part of the digestive system. It is the tongue. Hollow organs of the digestive system include the entire alimentary canal and the gall bladder with its associated duct system.

All tubular organs of the digestive system share a common histological plan, typically referred to as the four-layer plan. Before beginning your study of the microscopic anatomy of the digestive system, it is important for you to become thoroughly familiar with the four-layer plan. Master the names of each of the major layers or tunics, as well as each of the sub-layers or minor tunics. Be comfortable with the distinguishing features and characteristics of each layer and the modifications that are possible within each of the layers in different regions of the alimentary canal. By grouping different organs of the digestive system based on the structural features and details of the major and minor tunics, you will find that your mastery of this subject matter will proceed smoothly. Try to spend your time finding and keying on the features that one organ has in common with another. In this way, each item you learn will help you to learn the next because your approach is developing a knowledge base in a manner that relates one fact to another. Nothing should be learned in isolation.

What follows is a brief summary of the basic four-layer plan. Consult your textbook for a more thorough description. Each of the four layers is referred to as a tunic or coat. As you work to master this design, always progress from the lumen or luminal surface through the wall of the organ. Move from the inside (closest to the lumen) to the outside (closer to the outer wall of the organ). That means that as you move deeper into the wall of the organ, you are actually getting closer and closer to the outside surface of the organ. That means that the very deepest layer of a hollow organ is the one you can touch from outside the organ. Seems paradoxical but it isn't if you always work from the internal, luminal surface.

Proceeding in order from the lumen, the 4 major tunics are:

Tunica mucosa (or simply mucosa) - possesses 3 sub-layers or minor tunics.
1) Epithelium - only two specific epithelia will be seen. One is designed to withstand friction and abrasive forces and the other to accomplish secretion and/or absorption.
2) Lamina propria - an anchoring layer of irregular connective tissue in which small vessels and lymphatics may be seen. Multicellular glandular structures may or may not be present, depending on the specific organ being viewed.

3) Muscularis mucosa - thin smooth muscle layer which is sometimes very obvious and sometimes very difficult to pick out.

2. Tunica submucosa (or simply submucosa) - a single layer framework of irregular connective tissue which often contains larger visible blood vessels, lymphatic structures, and adipose. Multicellular glandular structures may or may not be present depending on the specific organ being viewed.

3. Tunica muscularis (or simply muscularis) - generally two layers of muscle, an inner (more superficial) circular layer and an outer (deeper) longitudinal layer. Typically it is composed of smooth muscle but in specific portions of one digestive organ, it contains or is composed entirely of skeletal muscle.

4. Tunica adventitia (or simply adventitia) - a second single layer framework of irregular connective tissue in which blood vessels and adipose are often seen. When its outer surface is covered by a simple squamous epithelium, it is referred to as a serosa (as in serous membrane). The visceral peritoneum is the serosa of the digestive system.

Histology images that support all elements of this exercise are included in the *Exploring A&P* CD that accompanies this manual.

Prelab Quiz - Histology of the Digestive System
    Complete the prelab quiz prior to arriving for lab.
    This quiz is available on the accompanying *Exploring A&P* CD in color.
    Use your textbook and on-line histology references to help complete this quiz.
    Part of your lab check-off will be based on the content of this quiz.
    Attached at the end of this exercise is the answer sheet.
    Bring your completed answer sheet to lab.

Part 1: Survey of Digestive Organs
In this exercise, you will be presented with a collection of four coded slides of different digestive system organs. For each of the four slides, determine if the organ presented on the slide is a solid epithelial organ, a solid muscular organ, or a hollow organ which follows the four layer plan. Circle your choice. Use the space below each slide to jot down or draw any detail that helped you reach your conclusion.

Slide #   **Nature of the Organ**

1.   solid & epithelial   solid & muscular   hollow

2.   solid & epithelial   solid & muscular   hollow

3.   solid & epithelial   solid & muscular   hollow

4.   solid & epithelial   solid & muscular   hollow

Part 2: Tongue

In this exercise, you will be presented with a slide of the tongue. Remember that the tongue is a solid, predominately muscular organ of the digestive system. Carefully observe this slide and attempt to answer the following questions.

1. The surface of the tongue is covered with epithelium. It is:

   ___ simple columnar   ___ simple cuboidal   ___ stratified squamous

   What <u>visible</u> features support your answer? Remember that "visible" means structural features that <u>you can see</u> in this slide.

   _____

   _____

   _____

   Explain how or why this particular type of epithelium fits with the role of the tongue in the digestive process.

   _____

   _____

2. Is the free surface of the tongue smooth and unbroken or is it characterized by the presence of slits, grooves, or crevices which divide it into hills and valleys? Scan the entire length of epithelium from one end to the other before answering.

   ___ smooth & unbroken   ___ hills & valleys

3. Taste buds are important structures found on the surface of the tongue. These are small, spherical structures located within the epithelium that lines grooves on the tongue surface called sulci (singular: sulcus). Try to identify a taste bud. Then, using the low power objective for observation, draw a small area of the tongue surface that clearly illustrates the placement (location) of the taste buds.

4. Deep to the surface of the tongue, you will find an abundance of muscle tissue. Are all the fibers or bundles that make up this muscle oriented along the same direction or are they oriented along different directions?

   ___ same direction   ___ different directions

   Observe this muscle carefully under the high power. Is it smooth muscle, cardiac muscle, or skeletal muscle?

   ___ smooth   ___ cardiac   ___ skeletal

5. Within the mass of the organ, look for evidence of epithelium (in addition to the epithelium that covers the surface of the tongue). What term best describes the cells that make up this epithelium?

   ___ columnar   ___ squamous   ___ cuboidal

6. This epithelium shows at least two different types of arrangements. In one arrangement, the cells are clustered together in small groups. In the other, the cells are arranged in single layers to form tubular structures. Using the low power objective, observe each of these different types of epithelial arrangements and provide a drawing of each.

   cluster   tube

   [drawing box   ]   [drawing box   ]

   Demonstrate that you have accomplished this by showing an example of each to your instructor.

7. Speculate on the function of each of these two epithelial arrangements.
   The clusters of cells act to …

   _____

   _____

   The tubular arrangements of cells act to … _____

   _____

PART 3: Digestive Glands

Most of the solid digestive system organs have an epithelial rather than a muscular core. In this exercise, you will be working with slides of three solid epithelial organs of the digestive system. These slides are the liver, the pancreas, and the submandibular gland (refer to the submaxillary gland slide). The submandibular gland is one of three major salivary glands. Observe these three slides under scanning, low-power, and then high power and attempt to answer the following questions.

1. In two of these organs, the epithelium that makes up the internal mass of the organ is arranged in spherical clusters or clumps of 8-10 cells. These clusters are the basic secretory units of the gland and are called acini (singular: acinus). In one of these slides, the epithelium that makes up the mass of the organ is arranged in plates or sheets of cells rather than in clusters or clumps. Which two organs show the spherical cluster arrangement and in which organ is the epithelium arranged in sheets or plates?

    Liver   solid mass   subunits

    Pancreas   solid mass   subunits

    Submandibular gland solid mass   subunits

2. Observe the arrangement of connective tissue associated with the interior of these organs. Despite the fact that there is some variation in the structure of these three glands, the connective tissue plays a similar role in each organ. Based on your observation, what appears to be its function?

    _____

    _____

3. Besides the two epithelial arrangements cited above, you may find epithelial cells forming channels or tubes through the organ. Carefully observe all three organs. Which of the three organs show(s) contains tubes or channels made from epithelial cells?

    ___ liver   ___ pancreas   ___ submandibular gland

    Speculate on the function of these epithelial channels. _____

    _____

    _____

Part 4: Hollow Digestive Organs: The GI Tract

The final digestive system exercise will give you some hands on experience with the histology of the four-layer plan. You will be working with three tubular digestive system organs, the esophagus, the small intestine (jejunem or duodenum), and the colon.

Indicate which small intestine slide you have: ___ jejunem ___ duodenum

Tunica Mucosa:
Compare the tunica mucosa in each of these three digestive system tubular structures. Use both low power and high power.

1. Which of these tunica mucosas show(s) a stratified epithelium? Look very carefully before you decide on your answer.

    ___ esophagus ___ small intestine ___ colon ___ none

2. Which of these three tunica mucosas contain(s) epithelium specialized for absorption?

    ___ esophagus ___ small intestine ___ colon ___ none

3. Which of these three tunica mucosas has the capability for producing the greatest amount of mucus?
    ___ esophagus ___ small intestine ___ colon

4. Two of these three organs show multicellular glands within the tunica mucosa. Which two?
    ___ esophagus ___ small intestine ___ colon

Tunica Submucosa:
Next, direct your attention to the tunica submucosa of these three organs. Use both low power and high power.

1. Which of these three digestive system organs contain(s) multicellular glands within the tunica submucosa?
    ___ esophagus ___ small intestine ___ colon ___ none

2. A common feature found throughout the alimentary canal within the tunica submucosa is the presence of large spherical collections of lymphatic cells. The nuclei of the lymphatic cells in these aggregations generally stain dark purple. The result is that these structures look like very dense concentrations of tiny dark dots. Can you find any of these lymphatic structures? Yes / No
    If yes, in which organ or organ(s) are they visible?

    ___ esophagus ___ small intestine ___ colon ___ none

What do you suppose is the function of lymphatic structures contained within the wall of the alimentary canal?

    __ secretion   __ absorption   __ structural support
    __ protection   __ coordination

Please explain your answer. _____

_____

_____

Tunica Muscularis:
Next, direct your attention to the tunica muscularis, the muscle layer of the alimentary tube.

1. For each of the three organs, determine the specific type of muscle tissue which makes up the tunica muscularis.

    Esophagus   smooth muscle   skeletal muscle

    Small intestine   smooth muscle   skeletal muscle

    Colon   smooth muscle   skeletal muscle

2. Compare the tunica muscularis of the small intestine with the tunica muscularis of the colon. Typically, the tunica muscularis is composed of two layers, an inner (more superficial) layer of circular muscle and an outer (deeper) layer of longitudinal muscle.

    Does the muscle of the tunica muscularis of the small intestine meet this description? Yes / No
    If not, how is the muscle of its tunica muscularis different from the standard description?

    _____

    _____

3. Does the muscle of the tunica muscularis of the colon meet this description? Yes / No
    If not, how is the muscle of its tunica muscularis different from the standard description?

    _____

    _____

4. Now consider the thickness of the two sublayers of the muscularis in each of these organs?

    Esophagus   thicker circular   thicker longitudinal   equal

    Small intestine   thicker circular   thicker longitudinal   equal

    Colon   thicker circular   thicker longitudinal   equal

5. When the muscularis is active, the length of the digestive tube changes or the diameter of its lumen changes. Consider how the contraction of each individual sublayer of the muscularis affects the digestive tube? In each case, select <u>only one of the four</u> possible choices.

    Circular muscularis   longer   shorter   constricted   dilated

    Longitudinal muscularis   longer   shorter   constricted   dilated

6. Which of these two layers likely plays the dominant role in moving material along within the digestive tube?

    ___ circular muscularis   ___ longitudinal muscularis

    Please briefly explain your choice. _____

    _____

Tunica Adventitia:
Finally, direct your attention to the tunica adventitia.

1. Is the adventitia visible on each of these organs?

    Esophagus   Yes / No   Small intestine   Yes / No

    Colon   Yes / No

2. If the adventitia is visible, is there a simple squamous epithelium covering the exposed surface of this adventitia, thereby making it a serosa?

    Esophagus   Yes / No   Small intestine   Yes / No

    Colon   Yes / No

If yes for any of these, be able to demonstrate it to your instructor.

Learning Outcomes: Histology of the Digestive System

Once you have done the preparation and completed the exercises dealing with the digestive system, you should be able to:

General Histological Knowledge of the Digestive System
1. Based on observation of even previously unviewed organ slides, categorize digestive organs as being solid epithelial, solid muscular, or hollow.
2. Describe and illustrate by example the four-layer plan followed by most hollow organs of the digestive system.
3. List and illustrate by example significant histological variations present within these layers as one journeys along the length of the alimentary canal.
4. Based on an overall observation of digestive system histology and the specific details which you have discovered, provide at least five significant examples of the principle of the complementary nature of structure and function.

Solid Digestive System Organs
1. For each of the solid digestive system organ slides studied, you should be able to recognize that particular organ of the digestive system by its specific name.
2. For each solid digestive system organ slide studied, you must be able to determine if its mass is predominately epithelial or muscular in nature.
3. For each solid digestive system organ slide studied, you must be able to determine if there is a covering layer of epithelium. If so, you should be able to identify the type of epithelium that is responsible for this covering.
3. If there is significant muscle associated with a solid digestive system organ, you should be able to identify the specific type of muscle tissue (smooth or skeletal) involved and its function within that solid organ.

Hollow Digestive System Organs
1. For each of the hollow digestive system organ slides studied, you should be able to recognize that particular organ of the digestive system by its specific name.
2. For each hollow digestive system organ slide studied, you should be able to determine how closely the histology of that organ corresponds to the generalized four-layer plan. If that organ significantly deviates from this generalized plan, you must be able to specifically describe the elements of that organ's histology which do not match.
3. For each hollow organ studied, you should be able to identify and describe the epithelium that is lining its lumen and the epithelium that is covering the outer surface of the organ (if one is present).
4. For each hollow digestive organ system slide studied, you should be able to describe (by tissue type and arrangement), locate, and name any muscular elements, glandular elements, and lymphatic elements contained within the wall of that organ. You should also have knowledge of the types of secretions produced by glandular elements and the functions of all elements identified.

Histology of the Digestive System: Prelab Quiz Name: _____

Complete this brief quiz prior to lab. Your instructor may collect this at the start of lab.

Question I
Supply the correct letter from the Prelab Quiz Question I slide/figure.

1. _____   Solid Muscular Digestive Organ

2. _____   Hollow Digestive Organ

3. _____   Solid Epithelial Digestive Organ

Question II
Supply the correct letter from the Prelab Quiz Question II slide/figure.

1. _____   Hollow Digestive Organ

2. _____   Solid Epithelial Digestive Organ

Question III
Supply the correct letter from the Prelab Quiz Question III slide/figure.

1. _____   Muscle of Tunica Mucosa

2. _____   Epithelium of Tunica Mucosa

3. _____   Tunica Submucosa

4. _____   Serosa

5. _____   Lumen of Organ

6. _____   Tunica Muscularis

Question IV
Supply the correct letter from the Prelab Question IV slides.

1. _____   Glands in Tunica Mucosa

2. _____   Tunica Submucosa

3. _____   Smooth Muscle in Tunica Muscularis

4. _____   Boundary Between Mucosa and Submucosa

Exercise H-4

Histology of the Endocrine System

Introduction

The endocrine system is composed of discreet organs located throughout the body and endocrine structures which are embedded within other organs of the body. Endocrine structures are generally composed of epithelial tissue but there are exceptions to this as in the case of the posterior portion of the pituitary gland. Among the organs of the endocrine system are the pituitary gland, thyroid and parathyroid glands, adrenal glands, gonads, and the islets of the pancreas. In this exercise, only three endocrine glands will be examined histologically, the pituitary, the thyroid, and the adrenals.

Consult your textbook for a discussion of the organs you will be examining. Histology images that support all elements of this exercise are included in the *Exploring A&P* CD that accompanies this manual.

Pituitary Gland:

The pituitary gland is composed of two histologically distinct portions which are a result of their very different origins. The anterior pituitary (adenohypophysis) shares an origin with other glandular structures of the body and therefore presents with a microscopic appearance that is consistent with that of other glands that have been viewed previously. The posterior pituitary, on the other hand, shares an origin with the nervous system. Microscopically it resembles other nervous system structures, much less cellular with a very high lipid content.

The pituitary gland is often referred to as the "master gland" of the body because the anterior portion produces a number of hormones which regulate the activity of other endocrine organs. These endocrine regulating hormones produced by the anterior pituitary are referred to as tropic hormones and include adrenocorticotropic hormone, thyroid stimulating hormone, follicle stimulating hormone, and luteinizing hormone. In addition, the adenohypophysis produces growth hormone and prolactin, and proopiomelanocortin from which melanocyte stimulating hormone is derived. The posterior pituitary (neurohypophysis) stores and releases from its axons two hypothalamic hormones, antidiuretic hormone and oxytocin.

Thyroid Gland:

The bilobed thyroid produces two hormones of note. The first is thyroid hormone. It is a mix of two active molecules, thyroxin and triiodothyronine, and it is produced by follicular cells that form the very numerous and prominent follicles of the gland. The primary effect of thyroid hormone is to stimulate metabolic activity and increase heat production. The other hormone is calcitonin which is produced by small clusters of parafollicular cells located within the interstitial tissue between the thyroid follicles. It is an important agent of calcium homeostasis.

Adrenal Glands:
The paired adrenal glands are each divided into two anatomically and histologically distinct regions. The outer, superficial cortex comprises the majority of the organ's mass and is further subdivided into three zones each of which produces different hormones. Starting most superficially is the very thin zona glomerulosa which produces the mineralocorticoid hormone, aldosterone, which plays an important role in fluid retention, fluid balance, and blood pressure regulation. The cells of this zone are arranged in small circular clusters of cells. Deep to the glomerulosa is the zona fasciculata. Its cells are arranged into long, straight chains or cords. The main product of this zone is cortisol, the principal glucocorticoid hormone, which exerts a powerful influence on carbohydrate and lipid metabolism and provides added fuel resources during times of stress. The deepest layer of the cortex is the zona reticularis. In it the cells are arranged more irregularly as a network of branching and intersecting cords. These cells produce steroid sex hormones, principally testosterone, in both males and females.

Deep to the reticularis of the cortex is the adrenal medulla. This region of the adrenal gland is considered to be among the most vascular tissues in the body. The medulla is characterized by obvious blood sinuses bordered by clusters of large cells. The cells that make up this portion of the gland actually share an origin with sympathetic nerve fibers. Their primary product is epinephrine which plays a central role in the "fight or flight" response and the body's response to stress.

Prelab Quiz - Histology of the Endocrine System
    Complete the prelab quiz prior to arriving for lab.
    This quiz is available on the accompanying *Exploring A&P* CD in color.
    Use your textbook and on-line histology references to help complete this quiz.
    Part of your lab check-off will be based on the content of this quiz.
    Attached at the end of this exercise is the answer sheet.
    Bring your completed answer sheet to lab.

Part 1: Survey of Endocrine Organs

In this exercise, you will be presented with a collection of three coded slides of the three different endocrine organs which will be studied. Based on the descriptive information provided above, determine which slide is the pituitary gland, which is the thyroid gland, and which is the adrenal gland. For each gland, indicate the slide of your choice. Use the space provided to jot down or draw any detail that helped you reach your conclusion.

Organ   **Slide #**

Pituitary gland   _____

Thyroid gland   _____

Adrenal glands   _____

Part 2: Pituitary Gland:
In this exercise, you will examine a slide of the pituitary gland. Carefully observe this slide, perform the indicated tasks, and attempt to answer the accompanying questions.

Anterior Pituitary
1. Find the <u>anterior</u> portion of the pituitary gland. Demonstrate this for your instructor.
   What <u>visible</u> structural features support your answer? _____
   _____

2. Which primary tissue type makes up the bulk of this portion of the organ?

   ___ epithelium   ___ connective   ___ muscle   ___ nerve

3. Do all cells of the anterior pituitary stain the same?   Yes / No

4. Describe the arrangement of cells in the anterior pituitary. _____
   _____
   _____

5. Is the microscopic appearance of the anterior pituitary consistent with the macroscopic appearance of the gland?   Yes / No   Briefly explain.
   _____
   _____

Posterior Pituitary
1. Find the <u>posterior</u> portion of the pituitary gland. Demonstrate this for your instructor.
   What <u>visible</u> structural features support your answer? _____
   _____

2. Which primary tissue type makes up the bulk of this portion of the organ?

   ___ epithelium   ___ connective   ___ muscle   ___ nerve

3. Describe the arrangement of cells in the posterior pituitary. _____
   _____

4. Provide an explanation for the staining character of the posterior pituitary.

_____

_____

5. Is the microscopic appearance of the anterior pituitary consistent with the macroscopic appearance of the gland?   Yes / No   Briefly explain.

_____

_____

_____

Part 3: Thyroid Gland
In this exercise, you will examine a slide of the thyroid gland. Carefully observe this slide, perform the indicated tasks, and attempt to answer the accompanying questions.

1. Find the cells of the thyroid which produce thyroid hormone. Demonstrate them for your instructor.

2. To which primary tissue type do these cells belong?

    ___ epithelium   ___ connective   ___ muscle   ___ nerve

3. Classify these cells more specifically by cell shape and organization (layering).

_____

4. Find the cells of the thyroid which produce calcitonin. Demonstrate them for your instructor.

5. Is the microscopic appearance of the thyroid consistent with the macroscopic appearance of the gland?   Yes / No
Briefly explain.

_____

Part 4: Adrenal Glands
In this exercise, you will examine a slide of the adrenal glands. Carefully observe this slide, perform the indicated tasks, and attempt to answer the accompanying questions.

1. Find the three zones of the adrenal cortex. Demonstrate each of them for your instructor.

2. Which primary tissue type makes up the bulk of this portion of the organ?

   ___ epithelium   ___ connective   ___ muscle   ___ nerve

3. Find the adrenal medulla. Demonstrate it for your instructor.

4. Demonstrate for your instructor the vascular spaces of the medulla.

5. Is the microscopic appearance of the adrenal gland consistent with the macroscopic appearance of the gland?   Yes / No
   Briefly explain.

   _____

   _____

   _____

Learning Outcomes: Histology of the Endocrine System
Once you have done the preparation and completed the exercises dealing with the endocrine system, you should be able to:

General Histological Knowledge of the Endocrine System
1. Identify each of the endocrine organs studied and the subregions that have been described for each.

Histology of the Endocrine System: Prelab Quiz   Name: _____

Complete this brief quiz prior to lab. Your instructor may collect this at the start of lab.

Question I
Supply the correct letter from the Prelab Quiz Question I slide/figure.

1. _____ Cells that Produce Oxytocin

2. _____ Cells that Produce Releasing Hormones

3. _____ Cells that Produce Antidiuretic Hormone

4. _____ Cells that Produce Tropic Hormones

5. _____ Anterior Pituitary

6. _____ Capillary of Portal System

7. _____ Posterior Pituitary

8. _____ Storage of Neurohormones

Question II
Supply the correct letter from the Prelab Quiz Question II slide/figure.

1. _____ Colloid

2. _____ Follicular Cell

3. _____ Parafollicular Cell

4. _____ Isthmus

5. _____ Lobe

Question III
Supply the correct letter from the Prelab Quiz Question III slide/figure.

1. _____ Adrenal Cortex   2. _____ Capsule

3. _____ Adrenal Medulla   4. _____ Kidney

5. _____ Deepest Zone of Cortex

Exercise H-5
Histology of the Reproductive System

Introduction

The organs of the reproductive system fall into two categories: the primary reproductive organs, or gonads, which have the job of producing gametes, eggs in the female and sperm in the male, and the secondary reproductive structures. The secondary reproductive structures are responsible for the delivery and maintenance of the gametes, and, in the female, for the development and protection of the various developmental forms resulting from the fusion of the egg and the sperm.

In the male, the gonad is the testis. The testis is a lobular organ encased in a thick, tough connective tissue sheath (tunica albuginea) and composed of very long, very narrow, highly coiled epithelial tubes known as seminiferous tubules. The walls of these tubes serve as sites for sperm production. The testicular epithelium provides the raw material from which sperm originate. Deep in the wall of the tubule (that is, furthest from the lumen) diploid basal cells called spermatogonia divide first by mitosis, becoming transformed into primary spermatocytes. These diploid cells then begin to divide by meiosis and slowly migrate towards the lumen of the tubes. As these cells migrate, they undergo first the reduction division of meiosis to form haploid secondary spermatocytes and then the equatorial division to form haploid spermatids. These spermatids then undergo a series of morphological changes which eventually lead to the formation of highly specialized sperm cells. In fact, sperm cells may provide one of the clearest and most striking examples of the close relationship between structure and function that will be encountered during the two semesters of study in A&P. Immature sperm cells are released into the lumen of the tubes by the sustentacular (Sertoli) cells which span the entire thickness of the wall of the seminiferous tubules and shepherd the process of sperm formation.

In the female, the gonad is the ovary. It is a paired solid organ composed of a fibrous and vascular central area called the medulla, and an extensive outer cortex. The cortex of each ovary contains thousands of follicles. Each follicle consists of an oocyte and surrounding layers of epithelium made up of follicular cells. Most of the follicles within an ovary are small and inactive. Actually, the vast majority of follicles within each ovary may never develop during a woman's reproductive lifetime. However, each month from the large supply of inactive follicles, a small number begin the developmental process. Shortly after this small group of follicles begins to grow, one follicle typically emerges as the dominant follicle and continues to develop. Occasionally more than one follicle continues to develop but usually the other follicles which started to grow quickly regress and disappear. As the dominant follicle develops, it enlarges because the number of follicular cells increases significantly. Later in the developmental process, the growing follicle develops a decided cavity called an antrum. As the follicle nears maturity, the oocyte becomes isolated within a mass of follicular cells (also called granulosa by this time) that extend into the antrum at the end of a stalk of follicular cells. Eventually, this mature (Graffian) follicle ruptures in a process called ovulation. When ovulation occurs, the oocyte encased in a mass of follicular cells is released into the peritoneal cavity and hopefully is captured by the fimbriae of the oviduct and then drawn into the uterine tube.

During the development of a follicle, it progresses through four different stages. Inactive or dormant follicles are called primordial follicles. They are formed by a single layer of squamous cells surrounding a small oocyte. When a follicle starts to develop, it enlarges gradually and becomes a primary follicle. In this case, the single layer of flat cells first becomes a single layer of cuboidal cells and then the number of layers of follicular cells increases. As the follicle increases in size, an internal chamber, the antrum, begins to form. As soon as the antrum is first visible, the follicle is considered a secondary or growing follicle. The final mature Graffian follicle is identified by its large size, very extensive antrum, and oocyte surrounded by a mass of granulosa cells (cumulus oophorus) suspended on a stalk of follicular cells. The innermost cell layer of the cumulus oophorus is generally considered the corona radiata. In the Graffian follicle, a clear zone exists between the oocyte and the cells of the corona. This acellular space is called the zona pellucida and plays an important role in the events of fertilization. Surrounding the granulosa of the follicle (and especially visible in more mature follicles) is a dense cellular layer called the theca. Cells of this layer synthesize androgen from which estrogens are synthesized by granulosa cells. Note: The description of developmental stages included above is consistent with descriptions in our text but may differ from schemes found in other references.

Secondary reproductive organs in both sexes are either glandular or tubular/hollow. Glandular organs in the male include the prostate gland, seminal vesicles, and the bulbourethral glands which provide secretions which support and protect sperm cells. In the female, the accessory reproductive glands include the vestibular and paraurethral glands which provide lubrication during sexual arousal. Tubular organs in the male provide a duct system for the storage, maturation and delivery of sperm. These include the rete testis, efferent ductules, epididymis, ductus deferens, ejaculatory ducts and the urethra. In the female, tubular/hollow organs allow sperm to be introduced into the female system (vagina) and support the process of development and birth (uterus and fallopian tubes). Tubular or hollow organs generally follow some type of a modification of the 4-layer plan with which you are already familiar. In the uterus, three layers are present. The inner lining is called the endometrium and is composed of epithelium supported by a connective tissue layer of variable thickness which contains multicellular glands. Deep to that is a muscular layer (myometrium) and an outer covering (perimetrium). The vagina is also three-layered with an epithelium anchored by connective tissue, a deeper fibromuscular layer, and an outer adventitia.

Histology images that support all elements of this exercise are included in the *Exploring A&P* CD that accompanies this manual.

Prelab Quiz: Histology of the Reproductive System
>Complete the prelab quiz prior to arriving for lab.
>This quiz is available on the accompanying *Exploring A&P* CD in color.
>Use your textbook and on-line histology references to help complete this quiz.
>Part of your lab check-off will be based on the content of this quiz.
>Attached at the end of this exercise is the answer sheet.
>Bring your completed answer sheet to lab.

Part 1: The Male

The Testis

1. Observe the entire testis slide first using the 4X objective. Is the tough outer capsule that was seen on gross inspection visible in this slide? Yes / No
    What is the name given to that outer capsule?
    _____

2. Find the tubes where sperm form. What are these tubes called?
    _____

    In your slide, what is the dominant view you have of these tubes?
    ____ longitudinal   ____ transverse

3. Which of the following best describes the cellular arrangement of the tubular epithelium?
    ____ simple   ____ stratified   ____ pseudostratified

4. Look for evidence of some type of cell division within these tubes. The best indication of division involves the appearance of very dark staining and dense material in the nuclei of the epithelial cells. Which of the following best describes the location of this type of activity?
    ____ In the spaces between the tubes
    ____ Toward the basal layer
    ____ In the middle of the wall of the tube
    ____ Close to the luminal surface

5. Try to find sperm cells. They are tiny, so use high power. Where in the tube are these cells found?
    ____ Within the walls of the tube
    ____ Attached to the luminal surface of the tube
    ____ Within the lumen of the tube
    ____ No sperm are visible in the slide
    ____ Two of these arrangements are correct

6. Look for collections or clusters of epithelial cells in the tissue between the tubes.
    Are these cell clusters made up of cells of the same type? Yes or No?
    Do these cells stain the same way as those that make up the tubule? Yes or No?
    Is each cell cluster made up of the same number of cells? Yes or No?
    What are these cells called? _____

    What do they do?
    _____

Epididymis

7. The epididymis is an organ of muscle and fibrous tissue surrounding a highly coiled tube or duct. It receives material from the testes via the rete testes and the efferent ductules. Observe the epididymis slide. What evidence do you see of a highly coiled tube?

   _____

   _____

8. In your slide, what type of epithelium makes up the duct of the epididymis?

   _____

   These epithelial cells participate in nurturing immature sperm during their maturation to mobile, fertile spermatozoa. This nurturing process involves exchange between the epithelial cell and the sperm seen with the epididymal lumen.

9. Which of the following specialized free surface features would facilitate the role described above?
   ____ cilia   ____ microvilli   ____ both   ____ neither

   Are either of the specialized structures listed above visible in your slide?
   Yes / No   If yes, demonstrate them to your instructor.

10. Identify the material inside the lumen of the epididymal duct. _____

11. The epididymis serves as the source of sperm released during ejaculation. There is muscle within the interstitium of the epididymis.
    What type of muscle is it?
    ____ smooth muscle   ____ skeletal muscle

    Which of the following best describes the arrangement of muscle within the epididymis?
    ____ A layered arrangement around the epididymal duct.
    ____ Multiple defined bundles oriented randomly.

    What is the role of this muscle? _____

    _____

Prostate Gland

12. Now observe the prostate slide.
    Which of the following descriptions best describes this organ?
    ____ Hollow with a single large central chamber
    ____ Solid but containing many small regular hollow structures
    ____ Solid but containing many small irregularly shaped hollow structures

13. The glandular units within the prostate are referred to as prostatic alveoli.
    Are any visible on your slide?   Yes / No
    On your slide, how they are stained?
    _____

    What primary tissue type makes up these glandular alveoli? _____
    _____

    Describe with a simple drawing the structure of a representative prostatic alveolus.

14. Prostatic concretions are calcified remnants of prostatic secretion which may be found within some alveoli. They are more likely to be seen in a tissue sample taken from an older individual.
    Are any concretions visible on your slide?   Yes / No
    If yes, describe or draw them below and demonstrate them for your instructor.

15. There is smooth muscle contained within the prostate gland. Based on your observation, which of the following is the most accurate description of its arrangement?
    _____ A single defined layer with all cells oriented in the same direction.
    _____ Two defined layers arranged at right angles to each other.
    _____ Individual fibers interspersed with the supporting connective tissue of the organ.

    What is the role of this muscle? _____

    _____

    _____

16. The prostate gland surrounds the urethra.
    Which of the following best describes the urethra?
    _____ solid   _____ tube   _____ sac

    Is the urethra visible on your slide?   Yes / No
    If yes, which of the following best describes the view of the urethra as it appears on your slide?
    _____ Transverse view of the whole organ
    _____ Longitudinal view of the whole organ
    _____ Partial view of only a portion of the organ

Part 2: Female
Ovary
1. Scan the entire ovary slide using the 4X objective. Once you have examined the whole slide and oriented yourself, switch to a higher magnification (10X objective) and place the tip of the pointer at what you consider the junction between the cortex and medulla of the organ. Verify your positioning with your instructor.

    Which of the listed structures is most abundant in the medulla?
    _____ follicles
    _____ vascular spaces
    _____ oocytes

2. Now direct your attention to the cortex. Which best describes the location of the resting or non-active (primordial) follicles:
    _____ Just deep to the surface of the organ
    _____ In the center of the cortex
    _____ Deep in the cortex, very close to the medulla

3. Find a follicle which has been activated and can be considered a primary follicle. Describe what you see.

   _____

   _____

   Demonstrate this stage of development to your instructor.

4. Find a secondary follicle and demonstrate it to your instructor. What feature that is visible tells you that it is a secondary follicle?

   _____

5. Is there a mature Graffian follicle visible in your slide?   Yes / No
   Remember that you should recognize it by its large size and the presence of a cavity in which an oocyte is suspended. If one is visible in your slide, demonstrate it to your instructor.

   If a Grafffian follicle is visible in your slide:
       Is an antrum clearly visible? Yes / No
       Is an oocyte clearly visible?   Yes / No
       Is the cumulus oophorus/corona radiata clearly visible? Yes / No
       Is the zona pellucida clearly visible? Yes / No
       Is the theca clearly visible? Yes / No

   Draw and label a Graffian follicle as it appears in your slide.

   Be prepared to demonstrate all of these structures to your instructor.

   Which of the named structures associated with the oocyte accompany it during ovulation?

   _____

Is it possible to see a Graffian follicle in your slide that does not seem to contain an oocyte or any of its surrounding elements? Yes / No
If yes, please explain how this can be true.

_____

_____

Uterus

6. Now turn your attention to the uterus slide. First, even before you examine the slide and based just on your observations from the recent gross anatomy exercise, indicate the most accurate statement about the basic structure of the uterus.
    ____ Hollow and thin-walled with a single large central chamber
    ____ Hollow and thick-walled with a single large central chamber
    ____ Solid but containing many small simple tubular structures
    ____ Solid but containing many small irregularly shaped hollow structures

7. Scan the entire slide using the 4X objective. Once you have examined the whole slide and oriented yourself, switch to a higher magnification (10X objective) and examine the whole slide in more detail. Based on your observation, what description best relates to the piece of uterine tissue on your slide?
    ____ Transverse view of the whole organ
    ____ Longitudinal view of the whole organ
    ____ Surface view of a portion of the organ
    ____ View of a sectioned portion of the organ

8. Explore the slide and locate the luminal epithelium. What type of epithelium lines the lumen of the uterus?

    _____

9. Are there any glands visible within the wall of the uterus? Yes / No
   If yes, which of the following best describes them?
    ____ Circular cell clusters
    ____ Straight non-branching tubes
    ____ Coiled non-branching tubes
    ____ Branching tubes

10. The glands of the uterus are found within the most superficial (closest to the lumen) layer of the uterine wall. This layer is called the endometrium. What process leads to significant repetitive changes in the histology of the uterus?

    _____

    As part of this process, the most superficial two-thirds of the endometrium (stratum functionalis) separates from the denser, deeper stratum basalis. In some slides it is possible to discern the junction between these two sub-layers of the endometrium because of a change in the density of the supporting connective tissue. Examine your slide carefully. If you can identify this junction, position the tip of your microscope pointer on it and share it with your instructor for verification.

11. Deep to the endometrium is the myometrium which contains the uterine muscle. What type of muscle makes up the myometrium?
    ____ smooth muscle   ____ skeletal muscle

    How is the muscle of the myometrium arranged?
    ___ In a single uniform layer
    ___ In two uniform layers
    ___ As multiple bundles oriented along different planes
    ___ As scattered cells located within the glandular layer
    ___ In some other way. Describe.

    What is the role of the muscle of the uterus? _____

    _____

Cervix

12. The cervix is the portion of the uterus that joins the rest of the organ at the internal os and abuts the vagina at the external os. Between these two openings lies the endocervical canal. What type of epithelium lines the endocervical canal.

    _____

    Are there glands visible in the underlying tissue of the cervix? Yes / No
    If yes, compare the glands to those seen in the body of the uterus.

    _____

13. Follow the epithelium lining the endocervical canal to the external os. At this point the epithelium of the cervix transitions. What type of epithelium now is seen?

    _____

    Place the pointer of your microscope at the junction between the two epithelial types and verify this with your instructor.

Vagina

14. Examine the luminal epithelium of the vagina. Compare it to that of the uterus.

    Is the epithelium of the vagina similar to that of the uterus? Yes / No

If different, how so?
_____

For what specific purpose is the epithelium of the vagina best suited?
_____

15. Next examine the tissue immediately deep to the epithelium. Which of the following best describes what you see in this area when examining this slide?
    ___ Blood vessels
    ___ Multicellular glands
    ___ Both blood vessels and multicellular glands
    ___ Neither blood vessels nor multicellular glands

If there are glands present, is the glandular makeup of the vagina similar to or different from that of the uterus?   ___ similar   ___ different
If different, how so?
_____
_____

Mammary Glands

16. Compare the slide of an inactive mammary gland with an active mammary gland. Base your comparison on the following characteristics:

    Densely packed alveoli with visible lumens
        Inactive -   Yes / No
        Active -   Yes / No

    Clearly defined lobules
        Inactive -   Yes / No
        Active -   Yes / No

    Relative amounts of interlobular connective tissue
        Inactive -   Abundant / Scarce
        Active -   Abundant / Scarce

    Visible secretory product
        Inactive -   Yes / No
        Active -   Yes / No

Specific Learning Outcomes: Reproductive System
As a result of your histological study of reproductive organs, students shall be able to recognize, identify, and discuss the function of the following organs and specific structures.

Human Testis (ts): tunica albuginea, seminiferous tubules, interstitial cells (of Leydig,)

Epididymis (ts): stereocilia, basal cells, spermatozoa

Human Prostate Gland: prostatic alveoli, fibromuscular stroma, concretions.

Ovary: germinal epithelium, cortex, medulla, primordial follicles, growing follicles, mature follicles, theca folliculi, follicular cells (granulosa), antrum, cumulus oophorus, corona radiata, zona pellucida, ovum.

Uterus: endometrium, uterine glands, myometrium.

Uterus at Cervix (ls): epithelial transition, mucous glands, fibromuscular stroma.

Vagina: mucosal rugae, vascular spaces, muscularis.

Inactive Human Mammary Gland: glandular follicles, interlobular stroma

Active Human Mammary Gland: glandular follicles, interlobular stroma

Histology of the Reproductive System: Prelab Quiz   Name: _____

Complete this brief quiz prior to lab. Your instructor may collect this at the start of lab.

Question I
Supply the correct letter from the Prelab Quiz Question I slide/figure.

1. _____   Cells that Produce Testosterone

2. _____   Cells that Produce Sperm

3. _____   Structure that Stores Sperm

4. _____   Gland that Surrounds Urethra

5. _____   Covering of Testis

Question II
Supply the correct letter from the Prelab Quiz Question II slide/figure.

1. _____   Mature Follicle of Ovary

2. _____   Surface of Uterus Shed During Menstrual Cycle

3. _____   Mammary Gland

4. _____   Gland of Uterus

5. _____   Germinal Epithelium

6. _____   (Primordial Follicle-not labeled) substitute Myometrium

7. _____   Developing Follicle of Ovary

Exercise H-6
Histology of Nerves and Blood Vessels

Introduction
Throughout your study of the microscopic anatomy of tissues and organs you have very often encountered blood vessels. This exercise provides an opportunity to take a close look at these types of structures. Histology images that support all elements of this exercise are included in the *Exploring A&P* CD that accompanies this manual.

Vessels:
While blood vessels can vary greatly in size and appearance, all vessels share an essential basic characteristic. They are all hollow structures with a definite lumen. In many specimens, red blood cells may be seen within this lumen. Excepting the smallest vessels (arterioles, capillaries, and venules), all small, medium, and large arteries and veins possess the same three layers. Closest to the lumen, vessels are lined with a simple squamous epithelium (endothelium) and a thin layer of supporting connective tissue. This layer is called the tunica interna or the intima. The middle layer of a vessel is a mix of connective tissue and smooth muscle called the tunica media. The outside layer of a vessel is a connective tissue layer called the tunica externa or tunica adventitia. As is always the case when studying anatomy using slides and the microscope, structures will appear differently based on the specific plane of the section through the structure and the specific type and size of vessel being examined.

As a general statement, the most prominent tunic in arteries is a substantial tunica media. In small to medium-sized arteries the media is characterized by abundant circular smooth muscle. The action of this vascular smooth muscle allows small to medium-sized arteries great ability to change their diameters and thereby influence the distribution of blood flow. In fact, in some texts these muscular arteries are also referred to as distributing arteries. In small to medium-sized arteries a very obvious internal elastic layer separates the intima and media. In large arteries such as the aorta or pulmonary arteries and their major branches, the internal elastic membrane is much reduced and the media is dominated by an obvious concentration elastic fibers mixed with the already mentioned smooth muscle. Because of their elasticity, these arteries are ideally suited to withstand the sudden surge of blood under pressure that is ejected from the heart with each beat.

In general, veins possess thinner walls than do similarly sized arteries, especially when viewed relative to the size of the vessel lumen. Because of this, they are less likely than arteries to exhibit a circular or regular shape in transverse section when viewed in thin histological specimens. Most veins show the same three layers as do arteries but with the externa is usually comprising the thickest or most noticeable layer. The adventitia is composed of a mix of collagenous and elastic connective tissue. In large veins such as the vena cavae, the adventitia possesses distinct bundles of smooth muscle as well. The media in most veins contains far less smooth muscle and much less elastic support. Generally the intima of a vein is minimal and an internal elastic layer is either absent or hard to find. Many veins (small and medium-sized) also exhibit valves. These valves are formed from out-pocketings of the tunica intima and resemble the semilunar valves of the heart. Lymphatic vessels resemble veins in that they are thin walled, do not maintain their shape well, and possess one-way valves similar in form to those found in veins. Lymphatic vessels also do not possess the distinctive three layer structure seen in most veins

In larger and larger vessels with thicker walls, the need for a separate blood supply to the tissue of the vessel wall increases. For this reason, the adventitia of larger vessels (both arteries and veins) is likely to contain varying numbers of smaller vessels to meet the nutritive needs of the tissue of the vessel's wall. These vessels are called vasa vasorum which literally means vessels of the vessel.

Nerves:
Nerves are solid structures made up of bundles of nerve fibers held together by bands of fibrous connective tissue. No lumen will be visible in a nerve section. Connective tissue encases each individual fiber and fills in the voids between the fibers within a bundle (endoneurium) and also wraps individual bundles (perineurium). Connective tissue also binds bundles together to complete the structure of the nerve (epineurium). The individual nerve fibers are tiny and thread like. However they are often covered with a fatty substance myelin. This covering is laid down in thin concentric layers by cells called Schwann cells. When these myelinated fibers are viewed longitudinally, the segmented nature of the myelin insulation becomes apparent and the exposed areas of nerve fiber (nodes of Ranvier) are visible. -Nerve slides may be stained darkly with osmic acid to make the Schwann cells visible, to highlight the fatty myelin, or to highlight any other lipid-rich cell or structure.

Prelab Quiz: Histology of Vessels and Nerves
    Complete the prelab quiz prior to arriving for lab.
    This quiz is available on the accompanying *Exploring A&P* CD in color.
    Use your textbook and on-line histology references to help complete this quiz.
    Part of your lab check-off will be based on the content of this quiz.
    Attached at the end of this exercise is the answer sheet.
    Bring your completed answer sheet to lab.

Part 1: Distinguishing Vessels and Nerves

From this collection of labeled slides provided, indicate the letter or letters of all slides which demonstrate the following. Some slides may satisfy more than one of the descriptions below.

1. _____ Lymph vessel or vein displayed longitudinally with valve visible.

2. _____ Small artery with substantial smooth muscle in its wall.

3. _____ Nerve cut in cross section.

4. _____ Large elastic artery with substantial elastic tissue in its media.

5. _____ Slide showing a combination of a small artery, a small vein, and a nerve, all cut transversely.

6. _____ Individual nerve fibers displayed intact with fatty covering and breaks in this covering clearly visible.

7. _____ Large vessel containing smaller vessels within its wall.

8. _____ Small artery with its inner lining showing elastic reinforcement.

9. _____ Large vein showing characteristic smooth muscle bundles.

10. _____ Vessel whose primary functional characteristic is the ability to constrict or dilate.

11. _____ Vessel whose principal functional characteristic is its ability to expand and recoil.

Part 2: Elements of Nerve and Vessel Structure and Function

1. What stain is used to stain myelin? _____

2. Is this stain specific for myelin or does it stain all fatty material?
   ___ myelin only   ___ all fatty material

3. Consider the appearance and organization of a nerve in cross section. What tissue that you have already studied (first semester) exhibits a similar appearance in cross section and follows a similar organizational plan.
   _____

4. Based on structure, what type of vessel has the greatest ability to change its diameter by muscle contraction or relaxation?
   ____ Large artery
   ____ Large vein
   ____ Small-medium artery
   ____ Small-medium vein

5. Based on structure what type of vessel has the greatest ability to adapt to large changes in pressure?
   ____ Large artery
   ____ Large vein
   ____ Small-medium artery
   ____ Small-medium vein

6. Based on structure, what 2 types of vessels tend to maintain their shapes. This is best appreciated when the vessels are viewed in transverse section?
   ____ Large artery
   ____ Large vein
   ____ Small-medium artery
   ____ Small-medium vein

Specific Learning Outcomes:

As a result of your histological study of the vessels and nerves, students should be able to recognize, identify, and discuss the functions of the following organs and specific structures.

Vessels:
1. Large and medium/small arteries:
    tunica externa or adventitia
    tunica media
    tunica interna (intima) - endothelium, elastic membrane
    vaso vasorum

2. Large and medium/small veins:
    tunica externa or adventitia
    tunica media
    tunica interna (intima)

Nerves:
3. Nerve bundles
    epineurium
    perineurium
    endoneurium
    axons
    myelin (area of myelination)
    Schwann Cell
    neurilemma

4. Teased nerve fibers
    myelin
    node of Ranvier

Histology of Vessels and Nerves: Prelab Quiz   Name: _____

Complete this brief quiz prior to lab. Your instructor may collect this at the start of lab.

Question I
Supply the correct letter from the Prelab Quiz Question I slide/figure.

1. _____   Nerve Fibers Stained for Myelin with Nodes of Ranvier

2. _____   Small Artery

3. _____   Elastic Artery

4. _____   Vessel with Valve

5. _____   Nerve in Cross Section

6. _____   Vein

Exercise H-7

Histology of the Respiratory System

Introduction

The respiratory system is made up of conducting passages and gas exchange structures. A system of conducting structures known as airways bring air to and from the functioning lung tissue. These airways are classified as cartilaginous (bronchi) or non-cartilaginous (bronchioles) based on the presence or absence of hyaline cartilage in their walls. Besides the presence or absence of cartilage, the type of epithelium lining the lumen of the tube and a number of other histological features help to identify specific areas and relate that area's structure to its function. Features of interest include the type of epithelium lining the tube, the presence or absence of cilia, the presence or absence of goblet cells, the presence or absence of vascular structures or multicellular glands, and the relative amount of smooth muscle in the wall of the tube.

A examination of the wall of the trachea shows it to be very similar in design to the 4-layer plan previously seen in the wall of alimentary tube. Bordering the lumen of the trachea is a mucosa composed of an epithelium anchored by a thin connective tissue lamina propria. Deep to the mucosa is a thicker submucosa in which vessels and/or multicellular glands may be visible. Deeper still is a muscularis of smooth muscle in which can also be seen rings of hyaline cartilage. Note: some references include the cartilage as part of the submucosa. Lastly an adventitia of loose connective tissue is generally visible.

The other major component of the respiratory system involves the gas exchange structures. These structures are thin-walled sacs composed of squamous epithelial cells, often defining a common central space. They are richly vascularized by capillaries, and together with these capillaries, create a tremendous surface area for gas exchange. Some references equate the total surface area for diffusion of gases in the lungs to that of an entire tennis court.

Organizationally, some conducting passages lie outside of the lungs and form the upper airways. This includes the nasal and oral passages, as well as the pharynx and larynx. Other conducting structures are within the lungs and form the lower airways. Most references refer to 8-10 generations of cartilaginous airways in the human lung. Distal to these are multiple generations of noncartilaginous airways called bronchioles. While there are numerous generations of bronchioles and they do taper as one progresses distally, the typical bronchiole has a lumen between 1 and 2 millimeters, possesses a relative abundance of smooth muscle compared to the thickness of the airway wall, and has an epithelium that gradually changes toward cuboidal. Some bronchioles may have a wall that is partly composed of gas exchange (alveolar) tissue. Because of this, these are referred to as respiratory bronchioles.

All structures involved with gas exchange are found within the lung. In fact, these gas exchange structures make up the vast majority of lung structure. The most proximal of the gas exchange structures are tubes composed entirely of alveolar tissue. These are called alveolar ducts. They lead in alveolar sacs which are composed of numerous individual alveoli.

Histology images that support all elements of this exercise are included in the *Exploring A&P* CD that accompanies this manual.

The prelab quiz that deals with the respiratory system is combined with the excretory system. It is included following the Histology of the Excretory System exercise (H-8)

PART I - Airways
1. Study a slide of the trachea.
   Proceed from the luminal surface progressively deeper into the wall.
   Can you distinguish all four of the layers of the tracheal wall? Yes / No

   If not, which layer(s) seem(s) to be missing? _____

   Now focus on the mucosa:
   First find the epithelium that lines the trachea. What type of epithelium is makes up this lining?
   _____

   Examine this epithelium carefully first under low power and then under high power.
   Are there any visible epithelial structures which produce a secretion? Yes / No
   If yes, what are these cells called?
   _____

   What type of product is produced by these cells? _____

   Are there any free surface structures visible in this epithelial layer?   Yes / No

   If yes, what structures are you able to see? _____

   Next examine the submucosa:
   Are there blood vessels visible in the submucosa?   Yes / No
   Are there multicellular glands visible in the submucosa?   Yes / No
   If yes, based on their staining characteristics, what type of product do they produce?
   ____ serous fluid   ____ mucous   ____ seromucous combination

   Next examine the muscularis layer:
   Is any hyaline cartilage visible in this slide?   Yes / No

   If yes, how is it arranged? _____

Is muscle visible in this slide?   Yes / No

If yes, how is it arranged? _____

Lastly, examine the deepest layer, the <u>adventitia</u>:
Is an outermost layer of connective tissue visible in this slide?   Yes / No

2. Now direct your attention to a lung slide. First examine the entire slide using the scanning objective. Then focus the slide under low power. Based on the information provided in the introduction, you should be able to locate a bronchus in the lung slide. Once you think you have found one, ask your instructor for verification. Use the visible structure of this bronchus to answer the following questions:
Find the epithelium which lines this bronchus. What type of epithelium is it?

_____

Are there cilia visible in this epithelium?   Yes / No
Are there goblet cells visible in this epithelium? Yes / No
Is there cartilage visible in this airway?   Yes / No

If yes, how is it arranged? _____

Is muscle visible in the wall of this airway?   Yes / No

If yes, how is it arranged? _____

3. Continue with the lung slide, and try to find a bronchiole. Use the structure of this type of airway to answer the following questions:
Find the epithelium which lines this bronchiole. What type of epithelium is it?

_____

Are there cilia visible in this epithelium?   Yes / No
Are there goblet cells visible in this epithelium? Yes / No
Is there cartilage visible in this airway?   Yes / No

If yes, how is it arranged? _____
Is muscle visible in the wall of this airway?   Yes / No

If yes, how is it arranged? _____

4. Continue with the lung slide, and try to find an alveolar duct. Use the structure of this type of airway to answer the following questions:
Find the epithelium which lines this airway. What type of epithelium is it?

_____

Are there cilia visible in this epithelium? Yes / No
Are there goblet cells visible in this epithelium? Yes / No
Is there cartilage visible in this airway? Yes / No

If yes, how is it arranged? _____

Is muscle visible in the wall of this airway? Yes / No

If yes, how is it arranged? _____

5. You have studied three intrapulmonary airways (bronchi, bronchioles, alveolar ducts) during this lab. Rank these different airways on the basis of their overall wall thickness.

    Thickest   Thinnest

    _____   _____   _____

6. Rank these same airways studied by the height of their lining epithelium.

    Tallest   Shortest

    _____   _____   _____

7. Rank these same airways studied by the relative concentration of smooth muscle to the wall thickness.

    Relatively most muscle   Relatively least muscle

    _____   _____   _____

    Which one of these three airway types is <u>always</u> involved in pulmonary gas exchange?
    _____

    Which one of these three airway types is <u>never</u> involved in pulmonary gas exchange?
    _____

8. Based on your observations, which of these three airway types produces the most secretion?
    _____

9. Based on your observations, which of these three airway types would be most actively involved in dilation and constriction?
    _____

10. Based on your observations, which of these three airway types is rigid and generally does not collapse?

    _____

11. Based on your observations, which of these three airway types would trap inhaled particulates on a sticky surface and move them proximally?

    _____

Part 2: Gas Exchange Structures

1. Find gas exchange structures on your lung slide. The individual units of exchange are called alveoli. Draw a single alveolus as viewed under the high power objective.

2. Alveoli are grouped together into clusters called alveolar sacs.
   Is there the same number of alveoli present in each alveolar sac?   Yes / No
   Do all alveoli in the sac possess the same diameter?   Yes / No

3. Look for capillaries associated with alveoli.
   How can you recognize a capillary? _____

   _____

   Based on your observation, capillaries are:
   ___ rare   ___ moderate in number   ___ numerous

4. If alveolar sacs were composed of fewer but larger alveoli than you see on your slide, alveolar surface area will:
   ___ increase   ___ decrease   ___ not change

295

Specific Student Outcomes: Respiratory System

As a result of your histological study of the respiratory system, you should be able to recognize, identify, and discuss the function of each of the following organs and specific structures.

1. Trachea: epithelium, cilia, goblet cells, submucosal glands and vessels, cartilage layer, muscularis, adventitia.

2. Lung: alveolar-capillary membrane, cartilaginous airway (bronchi), non-cartilaginous airway (bronchiole), alveolar ducts, alveolar sac, alveolus, pulmonary vessels.

Exercise H-8
Histology of the Excretory System

Introduction:
The excretory system is made up of the kidneys which produce urine by filtering and other modifications of the blood plasma and a number of hollow organs involved in the transport and storage of urine.

The kidneys are highly vascularized solid organs, receiving ~~over~~ between 10 and 20 percent of the blood pumped by the heart every minute. As is typical of solid organs, each kidney is composed of an outer cortex surrounding an inner medulla. The medulla of the kidney surrounds a collection chamber, the renal pelvis, from which urine exits the kidney. Within the kidneys are microscopic units called nephrons which filter the blood and modify the filtrate into urine. Nephrons are the basic structural and functional units within the kidneys. Each nephron is composed of a renal corpuscle (Bowman's capsule) and a series of tubules which lead from the capsule. The capsule itself is composed of epithelium and encloses a tiny tuft of capillaries called a glomerulus. It is here that the process of urine formation begins by filtration of plasma. From here the filtrate is greatly reduced in volume and modified in composition as it travels through the tubular elements of the nephron. The final formed urine is emptied from the pyramids of the medulla into the renal pelvis. The renal pelvis, and all urinary structures distal to it, are lined by a special epithelium designed to withstand stretching forces.

From the pelvis of the kidneys, the urine is conducted by long, narrow, muscular tubes, the ureters, to the urinary bladder. The bladder, located in the pelvis, is a muscular sac in which urine is stored. A single tube, the urethra, conducts the urine from the bladder while voiding. In addition to carrying the urine, the urethra serves a reproductive function in the male.

Histology images that support all elements of this exercise are included in the *Exploring A&P* CD that accompanies this manual.

Prelab Quiz: Histology of the Respiratory and Excretory Systems
    Complete the prelab quiz prior to arriving for lab.
    This quiz is available on the accompanying *Exploring A&P* CD in color.
    Use your textbook and on-line histology references to help complete this quiz.
    Part of your lab check-off will be based on the content of this quiz.
    Attached at the end of this exercise is the answer sheet.
    Bring your completed answer sheet to lab.

PART I - The Kidneys

1. With the scanning objective in place, examine a kidney slide.
   Is a covering visible on the outside surface of the kidney?   Yes / No
   If yes, what appears to be the nature of this covering?   fibrous / vascular

2. As mentioned above, the kidney is divided into two zones: a cortex and a medulla.
   In which zone does filtration occur?   cortex / medulla
   Support your answer based on your observations.

   _____

   _____

3. Within the cortex are circular elements called renal corpuscles. These structures have a vascular and epithelial component.
   Which component is superficial?   vascular / epithelial

   Emerging from the epithelium of the corpuscle is an epithelial tube. What type of epithelium makes up this tube?

   _____

   Does this tube show cilia and/or a brush border?

   ___ cilia   ___ brush border   ___ both   ___ neither

   If a specialized surface structure is present, briefly describe its function in the urine formation process.

   _____

   _____

4. Which zone of the kidney is largely made up of straight, parallel epithelial tubes?

   ___ cortex   ___ medulla

5. In the kidney, what type of epithelium makes up the walls of these tubes?

   _____

PART II - Tubular Excretory Organs

1. Study and compare slides of the three (3) hollow excretory system organs. Complete the following chart based on this comparison. In completing this chart, use a + to indicate that a particular feature is present, and a - to indicate that a particular feature is absent.

	URETER	BLADDER	URETHRA
Visible transitional epithelium lining the lumen			
Star-shaped lumen			
Visible muscularis of smooth muscle			

Specific Student Outcomes: Excretory System

As a result of your histological study of the urinary system, the student should be able to recognize, identify, and discuss the function of each of the following organs and specific structures.

1. Kidney: renal capsule, cortex, medulla, renal corpuscle with Bowman's Capsule and glomerulus, tubes of the nephron.

2. Ureter: epithelium, muscularis,

3. Urethra: epithelium, muscularis.

4. Bladder: epithelium, muscularis

Histology of the Respiratory & Name: _____
Excretory Systems: Prelab Quiz

Complete this brief quiz prior to lab. Your instructor may collect this at the start of lab.

Question I
Supply the correct letter from the Prelab Quiz Question I slide/figure.

1. _____ Trachea

2. _____ Bronchus

3. _____ Bronchiole

4. _____ Alveolus

5. _____ Renal Corpuscle

6. _____ Kidney Cortex

7. _____ Ureter

8. _____ Kidney Tubule

PART 3

Exercises in Human Physiology

Lab Exercise P-1

Skeletal Muscle Physiology-1:
The Frog Gastrocnemius

This week's exercise will include a demonstration of skeletal muscle contraction using the frog gastrocnemius muscle preparation. Students will observe the various elements of the demonstration and be given copies of the tracings that are generated. Using these, students will be required to perform various analyses in an attempt to better understand the mechanism of skeletal muscle contraction. In addition, there will be discussion of a number of elements of skeletal muscle physiology. This discussion will include the All or Nothing Rule, the muscle twitch, treppe, motor units, motor unit summation (recruitment), asynchronous motor unit activity, refractory period, wave (temporal) summation, series elastic elements, internal and external tension, tetanus, fatigue, and the effect of load on velocity and duration of contraction.

Set-up
The set-up for these demonstrations is pictured below (figure 1). The muscle is kept viable by regular irrigation with frog's Ringer's solution. The stimulator can be adjusted to provide single or repeated electrical shocks of adjustable voltage, duration, and frequency to the muscle. When the muscle is stimulated with a tracing of adequate strength, it contracts (shortens) and pulls down on the transducer lever. This mechanical signal is converted to an electrical signal and, using the ADInstruments Power Lab software, the computer generates a tracing which can be viewed on the screen, printed, and analyzed.

Figure 1: Muscle Twitch Demonstration Set-up

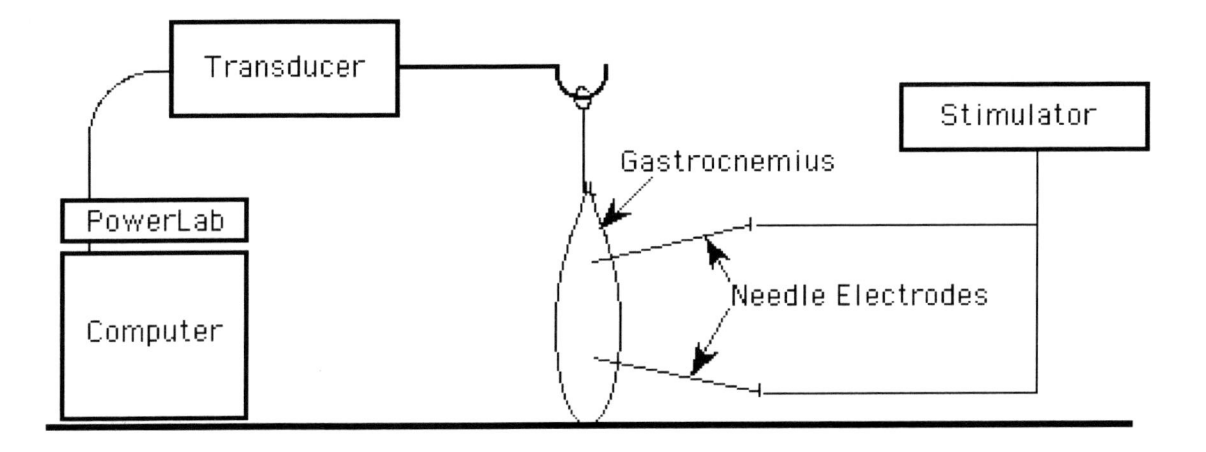

Background
Skeletal muscle contracts as a result of stimulation by a nerve impulse. In this case, the voltage applied to the muscle mimics nervous stimulation of the muscle. At the cellular level, skeletal muscle obeys the "All or Nothing Rule". It states that when a stimulus of at least threshold strength is applied to a skeletal muscle fiber, the fiber responds with a complete contraction (contracts as strongly as it can). If the stimulus is weaker than

threshold strength, the muscle does not respond at all. It is important that you recognize that the "All or Nothing Rule" applies to behavior at the level of an individual cell. The muscle twitch tracing being generated in this demonstration represents muscle behavior at the organ level.

Basic Twitch

Using the set-up depicted above, a single isolated muscle contraction generates a tracing showing both the application of a stimulus and the response of the muscle. Such a tracing is called a muscle twitch.

Figure 2: Muscle Twitch

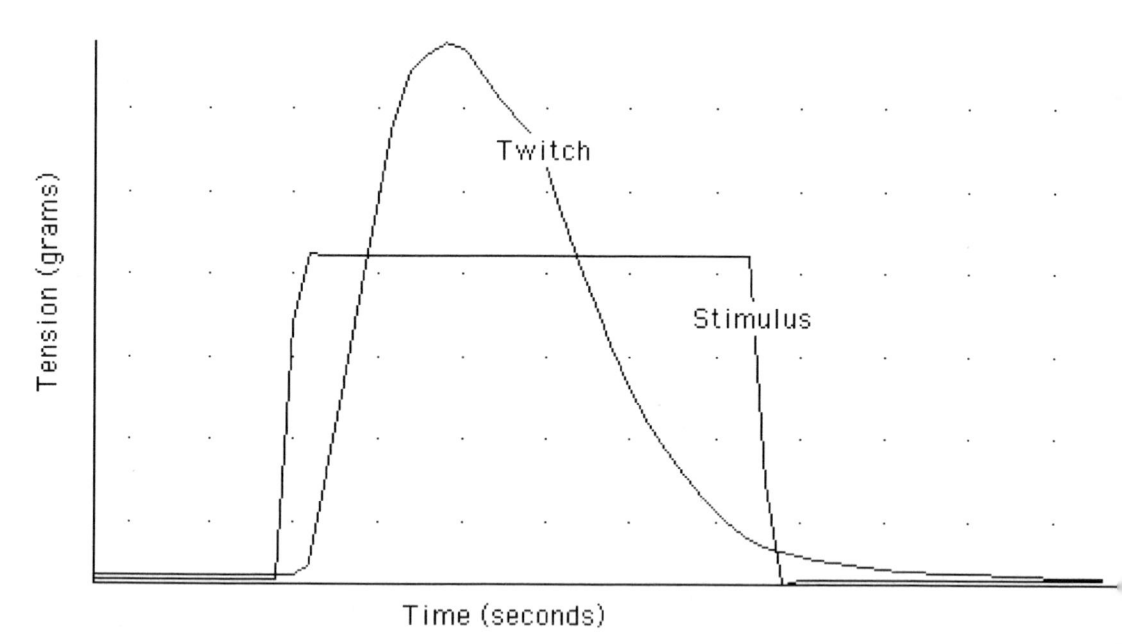

The twitch (figure 2) shown above is essentially a graph of muscle activity printed on a pair of axes. The vertical axis indicates tension generated by the muscle's contraction, generally in grams of force. The horizontal axis indicates time, generally in seconds or fractions of a second. It allows the careful and precise analysis of a muscle's twitch characteristics in terms of strength and rate of contraction. Three portions of a typical twitch tracing are identifiable: latent period (between application of stimulus and response of the muscle, contraction phase (period of muscle shortening), and relaxation (period of muscle lengthening). Given such a tracing, students should be able to identify the phases of a muscle twitch, the duration of each phase, and the peak tension generated by the muscle during the twitch.

Treppe

Sometimes when a muscle has been inactive and a constant, above-threshold stimulus is applied several times in succession, a progressive increase in contraction strength is sometimes observed. Following several initial contractions after which the muscle is allowed time to relax fully, contraction strength levels off to a constant repeatable tension. Although this at first seems a contradiction of the "All or Nothing Rule", it is not. The change in tension generated is more likely a result of improved distribution of calcium intracellularly as a result of successive contractions and possibly some change in fiber temperature. Figure 3 below illustrates treppe.

Figure 3: Treppe

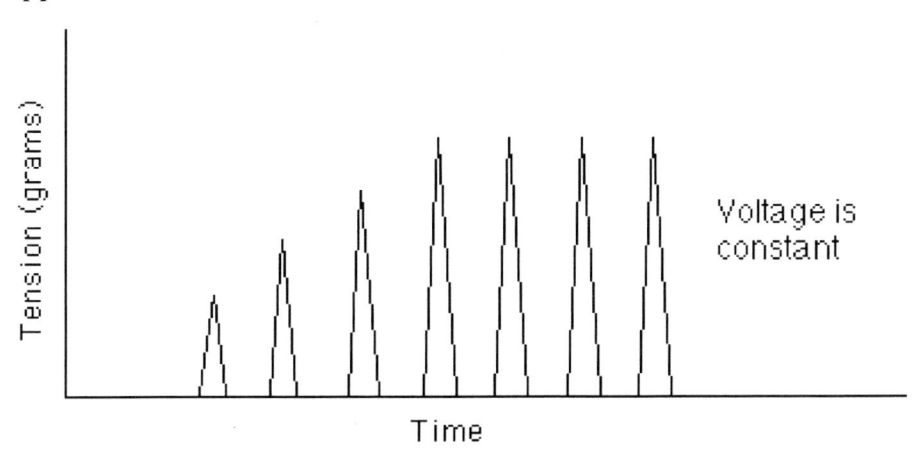

Voltage is constant

Summation

Muscles at the organ level are capable of virtually infinite gradation in contraction strength. Such variation in strength is a result of summation of individual contractions. One type of summation is called motor unit summation. It is elicited by stimulating a muscle with progressively stronger and stronger stimuli. A tracing of motor unit summation (showing triplets of stimuli that were applied and the corresponding muscle responses) is included below (figure 4). You should consider the range of muscle responses you see in this tracing carefully and reconcile it with the "All or Nothing Rule" that was described earlier. Note that the muscle responses range from no response through some response to a maximum level of response.

Figure 4: Motor Unit Summation

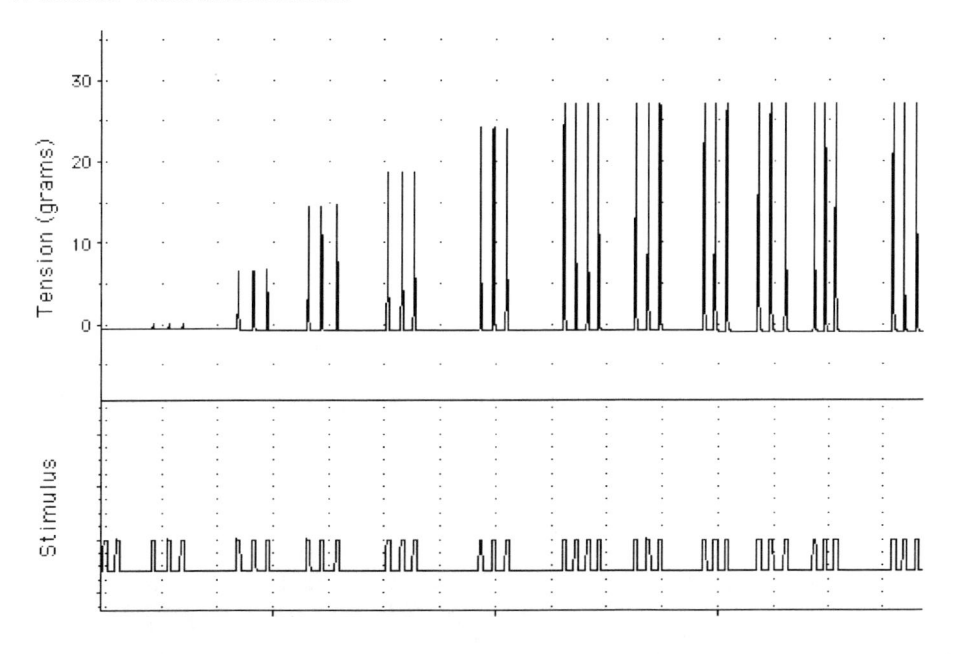

A second type of summation is elicited by applying an above threshold voltage of constant strength at faster and faster frequency. This is called wave summation. Two tracings demonstrating this type of summation are shown below (figures 5 and 6). Examine this tracing carefully and notice how tension changes as frequency of stimulation increases during the demonstration. Notice how the individual contractions merge to form a continuous sustained contraction at higher stimulus frequencies. This is called tetany (or tetanus). Again consider the tracing carefully. Can you reconcile what you observe and measure in this tracing to the "All or Nothing Rule" that was described earlier. Be prepared to share your conclusion and insights with your instructor. What do you think is happening in the muscle to cause wave summation? Note: In order to understand what is happening during wave summation, it is essential that you have a clear understanding of skeletal muscle microanatomy, especially as seen in transverse section. If you are in doubt about this, you should take out a microscope and relook at the skeletal muscle tissue once again.

Figure 4: Wave Summation-1

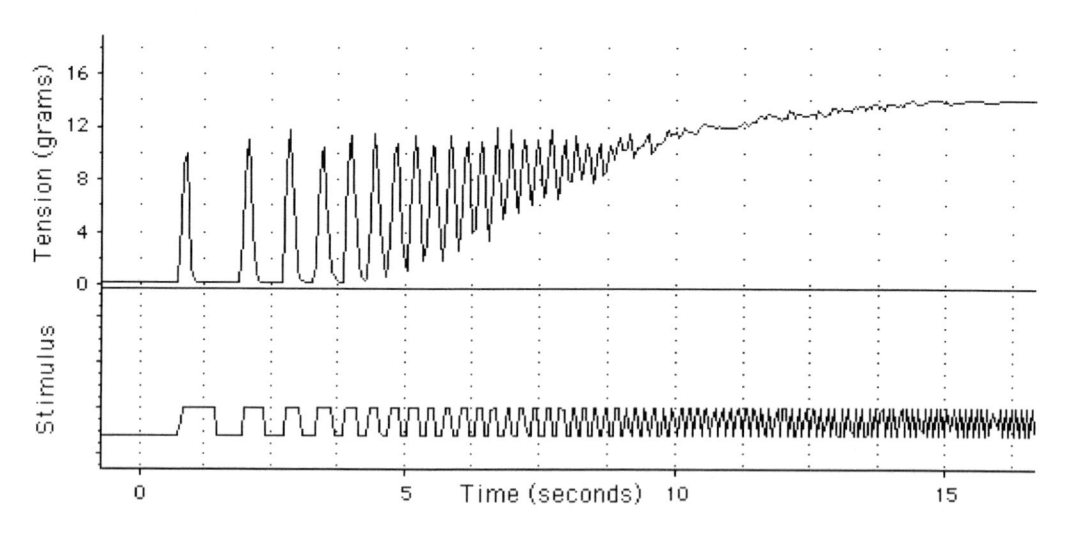

Figure 5: Wave Summation-2

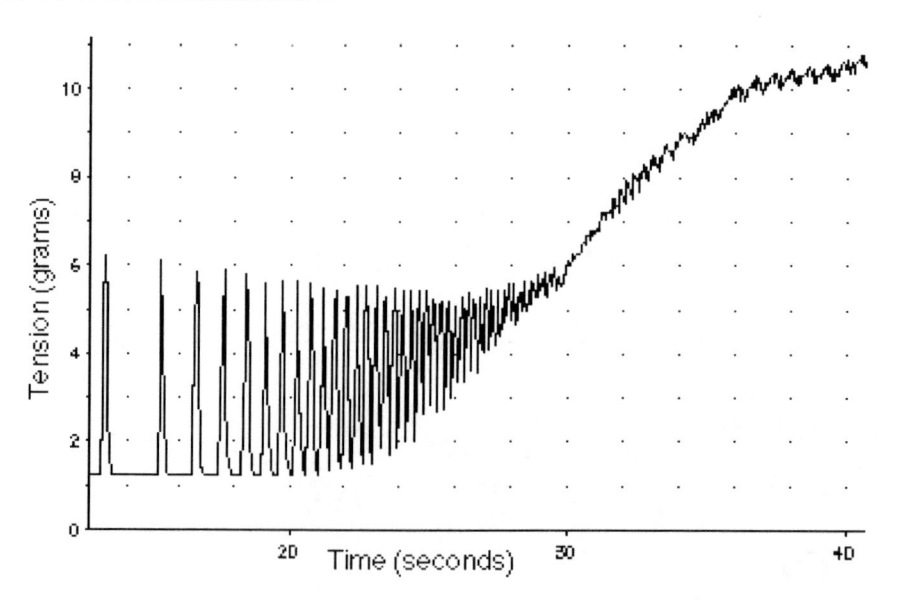

Asynchronous Summation

Although the activity level of any given motor unit in a muscle may range from complete inactivity to full activity, the asynchronous timing of motor unit activation insures that overall organ activity remains relatively constant. Figure 6 below illustrates this fact.

Figure 6: Asynchronous Summation (modified from Marieb, Human Anatomy and Physiology, 1st ed, Figure 9.15)

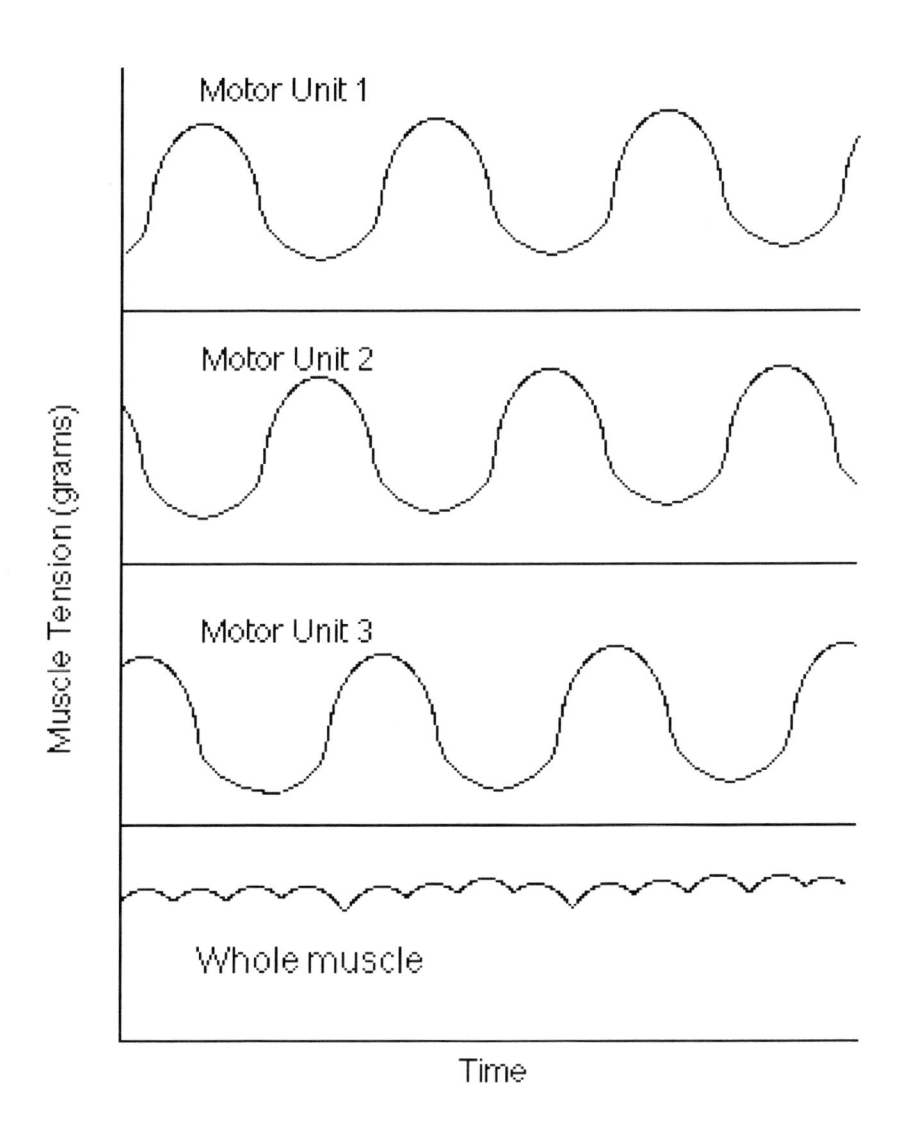

Effect of Stretch

The effect of stretching on muscle contraction strength is depicted in the graph shown below. In this demonstration, a constant, above threshold stimulus is applied singly to the muscle. However, before each stimulus application, the muscle is stretched slightly. Because it is difficult to reset the baseline after a certain amount of stretch has been applied, the tracing below (figure 7) exhibits a progressively higher and higher baseline. As you read the tracing, try to ignore the baseline and focus rather on the twitch which rises from it at each new level. What is the effect of continued stretch on contraction strength? Consider the sliding filament theory and try to reconcile it with the results obtained in this demonstration.

Figure 7: Effect of Stretch

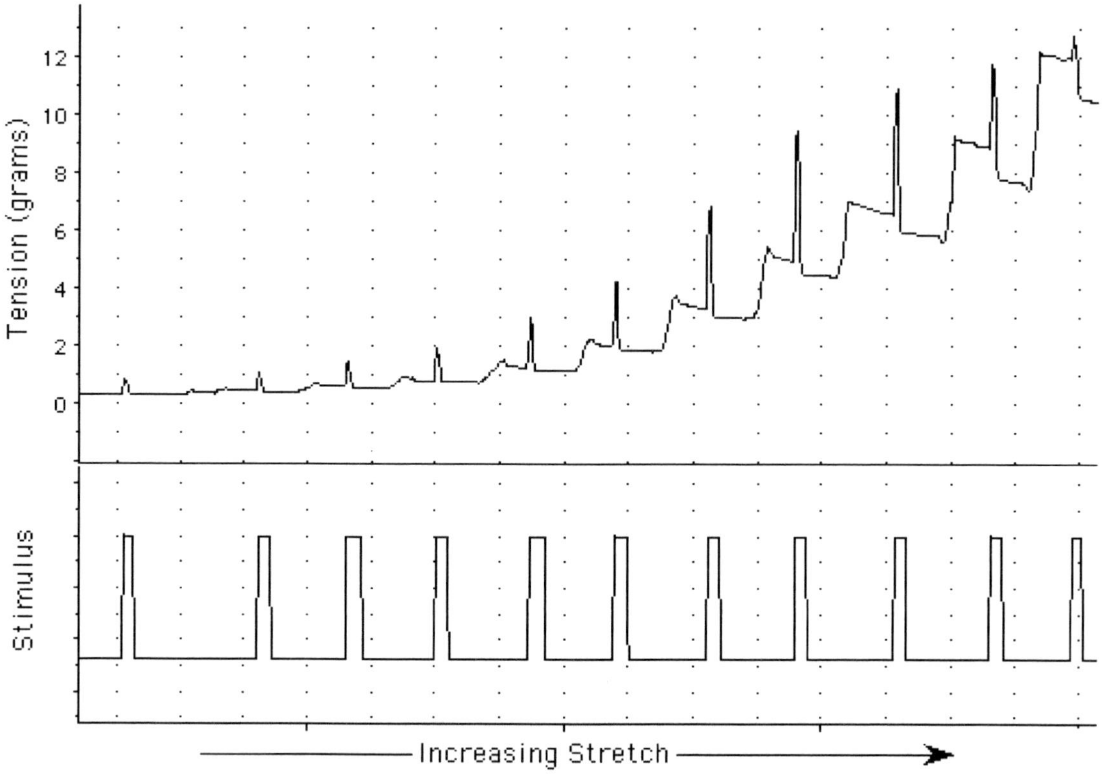

Summary and Assignment

Students should review the tracings generated during today's session. These will form the basis for the lab quiz on this material. Your instructor will provide you with an in-lab exercise that will help to test and clarify your understanding of today's demonstrations. Complete the check-off assignment before leaving the lab.

Additional illustrations taken from Marieb's <u>Human Anatomy and Physiology</u>, 5th edition, and relating to the discussion of skeletal muscle physiology follow.

Figure 8: **Internal and External Tension during Muscle Twitch (a) and During Tetany (b)** (Reprinted from Marieb, Human Anatomy and Physiology, 5ed., 2001, Figure 9.20 a and b.)

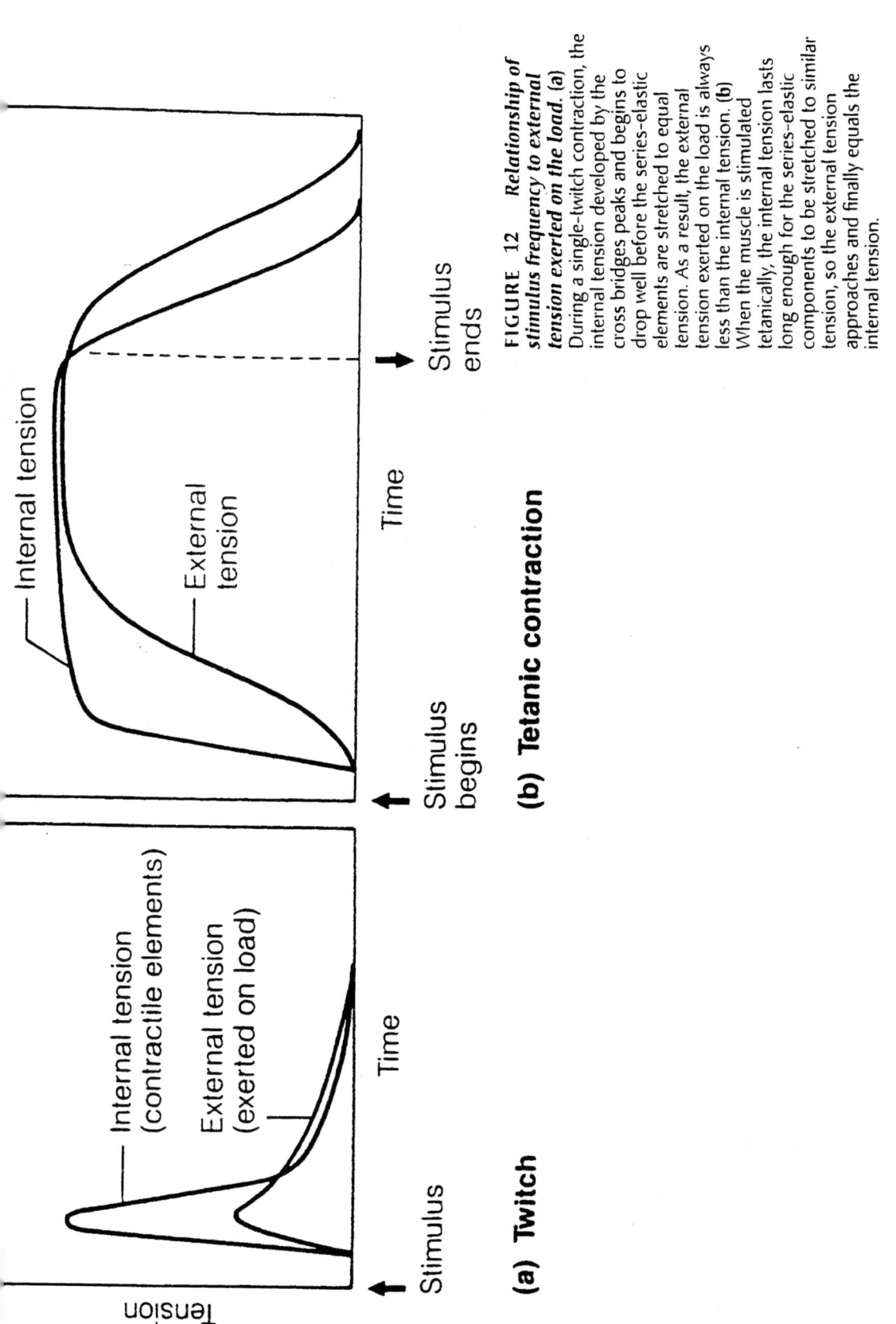

FIGURE 12 *Relationship of stimulus frequency to external tension exerted on the load.* **(a)** During a single-twitch contraction, the internal tension developed by the cross bridges peaks and begins to drop well before the series-elastic elements are stretched to equal tension. As a result, the external tension exerted on the load is always less than the internal tension. **(b)** When the muscle is stimulated tetanically, the internal tension lasts long enough for the series-elastic components to be stretched to similar tension, so the external tension approaches and finally equals the internal tension.

Figure 9: Length-Tension Relationships in Skeletal Muscle (Reprinted from Marieb, Human Anatomy and Physiology, 5ed., 2001, Figure 9.21a and b and c.)

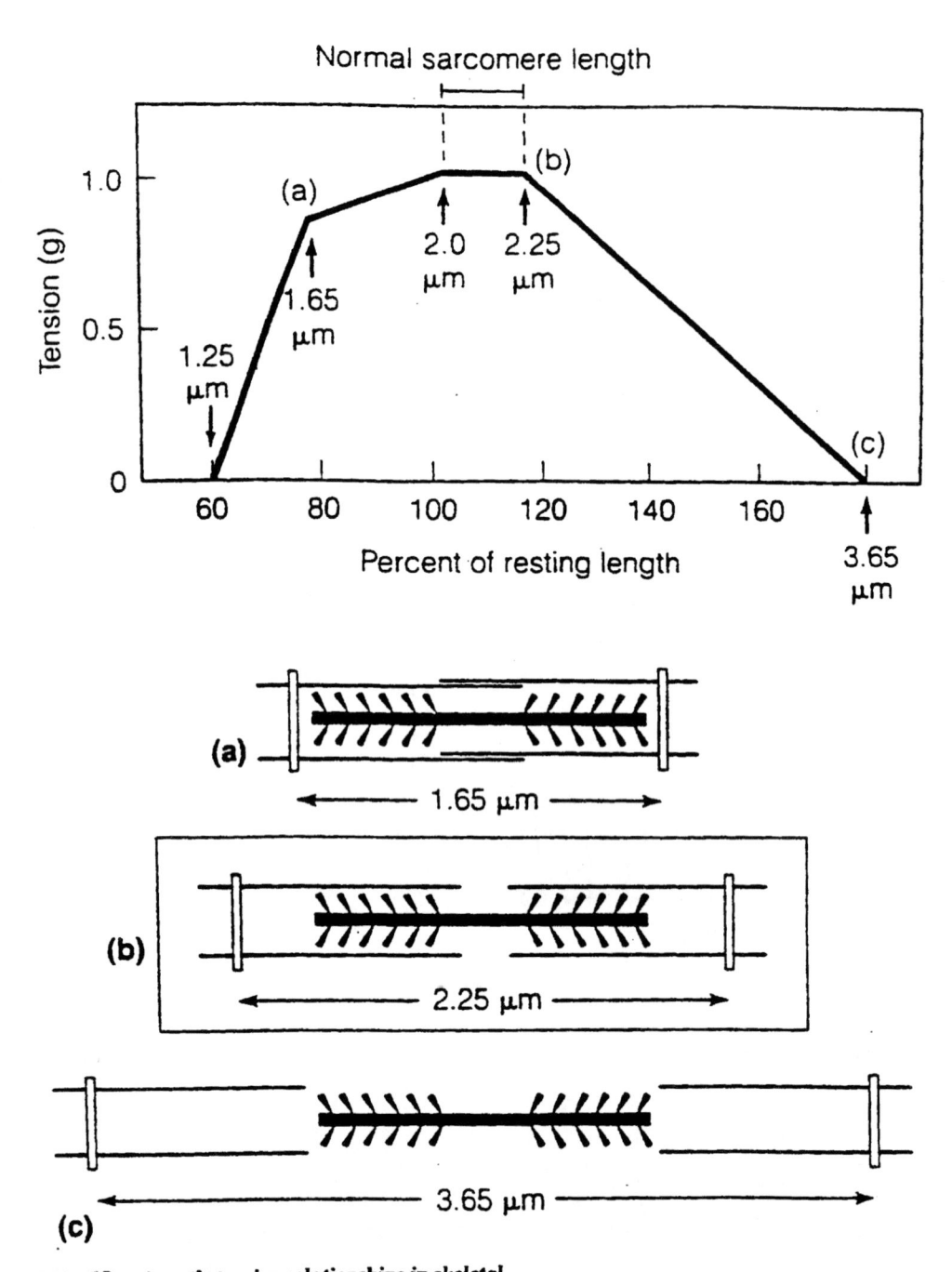

FIGURE 13 *Length-tension relationships in skeletal muscles.* Maximum force generation is possible when the muscle is a little over 100% of its resting length. Increases and decreases beyond the optimal range result in decreased force and finally an inability to generate tension. Depicted here is the relative sarcomere length in a muscle that is (a) strongly contracted, (b) at normal resting length, and (c) excessively stretched.

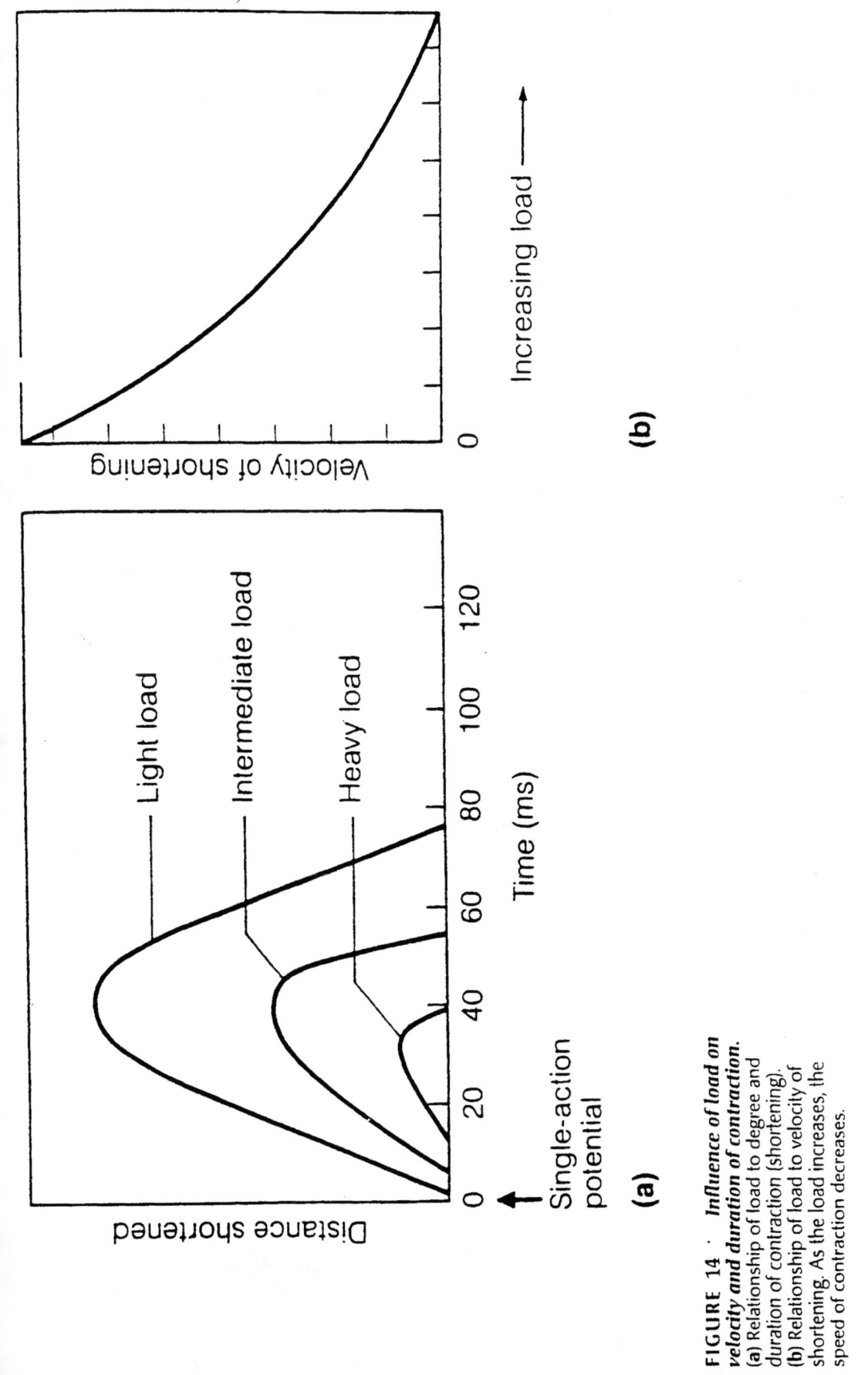

Figure 10: **Influence of Load on Velocity and Duration of Contraction** (Reprinted from Marieb, Human Anatomy and Physiology, 5ed., 2001, Figure 9.22a and b.)

FIGURE 14 · *Influence of load on velocity and duration of contraction.* (a) Relationship of load to degree and duration of contraction (shortening). (b) Relationship of load to velocity of shortening. As the load increases, the speed of contraction decreases.

Figure 11: Factors influencing force, velocity and duration of skeletal muscle contraction (Reprinted from Marieb, Human Anatomy and Physiology, 5ed., 2001, Figure 9.19a and b.)

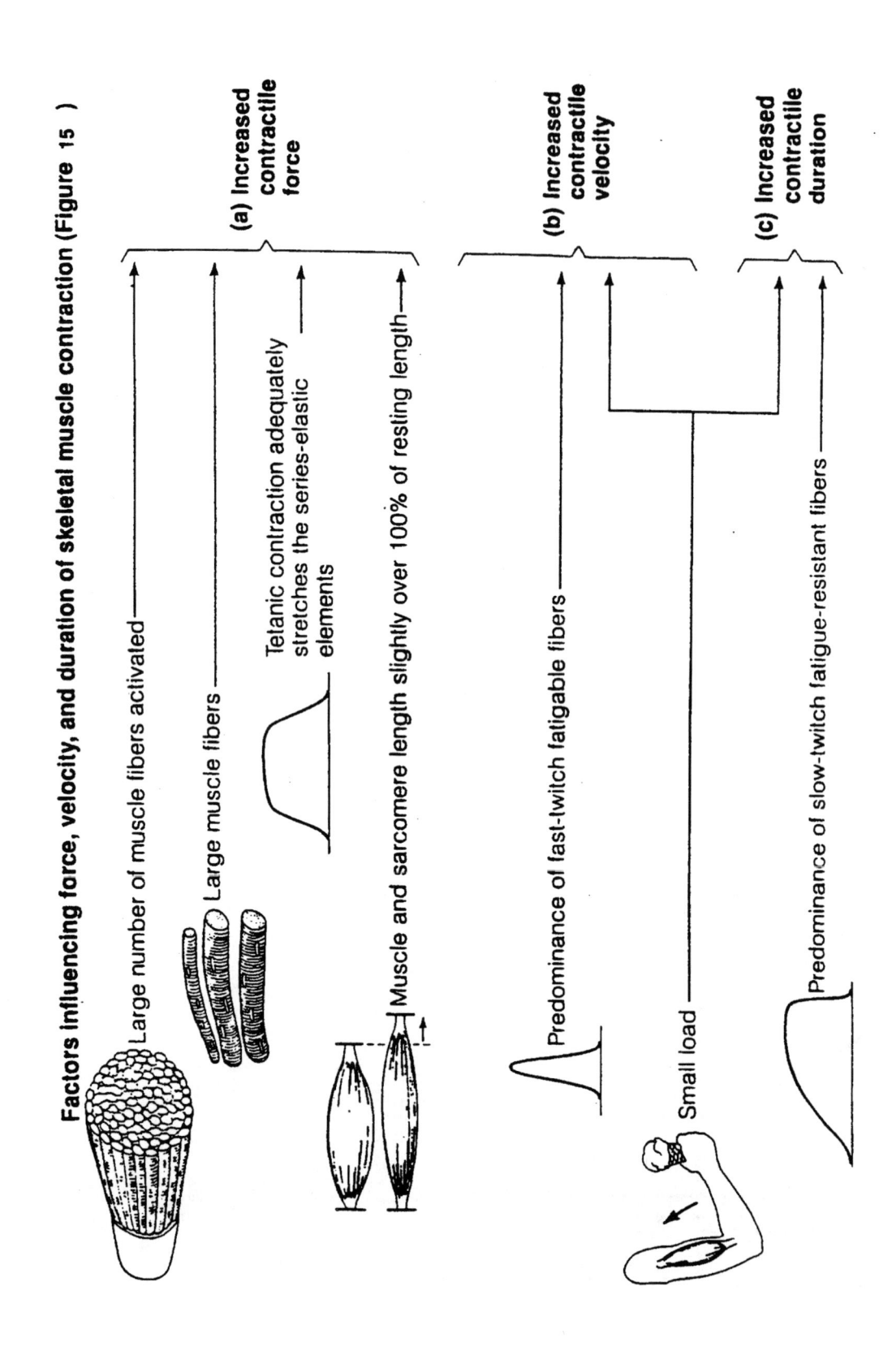

Exercise P-2
Electromyography

Introduction
A variety of specialized terms have been utilized to define or describe skeletal muscle contraction. Among these, isotonic and isometric are the most widely used. An isotonic muscle contraction has traditionally been defined as one in which the muscle shortens during the contraction and the tension exerted remains constant. However, it is more accurate to state that the tension generated during an isotonic contraction varies throughout the range of motion caused by the contraction. Therefore contraction strength is not unchanging and the term isotonic is a misnomer. The term isotonic is now often replaced by the terms concentric contraction (concentric activity) and eccentric contraction (eccentric activity) which describe contractions based on the nature of the length change the muscle undergoes while it is active. During concentric activity, the muscle shortens while during eccentric activity, the muscle lengthens. An isometric contraction, on the other hand, is one during which the length of the muscle remains unchanged throughout the contraction. The tension generated during the activity may vary tremendously during such activity.

This exercise will utilize electromyography, a type of biopotential that records the electrical activity of muscle, to more closely examine selected aspects of skeletal muscle contractions.

Equipment
The equipment required for this exercise includes the following:
> the Power Lab 410 physiological data recording system;
> an eMac with Power Lab software installed;
> USB cable;
> a five lead Bio Amp cable
> five EMG/EEG leads suitable for snap-on electrodes
> pre-pasted adhesive electrodes to which leads can snap; and
> alcohol swaps, abrasive pads, ball point pen, assorted dumbbells.

Equipment Set-up and Subject Preparation
Use the USB cable to connect the Power Lab unit to one of the USB connections provided on the eMac.

Next prepare the student volunteer for electrode placement. With an alcohol swab, firmly swab the skin over the wrist where the ground electrode or ground strap will be placed. Be careful and very lightly abrade this skin with a clean abrasive pad.

Now prepare the biceps and triceps sites for electrode placement as shown in the illustration that follows. With an alcohol swab, firmly swab the skin over the biceps and triceps muscle. Have the subject flex his or her arm; find the belly of the biceps muscle and place the two crosses approximately three centimeters apart along the long axis of the muscle. Mark the triceps in a similar fashion. Very lightly abrade the marked skin with the abrasive pad. When finished, discard the used abrasive pad.

313

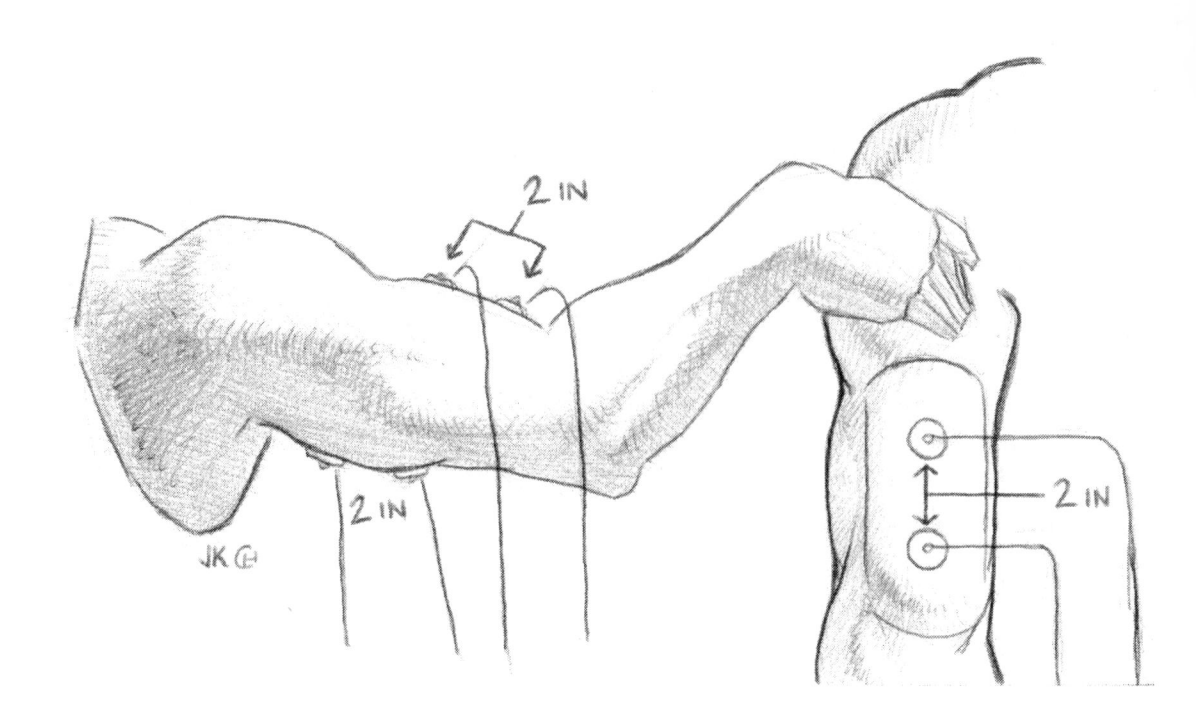

Position the five electrode leads into the sockets of the bio-amp cable. Each lead is marked with a letter that designates its recording function. "G" indicates ground. Two leads are marked with "B" for biceps, and two are marked with "T" for triceps. Plug the leads from the biceps recording electrodes into the channel 1 sockets of the bio-amp cable. Plug the ground lead into the remaining socket. Polarity for the biceps and triceps leads doesn't matter, but the channels must be correct. If a grounding strap is used, simply substitute the lead from the strap for the ground electrode lead.

Snap the adhesive electrodes onto the five leads (four if the grounding strap is used). Remove the backings to expose the adhesive and secure the electrodes to the subject in the designated areas. Check that all electrodes are properly connected to the volunteer and to the bio-amp cable before continuing.

Recording
Now, turn on the Power Lab unit and start up the eMac. Once the eMac starts up and the desktop is established, move the mouse cursor to the left side of the screen and find the icon for the Chart software. This software controls the Power Lab. Double-click on the Chart software icon. The Chart software will start up and begin to communicate with the Power Lab unit.

After a short time, you will be brought to a screen labeled "Experiments Gallery." In this window, select the EMG settings file, Figure 1.

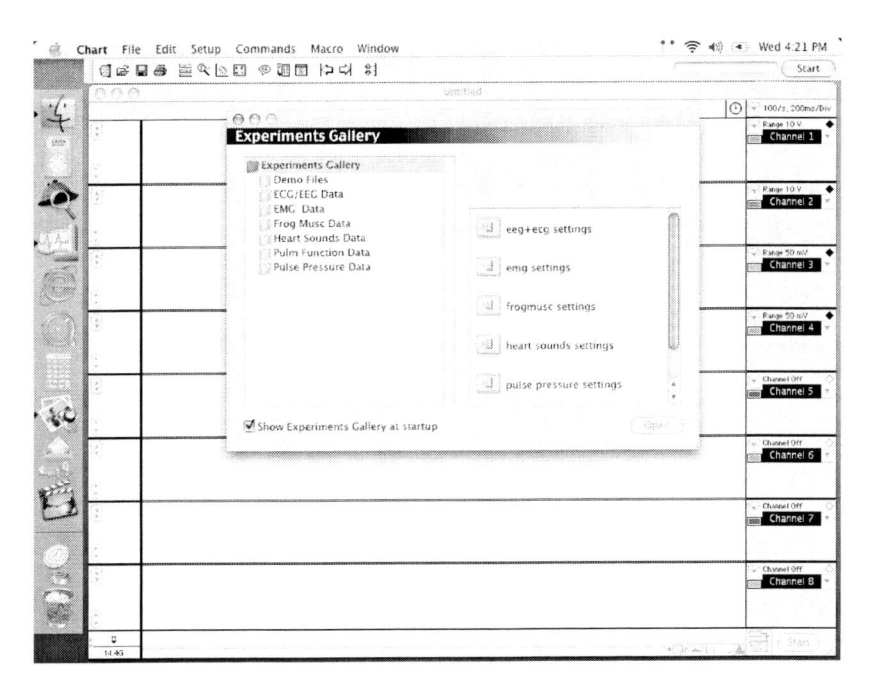

Figure 1

You will find this file along with a number of other settings files on the right side of the window in a small scrolling window. Double-click on this EMG settings file. An untitled EMG settings file will open, Figure 2.

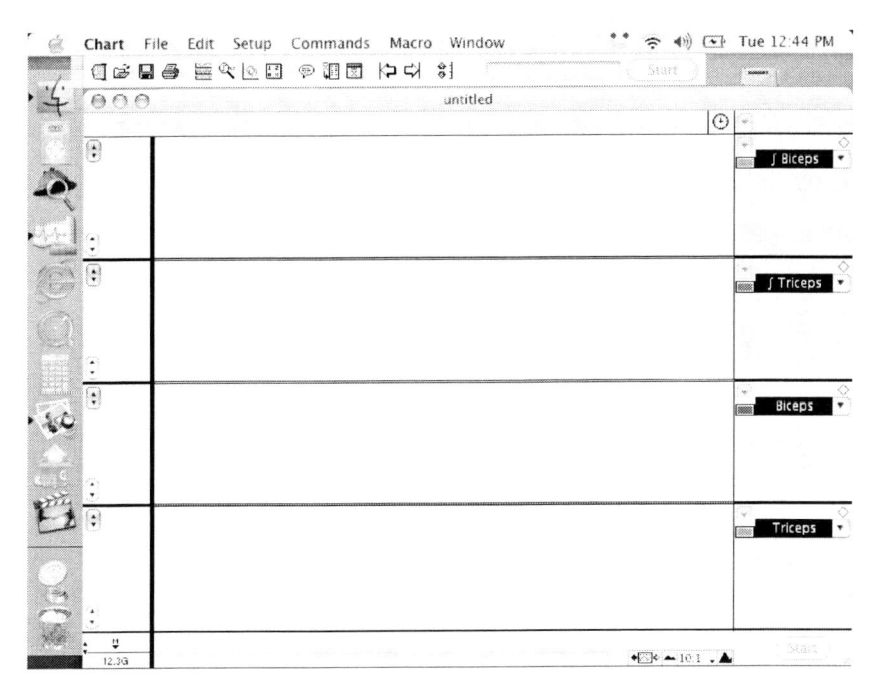

Figure 2

315

At this point, it is a good idea to convert the settings file to a data file, Figure 3. Do this by going to the File menu choice at the top menu bar and selecting Save. The file name needs to be entered since the default file name is "untitled". Name your file using the subject's name followed by "EMG". Now save this file. It should be saved into the Documents file of the home directory. If you need to reopen this file at some future time to review today's results, you can access the home directory from the desktop by selecting the Go menu choice in the top menu bar.

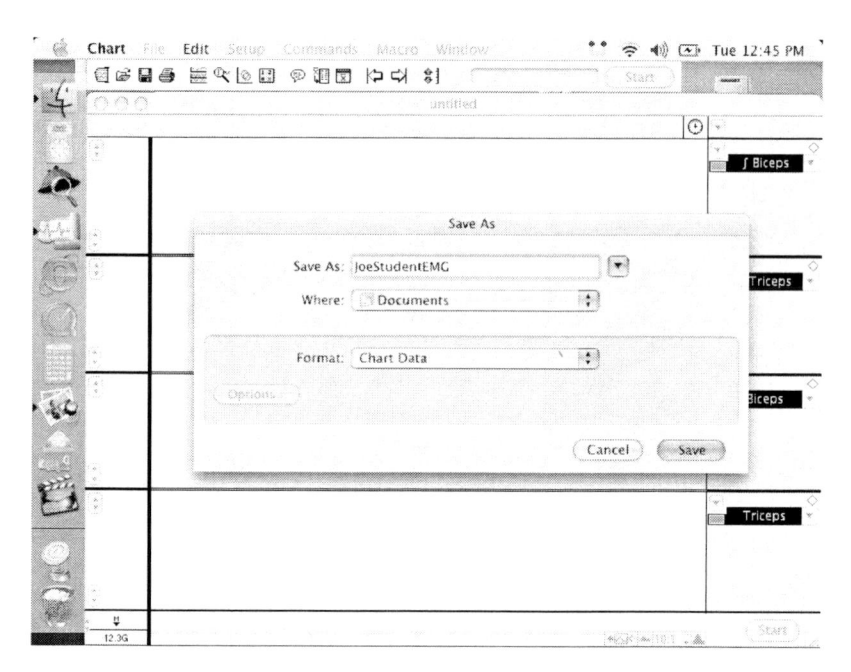

Figure 3

Once the file is saved the recording window provided by the Chart software is renamed to match the file name, Figure 4.

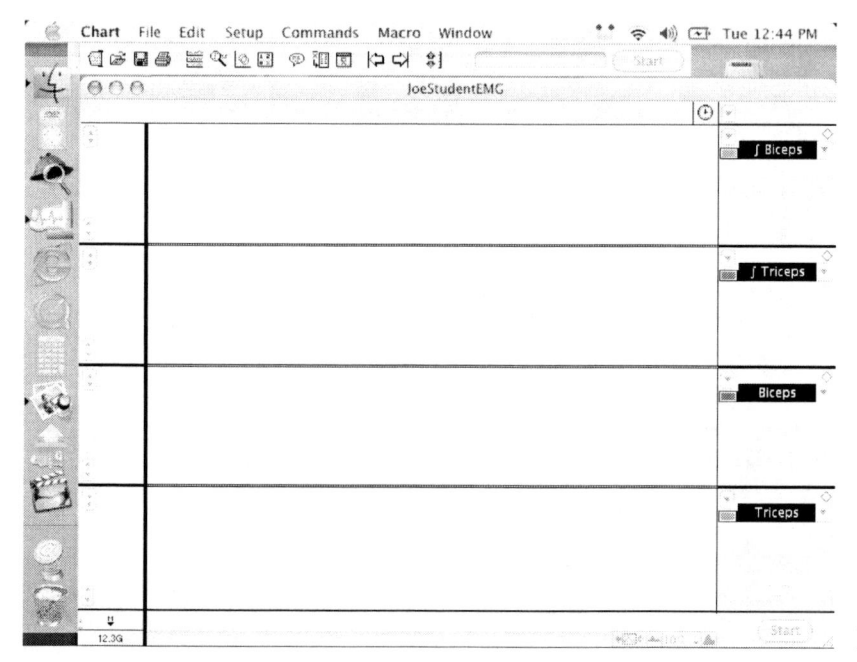

Figure 4

Have the subject sit comfortably facing the lab table. The subject should grip the tabletop with the hand of the monitored limb. Click the start button in the recording window. Wait three seconds and isometrically flex the arm through the elbow joint. Hold the contraction for three seconds. Relax and wait three seconds. Now isometrically extend the arm through the elbow joint. Hold the contraction for at least three seconds. Click the stop button to stop recording. If the subject is connected correctly, your tracing should look like this, Figure 5:

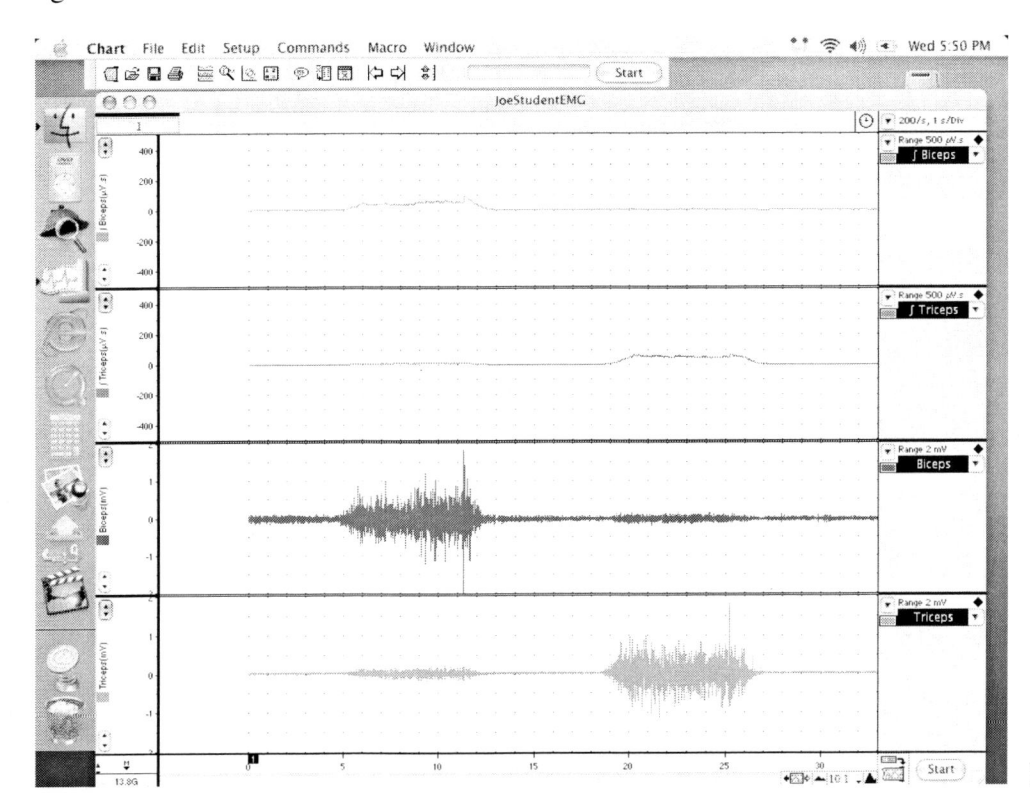

Figure 5

If you don't obtain a tracing like figure 5, check all your connections. If your connections seem secure, check with your instructor.

Notice that there are four recording channels, two for the biceps and two for the triceps. The top channel for each muscle calculates the integral from the corresponding raw data for each muscle. The raw data is displayed on the muscle's bottom channel. The integral reduces some of the lack of organization displayed by the raw data. At times it may be easier to ascertain the muscle's activity from the integral. The basis for interpreting the EMG tracing is straightforward. As motor units are activated, their muscle fibers depolarize. Since motor units behave in an asynchronous fashion, there will be continuous switching on and off of units during any activity. As a result the tracing may appear somewhat irregular or disorganized. However, the greater the number of motor units activated, the more depolarization events there are, and hence the greater the level of activity displayed on the EMG tracing. This increased activity is displayed on the EMG tracing and corresponds to an increase in tension generated by the muscle.

Figure 6 is an EMG recording which demonstrates increasing tension in both the biceps and triceps. Although both muscles are active and increasing in tension, the activity of the biceps is clearly much more significant.

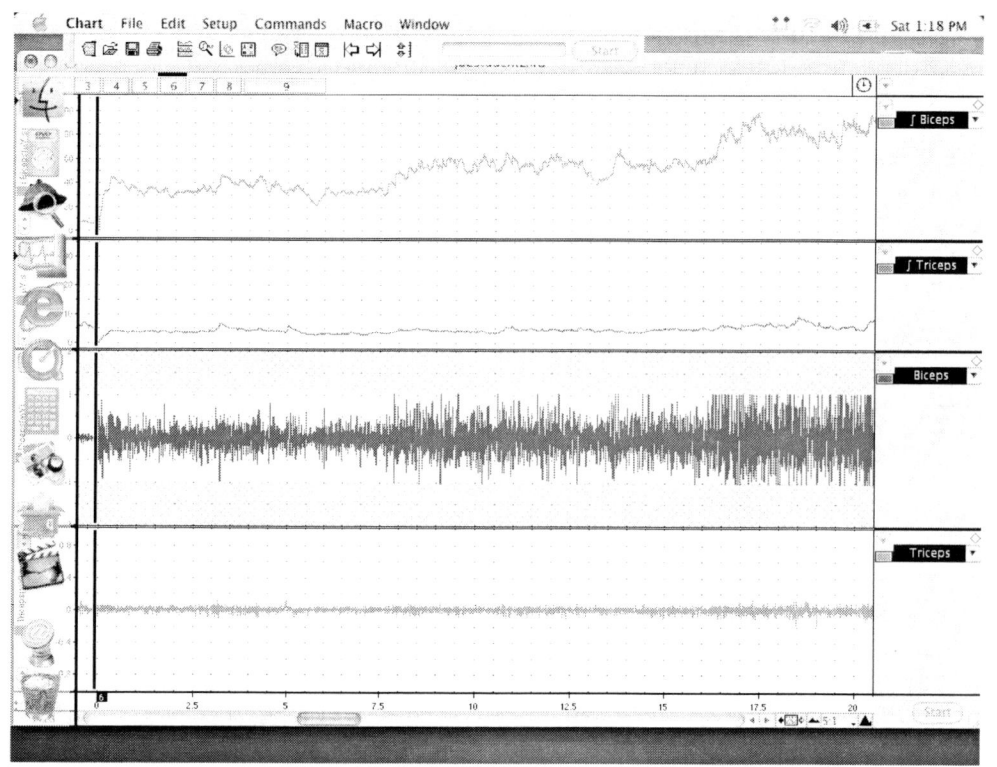

Figure 6

Adding Comments
It is possible to add comments to a Chart window. This may be done as the tracing is being recorded or after the tracing has been recorded. To add a comment while recording, position the cursor over the channel where you wish to add the comment and click the mouse button. A comment can now be added to this channel by a return key entry. The comment is placed at the time the return is entered. To add a comment to an existing record, position the cursor at the point you wish to enter the comment, click the mouse button and choose "Add Comment" from the Command menu in the Chart software. To add text into a comment or to edit a comment, use the Window menu in the Chart software and open the "Comments and Exclusions" window.

eMAC Printing
The eMac is set up to print to the printer in the A & P lab. In Chart, simply select the records you wish to print and select "Zoom Window" from the Window menu. The print commands are under the File menu. Select "Print Zoom" from the File menu to print the selected records. If you wish to print comments, open the "Comments and Exclusions" window and select "Print Comments" from the file menu.

Saving Your Work
It is a good idea to save your work often. To save your Chart data, select "Save" from the File menu.

The Lab Exercise

Prior to lab, students must review the detailed gross anatomy of the triceps and biceps muscles. including their specific origins, insertions, major and minor actions. Also prior to lab, each student should sit down with a dumbbell or other weight (e.g. textbook, dictionary, can of vegetables, etc.) and perform each of the movements described in these instructions. That means each of you will already have **individually completed the predictions section** for each movement to be performed as part of the exercise. Complete the prediction portion of each element of the exercise before the start of lab and be prepared to share it with your instructor before you are assigned to a group.

During the actual lab session, for each maneuver students in the group should discuss the predictions and come to a group consensus before performing the required maneuver. Once you are part of a group, you may revise your predictions based on discussions within the group. Include your revised predictions in the Discussion section for each activity. Once the data are collected for a maneuver, the members of the group must once again work together to evaluate the data and answer the questions that are posed. Because this is a group exercise, we are looking for consensus answers.

For this lab exercise, students will work in groups of four. One student will serve as the volunteer subject. Another student will be in charge of controlling the recording through the use of the Chart software. Rehearse each maneuver before actually generating the tracing. Perform each maneuver slowly and deliberately.

Activitiy 1

Starting with the arm straight, outstretched anteriorly and supported on a flat surface, the subject will slowly bend the arm at the elbow to 90°, pause, and then slowly return the arm to the straight position. For this a 5-10 pound load placed on an 8.5X11" sheet of paper will be used. This reduces friction between the weight and the tabletop, allowing it to slide easily during flexion and extension.

Prediction: In the space provided between the lines, draw the EMG tracing you expect this activity will produce.

Biceps:　　　　　　Flexion　　　　　　　　Extension

_____

Triceps:　　　　　　Flexion　　　　　　　　Extension

_____

Results:
- **Biceps during flexion:** Active / Inactive
  If active, contractions were: isometric / concentric / eccentric
  Contraction strength was: constant / increasing / decreasing

- **Biceps during extension:** Active / Inactive
  If active, contractions were: isometric / concentric / eccentric
  Contraction strength was: constant / increasing / decreasing

- **Triceps during flexion:** Active / Inactive
  If active, contractions were: isometric / concentric / eccentric
  Contraction strength was: constant / increasing / decreasing

- **Triceps during extension:** Active / Inactive
  If active, contractions were: isometric / concentric / eccentric
  Contraction strength was: constant / increasing / decreasing

Discussion:

_____

_____

_____

_____

Activitiy 2
Starting with the arm in the neutral position at his/her side and with no added weight, the subject will slowly bend the arm at the elbow to 90°, pause, and then slowly return to the neutral position.

Prediction: In the space provided between the lines, draw the EMG tracing you expect this activity will produce.

    Biceps: Flexion   Extension

    Triceps: Flexion   Extension

Results:

    Biceps during flexion: Active / Inactive
    If active, contractions were: isometric / concentric / eccentric
    Contraction strength was: constant / increasing / decreasing

    Biceps during extension: Active / Inactive
    If active, contractions were: isometric / concentric / eccentric
    Contraction strength was: constant / increasing / decreasing

    Triceps during flexion: Active / Inactive
    If active, contractions were: isometric / concentric / eccentric
    Contraction strength was: constant / increasing / decreasing

    Triceps during extension: Active / Inactive
    If active, contractions were: isometric / concentric / eccentric
    Contraction strength was: constant / increasing / decreasing

Discussion:

Activitiy 3
Repeat the same maneuver as in #2 while holding a 5-10 pound weight.

Prediction: In the space provided between the lines, draw the EMG tracing you expect this activity will produce.

Biceps: Flexion Extension

_____

_____

Level of activity compared to without load: more / same / less

Triceps: Flexion Extension

_____

_____

Level of activity compared to without load: more / same / less

Results:

Biceps during flexion: Active / Inactive
If active, contractions were: isometric / concentric / eccentric
Level of activity compared to without load: more / same / less
Contraction strength was: constant / increasing / decreasing

Biceps during extension: Active / Inactive
If active, contractions were: isometric / concentric / eccentric
Level of activity compared to without load: more / same / less
Contraction strength was: constant / increasing / decreasing

Triceps during flexion: Active / Inactive
If active, contractions were: isometric / concentric / eccentric
Level of activity compared to without load: more / same / less
Contraction strength was: constant / increasing / decreasing

Triceps during extension: Active / Inactive
If active, contractions were: isometric / concentric / eccentric
Level of activity compared to without load: more / same / less
Contraction strength was: constant / increasing / decreasing

Discussion:

_____

_____

_____

Activitiy 4

Starting with the arm straight, outstretched anteriorly and with the same 5-10 pound load as in #3, the subject will slowly bend the arm at the elbow to 90°, pause, and then slowly return to the starting position.

Prediction: In the space provided between the lines, draw the EMG tracing you expect this activity will produce.

    Biceps: Flexion   Extension
_____

_____

Level of activity compared to #3:   more / same / less

    Triceps: Flexion   Extension
_____

_____

Level of activity compared to #3:   more / same / less

Results: **Biceps during flexion**:   Active / Inactive
                If active, contractions were: isometric / concentric / eccentric
                Level of activity compared to #3:   more / same / less
                Contraction strength was: constant / increasing / decreasing

                Biceps during extension: Active / Inactive
                If active, contractions were: isometric / concentric / eccentric
                Level of activity compared to #3:   more / same / less
                Contraction strength was: constant / increasing / decreasing

                Triceps during flexion: Active / Inactive
                If active, contractions were: isometric / concentric / eccentric
                Level of activity compared to #3:   more / same / less
                Contraction strength was: constant / increasing / decreasing

                Triceps during extension: Active / Inactive
                If active, contractions were: isometric / concentric / eccentric
                Level of activity compared to #3:   more / same / less
                Contraction strength was: constant / increasing / decreasing

Discussion:
_____

_____

Activitiy 5

Starting with the arm straight, outstretched vertically and with the same 5-10 pound load as in #3, the subject will slowly bend the arm at the elbow to 90°, pause, and then slowly return to the starting position.

Prediction: In the space provided between the lines, draw the EMG tracing you expect this activity will produce.

    Biceps: Flexion   Extension

    Level of activity compared to #3:   more / same / less

    Triceps: Flexion   Extension

    Level of activity compared to #3:   more / same / less

Results:

    Biceps during flexion: Active / Inactive
    If active, contractions were: isometric / concentric / eccentric
    Level of activity compared to #3:   more / same / less
    Contraction strength was: constant / increasing / decreasing

    Biceps during extension: Active / Inactive
    If active, contractions were: isometric / concentric / eccentric
    Level of activity compared to #3:   more / same / less
    Contraction strength was: constant / increasing / decreasing

    Triceps during flexion: Active / Inactive
    If active, contractions were: isometric / concentric / eccentric
    Level of activity compared to #3:   more / same / less
    Contraction strength was: constant / increasing / decreasing

    Triceps during extension: Active / Inactive
    If active, contractions were: isometric / concentric / eccentric
    Level of activity compared to #3:   more / same / less
    Contraction strength was: constant / increasing / decreasing

Discussion:

Activitiy 6

With the arm at his/her side but bent at a 90° angle and holding a 5-10 pound weight, the subject will hold his/her hand in the pronated position. Slowly he/she will supinate the hand, pause, and then slowly return to the starting position.

Prediction: In the space provided between the lines, draw the EMG tracing you expect this activity will produce.

    Biceps: Supination   Pronation

_____

_____

    Triceps: Supination   Pronation

_____

_____

Results:

Biceps during supination: Active / Inactive
If active, contractions were: isometric / concentric / eccentric
Contraction strength was: constant / increasing / decreasing

Biceps during pronation: Active / Inactive
If active, contractions were: isometric / concentric / eccentric
Contraction strength was: constant / increasing / decreasing

Triceps during supination: Active / Inactive
If active, contractions were: isometric / concentric / eccentric
Contraction strength was: constant / increasing / decreasing

Triceps during pronation: Active / Inactive
If active, contractions were: isometric / concentric / eccentric
Contraction strength was: constant / increasing / decreasing

Discussion:

_____

_____

_____

_____

_____

Activitiy 7

Duplicate the supination/pronation maneuver in #6 but this time with the elbow and forearm supported on a stable surface.

Prediction: In the space provided between the lines, draw the EMG tracing you expect this activity will produce.

Biceps: Supination   Pronation

_____

_____

Triceps: Supination   Pronation

_____

_____

Results: **Biceps during supination:** Active / Inactive
If active, contractions were: isometric / concentric / eccentric
If active, level of activity compared to #6: same / greater / less

Biceps during pronation: Active / Inactive
If active, contractions were: isometric / concentric / eccentric
If active, level of activity compared to #6: same / greater / less

Triceps during supination: Active / Inactive
If active, contractions were: isometric / concentric / eccentric
If active, level of activity compared to #6: same / greater / less

Triceps during pronation: Active / Inactive
If active, contractions were: isometric / concentric / eccentric
If active, level of activity compared to #6: same / greater / less

Discussion:

Activitiy 8
With the arm at his/her side but bent at a 90° angle, the subject will hold a bag containing a 5-10 pound weight motionless for 5 seconds. After 5 seconds, another 5-10 pound weight will be added. After 5 more seconds, a third similar weight will be added.

Prediction: In the space provided between the lines, draw the EMG tracing you expect this activity will produce.

    Biceps: Starting weight   Add weight   Add weight

    Triceps: Starting weight   Add weight   Add weight

Results: **Biceps**:   Active / Inactive
If active, contractions were: isometric / concentric / eccentric
Level of activity: constant / increasing / decreasing

    Triceps: Active / Inactive
If active, contractions were: isometric / concentric / eccentric
Level of activity: constant / increasing / decreasing

Discussion:

Activitiy 9
With the arm at his/her side but bent at a 90° angle and with the hand in the supinated position, the subject will support a 10-25 pound weight. The subject will attempt to maintain an unchanging position for as long as possible as the muscles fatigue.

Prediction: In the space provided between the lines, draw the EMG tracing you expect this activity will produce.

Biceps: Weight in bag _____

_____

_____

Triceps: Weight in bag _____

_____

_____

Results: **Biceps:** Active / Inactive
If active, contractions were: isometric / concentric / eccentric
Level of activity: constant / increasing / decreasing

Triceps: Active / Inactive
If active, contractions were: isometric / concentric / eccentric
Level of activity: constant / increasing / decreasing

Discussion:

Exercise P-3

Physiology of the Nervous System:
Audition, Cutaneous Sensation, Sensory Adaptation, Vision

Introduction
Sensation is the perception of incoming information (either from outside or from internal viscera) that results from the stimulation of receptors (sensors) that respond to various types of change. Sensation is divided into two broad categories, general sensation and special sensation. General sensation relates largely to skin-related sensations such as touch, pressure, temperature, and pain and is usually detected by relatively simple sensory structures. Special sensation, on the other hand, is centered in the head and is mediated by much more complex sensory structures. Special sensation includes taste, olfaction, vision, hearing and equilibrium. In this exercise, you will examine some features or characteristics of several selected types of sensation.

Part 1: Audition
Air conduction carries sound waves through the external ear to the tympanic membrane. Vibrations of this membrane result in movements of the ear ossicles which result in waves of perilymph in the inner ear that stimulate the auditory receptors.

Sound vibrations may also be conducted through the bones of the skull to the inner ear. This may be demonstrated with a tuning fork placed on a bony surface. Rinne's and Weber's tests are used to distinguish between middle ear deafness and inner ear deafness. In localization by hearing alone, both differences in loudness at the two ears and differences in the time of arrival of sound at each ear are important.

Materials: Tuning forks (various frequencies)
                Sound generators (aka clickers)
                70% alcohol
                Blindfolds

A. Bone Conduction
1. To demonstrate bone conduction of sound waves, hold the handle of a vibrating tuning fork (these should first be cleaned with 70% alcohol) against the mandibular symphysis (also known as the mental symphysis). Start the fork vibrating by striking the tines against the palm of the hand (or gently against a hard surface such as a textbook).

2. Put the handle of the <u>vibrating</u> tuning fork in position in contact with the bone with both ears open. Notice the intensity and quality of sound perceived. Close the right ear. Note any change in the sound perceived.

Remove the fork, restart it vibrating and reposition it with both ears open. Now close the left ear. Note any change.

Remove the fork, restart it vibrating and reposition it with both ears open. Now with the assistance of a partner, close both ears. Note any change.

In each case, compare the change in the sound <u>intensity</u> and the change in sound <u>location</u> heard. Be sure to listen carefully to the vibrating tuning fork on the ~~mental~~ mandibular symphysis before anything is changed. This establishes a clear baseline (with both ears open) for sound intensity and location. Record your observations in the ~~spaces above~~ grid below and then answer the questions posed in the Analysis and Application section.

Bone Conduction			
Sound quality compared to both ears open	Louder	Softer	No Change
Right ear plugged			
Left ear plugged			
Both ears plugged			

B. Rinne Test
1. Now perform the Rinne test for middle-ear deafness by holding the handle of a vibrating tuning fork against the mastoid process. Of what bone is the mastoid process a part?

   The tines of the tuning fork should be pointed back away from the ear but not touching the head (only the base of the handle touches the head). This technique presents the sound by bone conduction.

2. When the sound can no longer be heard by bone conduction, hold the tuning fork by the handle with the tines positioned just outside of the external ear. This presents the sound by air conduction. Record below whether the sound is heard or not heard by air conduction <u>once bone conduction has ceased</u>.

Rinne Test		
Sound via air conduction after cessation of bone conduction	Present	Absent
Both ears open		
One ear plugged		

3. Simulate middle-ear deafness by plugging the ear to be tested with cotton and then repeating the test. Record your observations in the grid above.

4. Answer the questions in the Analysis and Application section.

C. Localization of Sound
1. Students will ideally work in groups of four (one subject, 2 sound generators, and 1 recorder). Blindfold the subject.

2. Using available sound generating devices ("clickers"), 2 students will randomly generate sounds approximately six inches
    (a) in front of the subject's head;
    (b) above the subject's head;
    (c) behind the subject's head;
    (d) on the right side of the subject's head; and
    (e) on the left side of the subject's head.

The sounds should be created and presented to the subject 3 times in varying order at <u>each</u> of the locations. The subject should indicate the location from which each sound is heard. The recorder will tabulate the responses in table 1 below. Enter 1 for a correct response; 0 for an incorrect response.

3. All team members shall then answer the questions posed in the Analysis and Application section.

Table 1: Localization of Sound

Correct response = +1; Incorrect response = 0

		Right	Left	In Front	Above	Behind
Subject 1	1					
	2					
	3					
	Total					
Subject 2	1					
	2					
	3					
	Total					
Subject 3	1					
	2					
	3					
	Total					
Subject 4	1					
	2					
	3					
	Total					

D. Analysis and Application:
1. Which mechanism of sound conduction (air or bone) is more sensitive (that is, able to detect softer sounds)? Defend your answer using experimental results you obtained.

2. Describe the Rinne test results you would <u>expect</u> from someone with middle-ear deafness.

3. In which location(s) was the subject best able to accurately localize the sounds?

   In which location(s) was localization accuracy the worst? _____

4. What factors help to explain why it was not always possible to correctly localize the source of a sound?

5. Based on the relative sensitivities of air and bone conduction, attempt to explain the results obtained in part A.

Part 2: Cutaneous Sensations

Cutaneous sensations include heat, cold, touch, pressure and pain. Most cutaneous receptors are distributed in a punctate manner, meaning that certain spots on the skin are more sensitive than others. <u>Tactile localization</u> refers to the ability to determine which area of the skin is being touched. <u>Tactile resolution</u> is the ability to discriminate two distinct sensations when the skin is simultaneously stimulated at two points. As the points of stimulation are brought closer and closer together, eventually only a single point is perceived. Pressure receptors are located more deeply in the skin than the touch receptors. Also, different areas of the body vary in their sensitivity to pressure and touch.

Receptor adaptation to stimuli occurs when the frequency of impulses caused by a stimulus decreases. Referred pain occurs when there is an error in localization so that a painful sensation is perceived as originating from a different area than that which is being stimulated.

Materials:
    50+ pieces of smooth paper   Bristles, pins, pencils, rulers
    Assorted esthesiometers (from 1 to 15 mm, in 1 mm increments)
    Paper cups/glass beakers   Warm, room temperature and ice water
    Tincture of iodine, tincture of wintergreen, tincture of cloves

A.   Localizing a Stimulus
1. The subject is instructed to close his/her eyes. The experimenter will then touch the palm of the subject's hand with a pencil or probe.

2. Using a similar probe, the subject then tries to place the point of another pencil or probe upon the precise spot stimulated. The subject may open his/her eyes to help position the pencil but should not look for the mark left by the experimenter's pencil/probe.

3. Another student then measures, in <u>millimeters</u>, the distance (if any) by which the subject missed the precise site of stimulation. Repeat this procedure two more times. In the data grid which follows (table 2), record the individual values obtained along with the average of the three determinations at each site.

4. Repeat the foregoing procedure on the palm and the back of the hand, the ventral and dorsal surfaces of the forearm, the ventral surface of the shoulder, the medial surface of the calf and the sole of the foot. Your instructor may change some of the sites being assessed.

Tactile Localization						
Subject 1		Index Finger	Palm of Hand	Back of Hand	Bicep	Tricep
	1					
	2					
	3					
	Avg					
Subject 2		Index Finger	Palm of Hand	Back of Hand	Bicep	Tricep
	1					
	2					
	3					
	Avg					
Subject 3		Index Finger	Palm of Hand	Back of Hand	Bicep	Tricep
	1					
	2					
	3					
	Avg					

B. Tactile Resolution

1. For purposes of this exercise, tactile resolution is the smallest distance at which two points of stimulation can be perceived as two distinct and separate stimuli. To determine tactile resolution, devices known as esthesiometers are used. Simple esthesiometers are composed of two pins/toothpicks securely taped together and held at precise, known distances apart.

2. The experimenter(s) collects a full set of esthesiometers. Before starting, the tips of the esthesiometers are cleaned with 70% alcohol. The subject is then blindfolded.

3. The experimenter(s) first determine(s) (in millimeters) the tactile resolution distance of the ventral surface of the index finger. This is done by applying various esthesiometers to the skin until a clear pattern emerges and a definite tactile resolution distance has been obtained. A "bracketing method" is the most straightforward approach to accomplishing this. Start with the points far apart. If the subject feels 2 points, halve the distance between the points and repeat. If still 2 points are felt, halve the distance again. If the subject feels only one point,

increase the distance by one-half and repeat. If the subject now feels 2 points, this is probably the tactile resolution distance that should be recorded. The experimenter(s) record(s) the results (in <u>millimeters</u>) in the data grid which follows (table 2).

4. Repeat this procedure for the other sites listed or for other sites as directed by your instructor. Record your results on the data grid (table 2) found on the next page.

5. Only if time allows, will determinations at all sites be repeated from which an average tactile resolution distance can be calculated.

6. When finished, clean the tips of the esthesiometers with 70% alcohol.

Tactile Resolution						
		Index Finger	Palm of Hand	Back of Hand	Bicep	Tricep
Subject 1						
Subject 2						
Subject 3						
Subject 4						
Subject 5						
	Avg					

C. Pressure Sensation
1. The experimenter places a single bristle on a smooth, hard surface and covers it with 1 or more sheets of construction paper (count them). Do this while the subject's eyes are closed or he/she is looking elsewhere.

2. The subject now attempts to determine the location of the bristle by pressing the tip of the index finger across the surface of the papers. Determine the <u>maximum number</u> of sheets of paper through which the subject can still feel and correctly locate the bristle.

3. Using the same amount of pressure, repeat the test using the metacarpal/phalangeal knuckle of the index finger, proximal portion of the palm of the hand, back of the hand, ventral surface of the forearm, and the dorsal surface of the forearm. In the data grid (table 2) which follows, record the maximum number of sheets of paper through which the bristle could be detected and accurately located.

Pressure Sensation		Index Finger	Heel of Hand	Back of Hand	Ventral Forearm	Dorsal Forearm
Subject 1						
Subject 2						
Subject 3						
Subject 4						
Subject 5						
	Avg					

D. Referred Pain

1. The subject is instructed to place one elbow in a tray of ice water, deep enough to cover the entire elbow.

2. The elbow is positioned long enough for the subject to feel the following progression of sensations:
   a) some general discomfort in the region of the elbow;
   b) actual pain sensations that are felt elsewhere.

3. Was the sensation of mild discomfort gradually replaced by one of pain? Yes / No

4. If pain was felt, describe the specific pattern or location of the pain that was experienced.

Analysis and Application:

1. In the <u>localization</u> of a single tactile stimulus experiment, was there any pattern to the subject's ability to localize the stimulus?   Yes / No
   If yes, please describe it.
   _____
   _____

   What could be the anatomical basis for this difference? _____
   _____
   _____

2. In the <u>tactile resolution</u> experiment, was there a difference in tactile resolution in different parts of the body?   Yes / No
   If yes, what could be the anatomical basis for this difference? _____
   _____
   _____

3. What areas of the body were most sensitive to pressure? _____
   _____

   What areas were least sensitive? _____
   _____

   What could be the anatomical basis for this difference? _____
   _____
   _____

4. Give an explanation for the phenomenon of referred pain. _____
   _____
   _____
   _____

Part 3: Sensory Adaptation

    A.   Temperature Receptor Adaptation

           1.   Immerse one index finger in a cup of warm water for two minutes. Then, without removing the first finger, dip the other index finger into the same container of warm water. Describe the difference between the sensations experienced in each of the fingers.

           2.   Now immerse one index finger in a cup of <u>warm</u> water and the other in a cup of <u>ice</u> water. After two minutes, immerse both fingers in the same container of <u>room temperature</u> water. Describe the difference between the sensations experienced in each of the fingers.

Analysis and Application:

1. Is it advantageous for receptors to adapt?   Yes / No
   Why?

2. Explain the results of the temperature adaptation experiments.

   Experiment 1:

   Experiment 2:

3. Why is it advantageous for pain receptors to show <u>limited</u> adaptation? _____

Part 4: Vision
Specialized receptors which respond to light are located within the retina of the eye. Each one contributes a single nerve fiber to the optic nerve which emerges from the posterior portion of the eyeball. The cornea is the clear anterior layer through which light must first pass as it enters the eye and which first begins to bend the light so that it is correctly focused on the retina. The lens behind it further bends the light so that an image is focused on the receptors in the retina. The iris regulates the amount of light which enters the eye.

Materials:
    Blind spot test cards   Snellen eye chart   Astigmatism eye chart
    Penlights   Ophthalmoscope

A. Blind Spot Verification
 1. Obtain an index card with a large plus sign (+) and a single large black dot printed on one side.

 2. Cover one eye. Hold the card at arm's length and focus on the <u>medial</u> of the two images on the card. Maintain focus <u>on just this image</u> as you move the card slowly toward you.
 As you move the card closer and closer to your face, does the other image disappear from your peripheral view? Yes / No

 3. Repeat this experiment with the other eye closed.
 As you move the card toward you again, does the lateral image disappear from your peripheral view? Yes / No

 4. Repeat this demonstration with <u>both eyes open</u>.
 Are you now able to demonstrate the presence of a blind spot? Yes / No.
 Please explain your findings in the Analysis and Application section.

B. Visual acuity
 Stand approximately 20 feet from the wall mounted Snellen chart. With the assistance of your partner, test the visual acuity of both your eyes (with and without glasses if possible). The terminology used to report basic visual acuity is simple. The visual acuity of each eye of the subject when standing 20 feet from the object being viewed is compared to that of a person with normal visual acuity. The first number refers to the subject while the second number refers to the distance at which a normally sighted could accurately read the same line on the Snellen chart. Record your visual acuity in the spaces below. If you wear corrective lenses, do this with and without your lenses in place.
 With no corrective lenses:
     Right eye: 20 / _____   Left eye: 20 / _____
 With corrective lenses:
     Right eye: 20 / _____   Left eye: 20 / _____

What is better, a visual acuity of 20/200 or a visual acuity of 20/15?
     ___ 20/200   ___ 20/15
Explain.

_____

_____

_____

_____

_____

C. Astigmatism:
  An astigmatism results when there is an irregular curvature of either the cornea or the lens such that light is not bent uniformly as it proceeds toward the retina. As a result, the radiating lines on the chart do not appear uniform and consistent (Some are darker than others; some seem to vibrate; etc.) Using the wall mounted astigmatism chart, determine if you possess an astigmatism in either eye. Stand close enough to the chart so that you can see the lines clearly. Cover one eye and look carefully at the chart.
  Do all lines on the chart appear uniform? Yes / No
  Based on this, is an astigmatism present? Yes / No

  Often eyeglasses can correct an astigmatism but such is not always the case with contact lenses. Only some contact lenses can correct this condition. Try to explain why this is so.

_____

_____

_____

_____

_____

_____

_____

D. Pupillary reflexes:
Accommodation to distance
This reflex involves changes in pupillary size associated with how far from the subject the object being viewed is. Have a subject change focus <u>from a distant to a near object</u> and then back. Note: Those with lighter colored eyes are the best subject's for this since their dark pupils will be more easily seen. Observe the pupils for any change in size. Record your observation in the grid below.

Accommodation to Distance	Dilate	Constrict
From near to distant		
From distant to near		

Please explain the change in the size of the pupils. _____

_____

_____

_____

How must the shape of the <u>lens</u> change during this demonstration?

___ Rounder   ___ Flatter

Please explain. _____

_____

_____

_____

_____

Accommodation to light intensity
Observe the size of the subject's pupils in dim light. Using the penlight supplied, illuminate one pupil by moving the light source slowly over the eye from lateral to medial. How did the size of the illuminated pupil change?

Accommodation to Light Intensity	Dilate	Constrict	Not Change
Illuminated eye			
Non-illuminated eye			

Explain the response of the illuminated pupil. _____

Explain the response of the **non**-illuminated pupil. _____

Exercise P-4
Biopotentials: The ECG and EEG

Introduction
The electroencephalogram (EEG) and the electrocardiogram (ECG or EKG) are examples of biopotentials. Excitable tissues are able to experience action potentials which involve ion flow across cell membranes. Although the primary effect of such ion flow is intracellular, there is nonetheless a change in electrical charge in extracellular fluid associated with the generation and propagation of these action potentials. Since the skin is in contact with the ECF, electrical changes that occur in ECF can be sensed by electrodes placed on the surface of the skin. These changes, once detected, can be magnified and result in the generation of tracings that can then be examined and analyzed. When this electrical activity is associated with the heart cycle, it is recorded as a wave pattern called an electrocardiogram. When this electrical activity is associated with the synaptic potentials in the gray matter of the cortex, it is recorded as a wave pattern called an electroencephalogram.

A simple biopotential record can be obtained by using two recording electrodes and a ground electrode. If multiple biopotentials are being recorded from the same subject, a different pair of recording electrodes is required for each record but a ground electrode can be shared. A biopotential is measured when an electrical energy gradient exists between recording electrodes. This energy gradient is measure in volts or some unit derived from volts, such as millivolts or microvolts. The energy gradient represents a path along which electrons can travel. The movement of electrons along such a path is an electrical current. If this path is an up-hill path, the measured voltage is negative. If this path is a down-hill path, the measured voltage is positive. A path or gradient for electrons exist when a charge difference exists between the points measured by the recording electrodes. One recording electrode will be a negative electrode; the other positive. If the positive recording electrode is measuring an environment which, relative to the negative recording electrode, is more positive, a positive voltage is measured. This establishes a down-hill path for negative electrons. If the positive recording electrode is measuring an environment which, relative to the negative recording electrode, is more negative, then a negative or minus voltage is measured. This establishes an up-hill path for negative electrons. If there is no charge difference between the electrodes there is neither an up-hill or down-hill path for electrons, and the voltage is zero.

Action potentials in the case of the ECG and graded synaptic potentials in the case of the EEC cause changes in charge distribution in the extracellular fluid compartment. If recording electrodes are properly positioned and recording instrumentation is properly calibrated, it is possible to measure and record these changes.

Equipment
The equipment required for this exercise includes the following: the Power Lab 410 physiological data recording system, an eMac with Power Lab software installed, USB cable, a five lead BioAmp cable, five ECG/EEG leads suitable for snap-on electrodes, pre-pasted adhesive electrodes to which leads can snap, an ace bandage with clip, and alcohol swaps.

Equipment Set-Up and Subject Preparation
For this lab exercise, students will work in groups of four. One student will serve as the volunteer subject. The other members of the group will prepare the equipment and the subject for the ECG and EEG recording. One group member will be responsible for operating the eMac and Chart software.

Use the USB cable to connect the Power Lab unit to one of the USB connections provided on the eMac.

Next prepare the student volunteer for electrode placement. With alcohol swabs firmly swab the following locations (ECG sites are shown below and to the right):
>Skin just below the mid clavicle on the right anterior trunk;
>Skin just below the costal margin on the left mid-clavicular line;
>Skin of scalp in left frontal area;
>Skin of scalp in left occipital area;
>Skin just below the costal margin on the right mid-clavicular line.

The right mid-clavicular subcostal location is for the shared grounding electrode. All other areas will receive recording electrodes. If there is a grounding strap in place of the fifth electrode, it should be placed around the right ankle.

Position the five electrode leads into the sockets of the bio-amp cable. Each lead is marked with its recording function. "G" indicates ground. Two leads are marked with "ECG" and two with "EEG". Plug the ECG leads into the channel 1 sockets of the bio-amp cable. Plug the EEG leads into the channel 2 sockets of the bio-amp cable. Plug the ground lead into the remaining socket. Polarity for the ECG can be corrected by the computer and polarity for the EEG doesn't matter but the channels must be correct for both ECG and EEG.

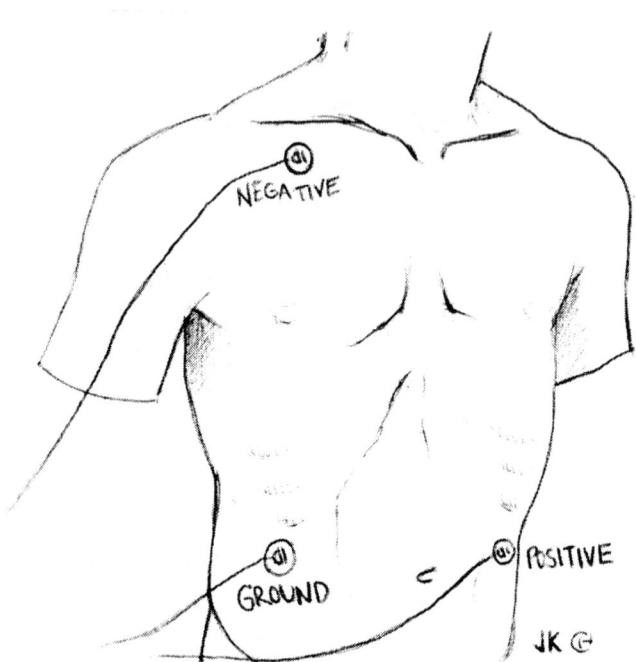

Snap the adhesive electrodes onto the five leads. Remove the backings to expose the adhesive. Trim the EEG electrodes with a clean scissors to reduce the adhesive surface placed on the subject's hair. Secure the ECG and ground electrodes to the subject in the designated areas. Expose the subjects scalp by moving hair and place the EEG electrodes on the prepared regions. Place a roll of gauze on the occipital electrode before wrapping ace bandage snugly over the scalp electrodes to stabilize their position. The roll of gauze on the occipital electrode increases the pressure at that point and improves the contact to the skin. Clip the bandage in place. Check that all electrodes are properly connected to the volunteer and the bio-amp cable before continuing.

Recording

Now, turn on the Power Lab unit and start up the eMac. Once the eMac starts up and the desktop is established, move the mouse cursor to the left side of the screen and find the icon for the "Chart" software. This software controls the Power Lab. Double-click on the chart software icon. The chart software will start up and begin to communicate with the Power Lab unit. After a short time, you will be brought to a screen labeled "Experiments Gallery." In this window, select the "eeg+ecg settings" file, Figure 1.

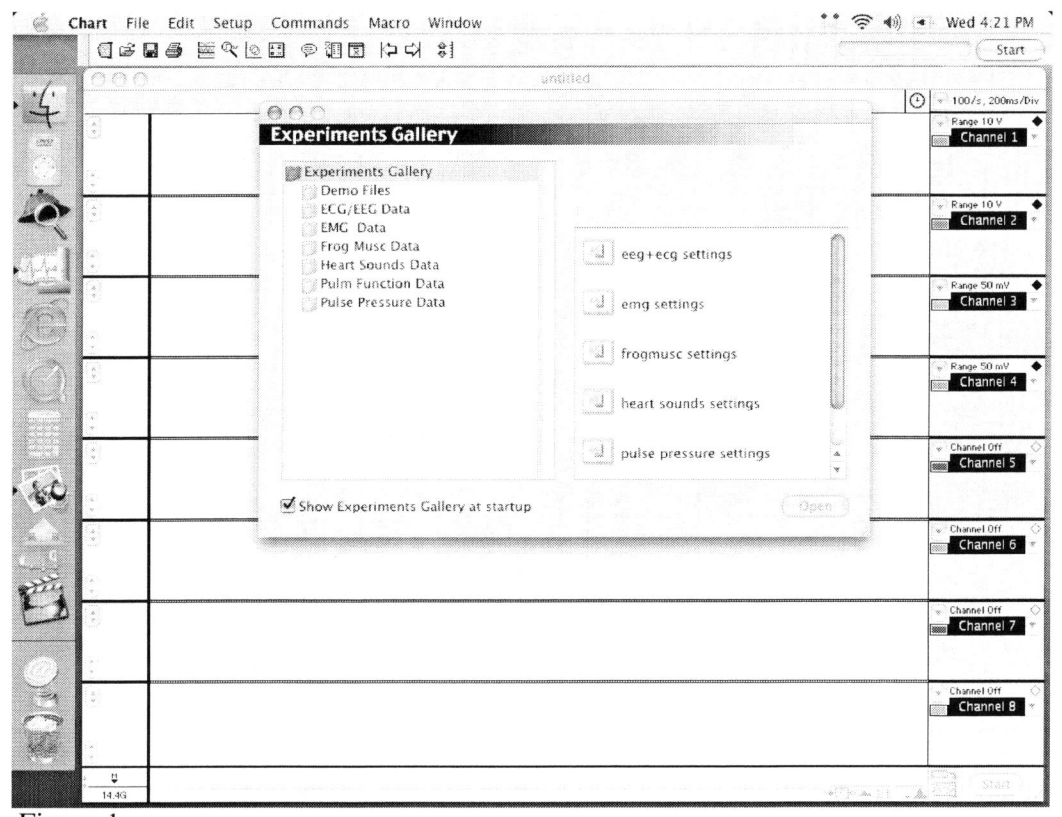

Figure 1

You will find this file along with a number of other settings files on the right side of the window in a small scrolling window. Double-click on this "eeg+ecg settings" file. This opens an untitled settings file, Figure 2.

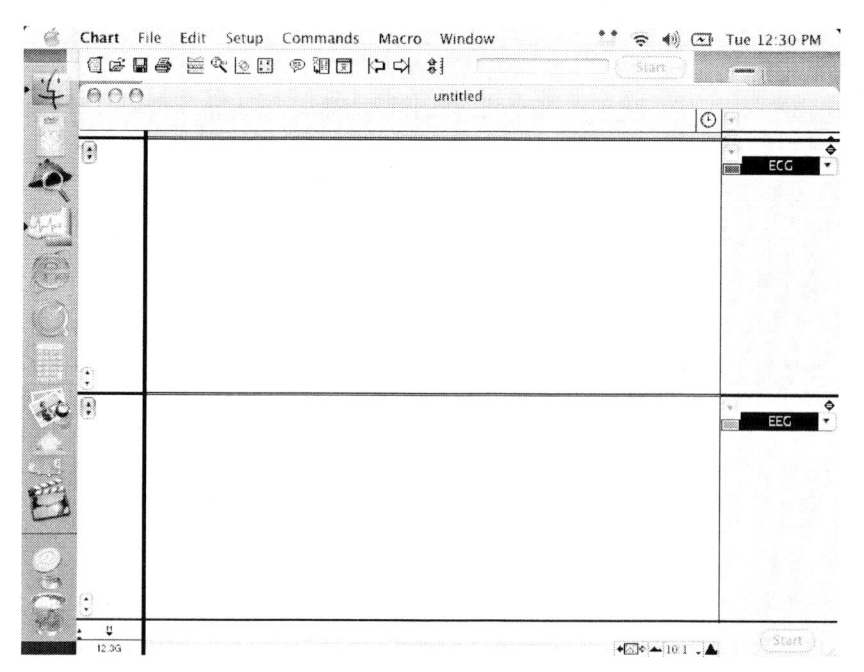

Figure 2

At this point, it is a good idea to convert the settings file you have just opened to a data file, Figure 3. Do this by going to the "File" menu choice at the top menu bar and selecting "Save". The file name needs to be entered since the default file name is "untitled". Name your file using the subjects name followed by "eegecg". Now save this file. It should be saved into the Documents file of the home directory. If you need to reopen this file at some future time to review today's results, you can access the home directory from the desktop by selecting the "Go" menu choice in the top menu bar.

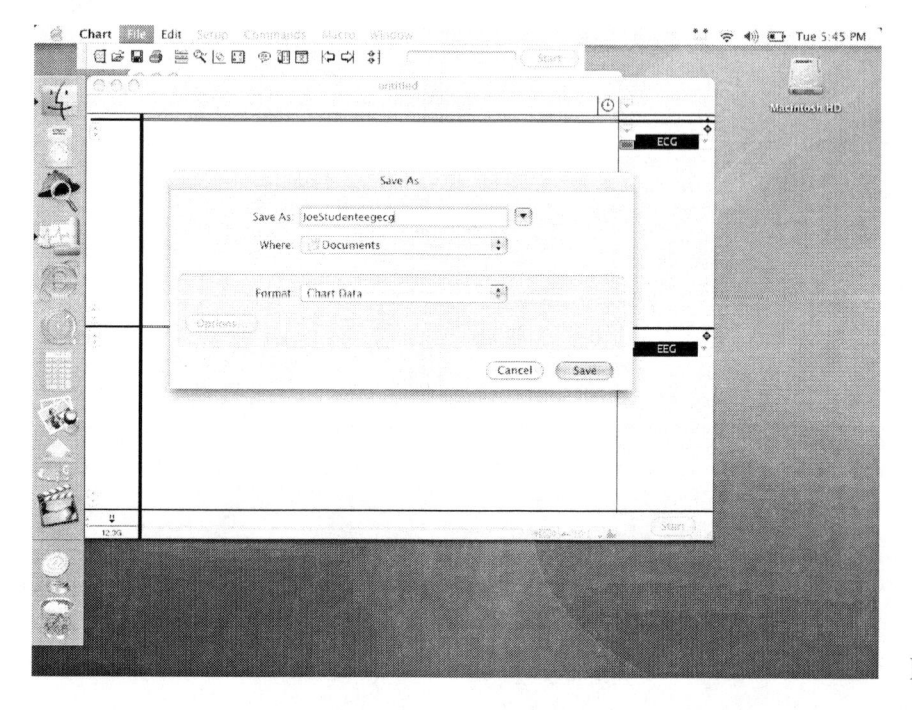

Figure 3

Once the file is saved, the recording window provided by the chart software is renamed to match the file name (Figure 4).

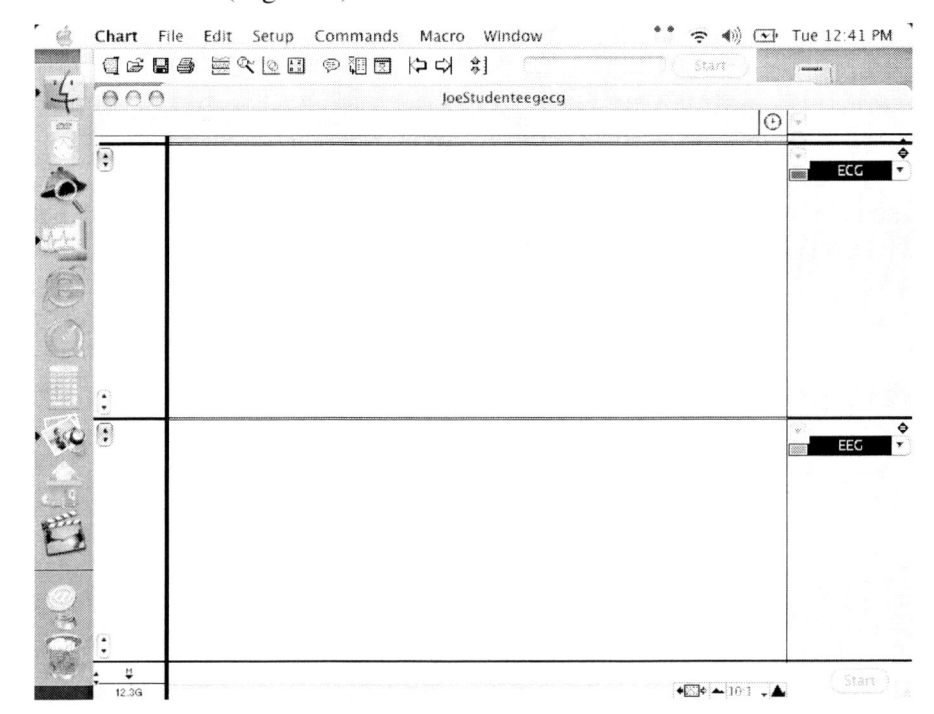

Figure 4

Have the subject sit comfortably. Click the start button in the recording window. The chart software will record a 6 second sample of ECG and EEC. If the subject is connected correctly, your tracing should look like this (Figure 5):

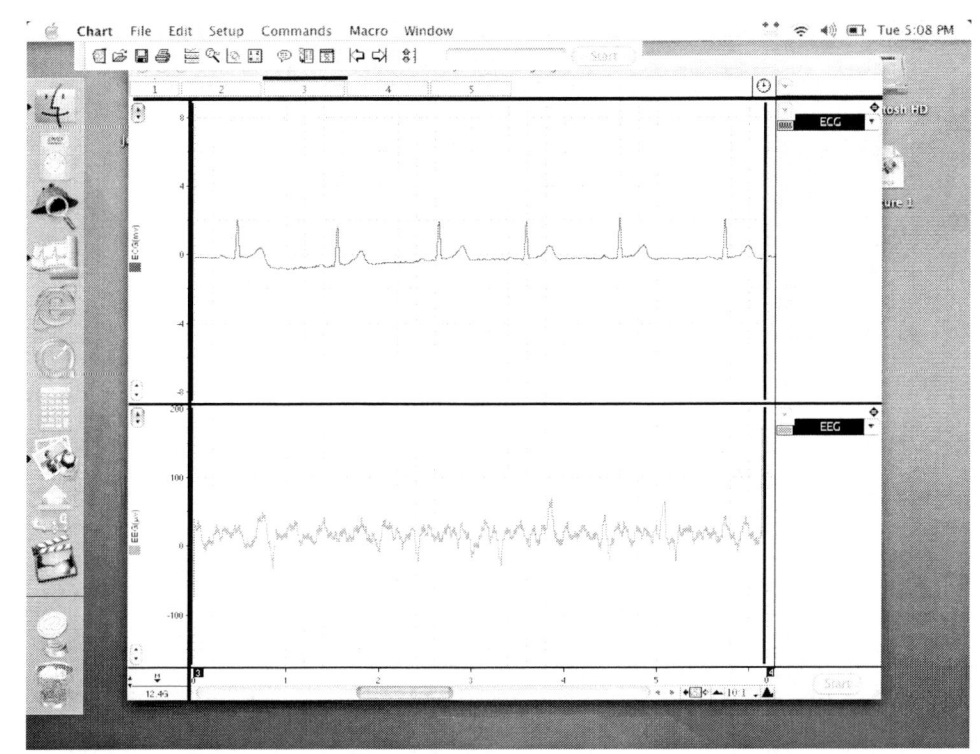

Figure 5

Notice that there are two recording channels, the top channel displays the ECG and the bottom channel shows the EEG. If you don't get a tracing like Figure 5, check all your connections. If your connections seem secure, check with your instructor.

Adding Comments
It is possible to add comments to a chart window. This may be done as the tracing is being recorded or after the tracing has been recorded. To add a comment while recording, position the cursor over the channel where you wish to add the comment and click the mouse button. A comment can now be added to this channel by a return key entry. The comment is placed at the time the return is entered. To add a comment to an existing record, position the cursor at the point you wish to enter the comment, click and choose "Add Comment" from the Command menu in the Chart software. To add text into a comment or to edit a comment, use the Window menu in the Chart software and open the "Comments and Exclusions" window.

eMAC Printing
The eMac is set up to print to the printer in the A & P lab. For the ECG and EEG, it is customary to work with a 6 second sample displayed over a distance of 6 inches. To achieve this standard display, simply select the six second record you wish to print. The print commands are under the File menu. First select "Page Setup" and set the orientation to the first "Landscape" option. Next scale the output to 75% and click OK. Next go back to the File menu and choose "Print Selection". Fill in the number of copies you require and click "Print". If you wish to print comments, open the "Comments and Exclusions" window and select "Print Comments" from the File menu.

Saving Your Work
It is a good idea to save your work often. To save your chart data, select "Save" from the File menu.

The Lab Exercise

Obtaining a ECG and an EEG

Once the group is comfortable with the equipment and can produce a reliable record, everyone should be quiet and have the subject close his or her eyes and begin recording. After three seconds have the subject open his or her eyes and complete the six second record. Show the results to your instructor. If acceptable, your instructor will direct you to print the record obtained.

Principles of analysis

Wave patterns like the ECG and EEG are analyzed on the basis of amplitude (or wave strength) and frequency (or wave timing). As already stated, biopotentials are voltage measurements. ECG amplitudes are typically measured in millivolts; EEG amplitudes in microvolts. The "Settings" file provides the proper calibration to allow easy measurement of wave amplitude in both the ECG and EEG. A vertical scale with the proper units is visible along the left side of each recording channel. Also the Chart software allows direct on-screen measurement of wave amplitude. Simply click the small rectangle in the lower left corner of the recording window. This activates the chart marker, a small triangle labeled "M", Figure 6 .

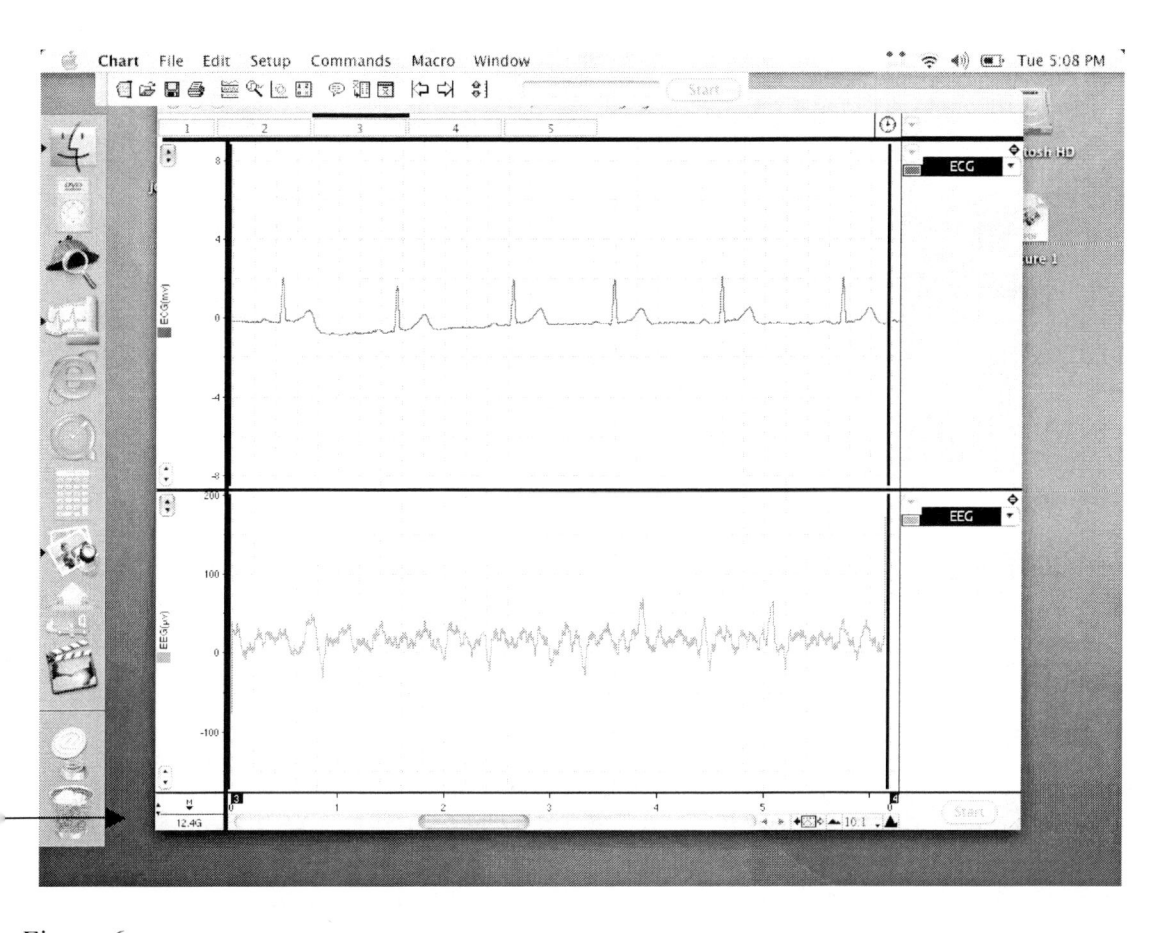

Figure 6

Use the mouse to position this marker anywhere on a tracing. Now move the cross hair cursor to any point on the same tracing. The voltage difference between the marker and the cursor is displayed above the name of the channel on the right side of the Channel window, Figure 7.

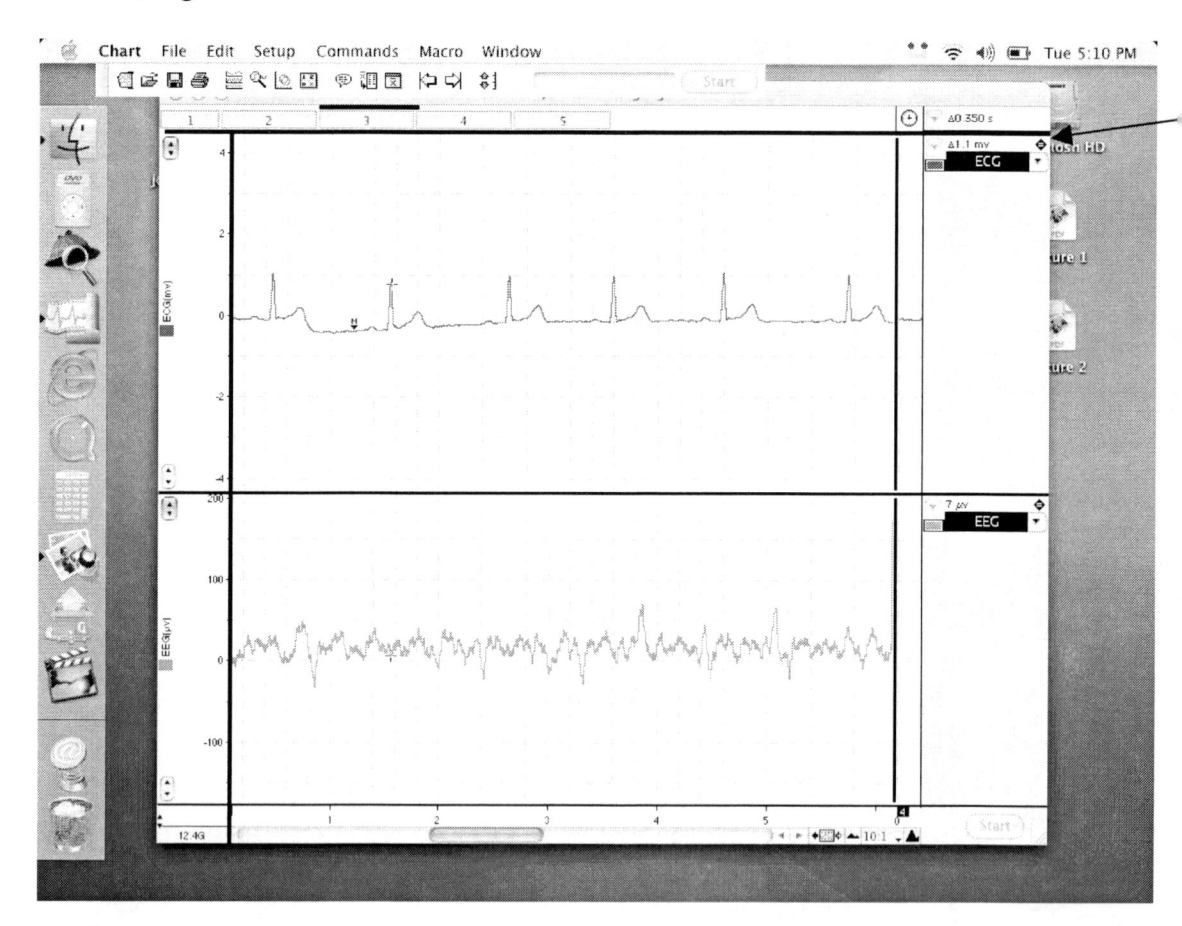

Figure 7

For traditional non-digital ECG and EEG waves, voltage can be determined by measuring vertical distances on a paper tracing. These records are generated mechanically by pens tracing on a moving paper chart. For a properly calibrated, mechanically generated ECG or EKG, 1 centimeter of vertical distance corresponds to 1 millivolt or 1 millimeter of vertical distance corresponds to 0.1 millivolt. For a properly recorded, mechanically generated EEG, one (1) millimeter of vertical distance corresponds to 10 microvolts (Note: 10 microvolts equals 0.01 millivolts).

Horizontal distance corresponds to time. The Chart software allows direct on-screen measurement of time. Once again, simply click the small rectangle in the lower left corner of the recording window. This activates the Chart marker, a small triangle labeled "M". Use the mouse to position this marker anywhere on a tracing. Now move the cross hair cursor to any point on the same tracing. The elapsed time between the marker position and the cursor position is displayed above the voltage on the right side of the Channel window, Figure 8. For traditional mechanically-recorded ECG and EEG tracings, time can be determined by measuring horizontal distances on a paper tracing. For a properly calibrated, mechanically-generated ECG or EEG tracing, one (1) millimeter of horizontal distance corresponds to 0.04 seconds. From this, a number of other temporal relations can be derived.

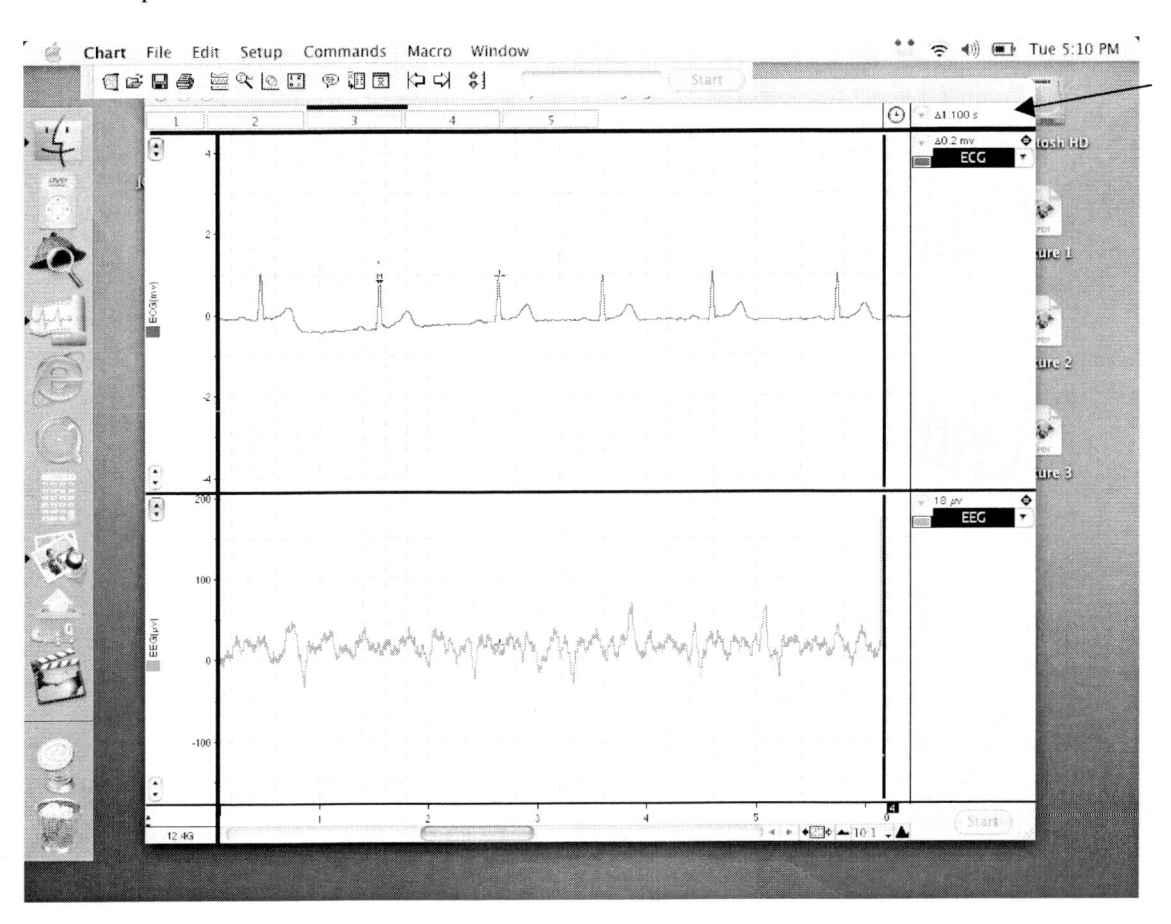

Figure 8

The following summarizes the most important:
    2.5 centimeters of horizontal distance = 1 second
    15 centimeters of horizontal distance = 6 seconds
    1 inch of horizontal distance = 1 second
    6 inches of horizontal distance = 6 seconds
    frequency per minute of an event = frequency in 15 centimeters or 6 inches X 6

* cycles per minute = 60 seconds /time for 1 cycle in seconds

* cycle is measured from a point on a particular wave to the same point on the next wave of that type

If the printing instructions contained earlier in this exercise are followed, all printed tracings can be analyzed for time and frequency according to these rules. That is, for the purpose of time-related analysis, they can be treated as mechanically-generated tracings.

353

Part 1: The Electrocardiogram:

Background

Impulse conduction through the heart generates electrical currents that may be detected. Each portion of the cardiac cycle produces a different electrical impulse which can be sensed on the skin surface by electrodes. These impulses are recorded as a series of up-and-down waves called deflection waves.

The electrocardiogram (ECG or EKG) is used to examine the physiological nature of cardiac muscle activity and also is used as an important diagnostic medical tool. The human body is visualized as a large sack containing electrolyte solution. Within this sac sits the heart, containing several sources of electrical potential. These potentials vary in intensity, time, and space. Electrodes placed on the surface of this electrolyte-filled sac may be used to record these changes.

In a normal cardiac cycle, electrical events follow a standard sequence:
1) depolarization and repolarization of the sinoatrial (SA) node;
2) depolarization and repolarization of the atria;
3) depolarization and repolarization of the AV (atrioventricular) node and AV bundle; and
4) depolarization and repolarization of the ventricular musculature.

Although depolarization and repolarization are transmembrane potentials, as these events occur and travel along the conduction path in the heart, they establish extracellular gradients. Simply put, one place along the path will depolarize or repolarize before another. As repolarization and depolarization are occurring, properly placed electrodes will record these extracellular differences as voltage changes over time. These wave forms will serve as a record of depolarization and repolarization events. When both electrodes are monitoring the same condition, either complete depolarization or complete repolarization, no voltage exists between the electrodes and a zero voltage horizontal line is recorded. Such a region is referred to as isoelectric.

The standard ECG has been derived from the examination of thousands of ECG tracings. It is altered by such factors as age, body build, electrode position, physical orientation of the heart within the body, previous cardiac history, and various other factors. Medical electrocardiography for diagnostic purposes normally involves vectorcardiographic techniques which utilize electrodes on the extremities and around the thoracic or esophageal regions to provide up to 12 leads or different electrical views of the heart. However, the three basic limb leads with electrodes attached to the extremities or trunk are more than adequate for basic study.

A lead is an arrangement of electrical conductors, one positive and the other negative, through which electrical activity from the body is brought to a recording device. Lead can also refer to the recording obtained from such an arrangement (as in a "Lead II tracing"). As the line between the positive and negative electrodes is moved, the orientation of the lead is changed. When the net wave of depolarization traveling through the heart moves toward the positive electrode of a given lead, the recording pen is deflected in a positive (upward) direction. When the net depolarization wave moves away from the positive electrode, a negative deflection occurs. Since the orientation of the three basic limb leads are each different, these leads provide three different perspectives on the electrical activity of the heart. The standard "12 lead ECG" therefore provides twelve different perspectives on the same electrical activity. In a sense, each lead "looks" at the heart's electrical activity from a different direction.

Consider the following analogy. You take eleven of your classmates out to the parking lot so they can see your new car. Everyone stands around the car and admires it. Each person sees something different because each person has a different perspective... of the same car. It's the same with the 12 cardiac leads. Twelve different perspectives of the same heart activity. Twelve different typical ECG tracings; one for each of the 12 different leads.

Under these standard conditions, a typical electrocardiogram is recorded (see Figure 9 below). Duplicate this typical electrocardiogram in the space provided in the results section. Label it according to the information which follows:

1. P Wave: This wave represents the electrical activity of the original impulse from the SA node and its subsequent spread through the atria. If the P waves are present and of normal and consistent size and shape, it is assumed that the stimulus began in the SA node. If they are absent or aberrant, it implies that the impulse originated someplace in the atrium other than the SA node.

2. P-R Interval: The period from the start of the P wave to the start of the QRS complex is called the P-R interval. It represents the time taken for the original impulse to reach the ventricles and initiate ventricular depolarization. During this period, which normally does not exceed 0.20 seconds, the impulse has traversed the atria and the AV node. Prolongation of the interval indicates a conduction delay from atria to ventricles.

3. QRS Complex: These waves represent depolarization and contraction of the ventricular muscle. They consist of an initial downward deflection (Q wave) which is generally not present; a large upward deflection (R wave); and a second downward deflection (S wave). Together, this complex represents the time necessary for the impulse to spread through the atrioventricular Bundle of His and the bundle branches to complete ventricular activation. Duration of this impulse is normally less than 0.12 seconds. An increase in duration indicates delayed, abnormal impulse conduction through the ventricles.

4. ST Segment: This interval represents the period between completion of depolarization and repolarization (recovery) of the ventricular muscles. Injury to the muscle may cause this segment to be elevated or depressed.

5. T Wave: This wave represents the recovery phase after contraction. If repolarization is abnormal, due to tissue injury or ischemia, this wave may be abnormal.

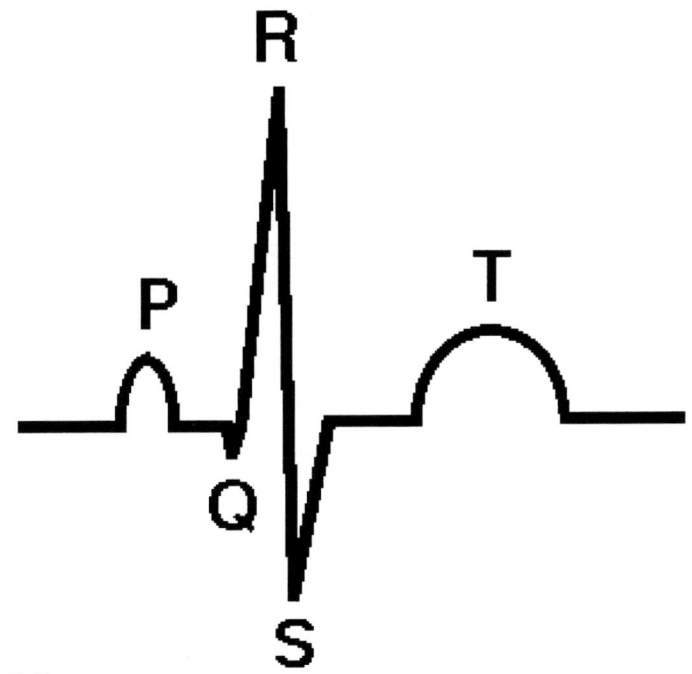

Figure 9: Typical ECG

Analysis
Using the 6 inch tracing recorded and printed by your group calculate the following information. Record this information in the Results section of your lab report.

1. Rhythm: Note the regularity of the R waves. If they occur at regular intervals (not more than 3mm difference in the length of R-R intervals), the ventricular rhythm is normal. If the rhythm is not regular, it is classed as irregular.

   To determine this, measure the time between five successive R waves (remember that each small square is 1 mm on a side and that it takes the pen 0.04 seconds to move 1 mm). If any of the four time intervals (R-R intervals) is different by .12 seconds (3 mm) or more from any other assume some irregularity of ventricular rhythm. Record the four time intervals and your conclusion concerning ventricular rhythm in the Results section. Your instructor may also show you how to quickly determine rhythm using a simple caliper.

2. Heart Rate
   This can be done in the following ways, depending on the ventricular rhythm.
   a. Count the number of R waves in a 6-inch segment of the electrocardiographic tracing (equal to a 6-second time interval) and multiply by 10 to get the rate per minute. This method is quick, easy and best if the ventricular rhythm is irregular.

   b. Count the number of small squares (millimeters) between two successive R waves (R-R interval) and divide this number into 1500. 1500 is the number of small squares (millimeters) the recording pen crosses over in one full minute. This method is a bit more involved than the above but provides a more precise result. However, it is valid <u>only if the heart rhythm is regular</u>.

   c. A third approach for use <u>only with regular rhythms</u> is to count the number of R-R <u>intervals</u> and multiply by 10. With this method, you must examine the portions of R-R intervals at the start and end of the tracing and combine them to estimate the fractions of R-R intervals they represent together. For example, if there are 6 complete R-R intervals plus ½ of an interval at the start and ¾ of an interval at the end, then there are 7 and ¼ R-R intervals in total. 7.25 X 10 equates to a heart rate of 72.5 bpm.

3. Compare the atrial and ventricular rates. Ventricular rate has already been determined above. For the same 6-inch strip, determine atrial rate by counting the number of P waves in a 6-inch strip and multiplying by 10. Are atrial and ventricular rates the same? If not, it may simply be that the tracing starts or ends in the middle of one cycle or it could indicate a possible conduction blockage. Record your results.

4. Examine the P waves. If P waves are present:
   a. Are all P waves of equal amplitude?   Yes / No
   b. Does a P wave precede each QRS complex?   Yes / No
   c. Is every P wave followed by a QRS complex?   Yes / No

   If the answer to each of the above is "yes". then the heart beat originates in the sinus node and a sinus rhythm exists. If the P waves are absent, are of variable amplitude or if their positions vary with respect to the QRS complex, the impulse may have started outside of the SA node and an ectopic (starts in a different location) pacemaker may be in command. Record the duration and amplitude of 5 P waves in your Results section. Compute the average duration and amplitude using your five observations.

5. Measure the P-R interval. Record the time represented by 5 P-R intervals in the Results section. Calculate the average P-R interval and record this information. The normal duration for the P-R interval is less than or equal to 0.2 seconds. If the

interval is prolonged in time from this value, it indicates a defect in the conduction system between the atria and the ventricles.

6. Examine the QRS complex. Is a Q wave present? Yes / No If yes, determine the amplitude of this complex based on the average of 5 observations. Determine the duration of the QRS complex again calculating an average based on the duration of 5 such complexes.

7. Determine the duration of the Q-T interval. This interval represents the time between the beginning of the QRS complex and the end of the T wave. Use the average based on the measurement of 5 Q-T intervals.

8. Compare your results with standard values as contained below.

Normal ECG Values (based on a heart rate of 70 bpm)

	Duration (sec) Average	Range	Amplitude (mV)
P Wave	0.08	0.06-0.12	≤ 0.3
QRS Complex (any single lead)	0.08	0.06-0.12	≤ 2.5
P-R Interval	0.18	0.12-0.20	
T Wave	0.18	------------	≤ 0.5
Q-T Interval	0.36	0.31-0.38	

Note: P-Q interval (PQI) is the same thing as P-R interval (PRI).
QRS interval is the same thing as QRS complex.

Results: Student Name: _____
                    Typical EKG   EKG ID _____

1. **R wave regularity**

interval	duration
1	_____
2	_____
3	_____
4	_____

                       Regular / Irregular

2. **Heart rate per minute (methods a and b)**

   a. _____ bpm

   b. _____ bpm

3. **Atrial and Ventricular Rates per minute**

   Ventricular Rate   _____ bpm
   Atrial Rate   _____ bpm
   Comments:

4. **P waves**   Duration (sec)   Amplitude (mV)
                    1. _____   1 _____
                    2. _____   2 _____
                    3. _____   3 _____
                    4. _____   4 _____
                    5. _____   5 _____
                    Avg _____   Avg _____

   Comments:

5. **P-R Interval :**   Duration (sec)   1 _____
                                          2 _____
                                          3 _____
                                          4 _____
                                          5 _____   Avg _____

   Comments:

6. **QRS Complex:**   Q Wave: present / absent

   Duration (sec)   Amplitude (mV)
   1. _____   1 _____
   2. _____   2 _____
   3. _____   3 _____
   4. _____   4 _____
   5. _____   5 _____
   Avg _____   Avg _____

   Comments:

7. **Q-T Interval:**   Duration (sec)   1 _____
                                          2 _____
                                          3 _____
                                          4 _____
                                          5 _____   Avg _____

   Comments:

Interpreting the Abnormal EKG (Optional)
Read the following materials for a basic explanation of some common electrical abnormalities. Your instructor may provide you with a selection of abnormal ECG tracings for your inspection and analysis. If so, use this information and other available reference material to identify the arrhythmia or abnormality shown in each of the accompanying EKGs.

1. Abnormal Rates and Rhythms
   The rate of the heartbeat and its rhythm are easy to ascertain from the typical electrocardiogram. The normal rate is about 72 (60-80) beats/min. A very slow rate, termed bradycardia, unassociated with other cardiovascular abnormalities, is not considered pathological. Such a rate is commonly seen in aerobically conditioned individuals. An increased rate (generally greater than 100 bpm), termed tachycardia, is more often associated with poor cardiac health or actual disease. As indicated above, slight variations in rhythm are normal. Pronounced irregularity suggests a cardiovascular disorder. One such example is paroxysmal tachycardia in which the heart will abruptly speed up for a few seconds and then slow down.

   The rate may become so great as to be compared to the rapidly fluttering wings of a bird. For this reason, regular rates over 200 beats/min are referred to as flutter. The atria are more prone to flutter than the ventricles. Rates up to 350 beats/min have been recorded. Despite the rapid rate, the contractions are coordinated; that is to say, the sequence of events is the same as at normal rates, the only difference being one of rapidity. However, contraction may become discoordinated (grossly irregular or chaotic), a state in which small areas of myocardium contract and relax independently of other areas. The rate is very rapid. Rapid, discoordinated contraction is termed fibrillation because individual fibers, rather than the myocardium as a whole, contract. Fibrillation of the atria is compatible with life, but ventricular fibrillation is not. A fibrillating ventricle does not contract as a single unit and is incapable of elevating pressure high enough to open the aortic valve and eject any blood. Stroke volume and cardiac output are therefore zero. Atrial fibrillation, on the other hand, prevents the atria from pumping blood into the ventricles, but such atrial pumping probably accounts for at best 25 percent of ventricular filling. The greater percentage (roughly 75% or more) is due to venous pressure gradients. Thus, though atrial fibrillation decreases the efficiency of the heart, it is not fatal as is ventricular fibrillation.

2. Premature and/or Ectopic Contractions
   A premature contraction is one which occurs ahead of schedule. It may originate in the atria and therefore cause both the atria and the ventricles to contract early. Or it may originate in the A-V node or the muscle mass of the ventricles and affect only the activity of the ventricles. An ectopic beat is one which originates from a location in the heart other than part of the normal conduction system. An impulse thus generated will pass through the tissue of the heart by a pathway that is different from normal. Since the skin sensors (electrodes) will "see" an

electrical impulse that is different from what is usual, the wave forms (P waves or QRS complexes) generated on the tracing will look different (sometimes very different).

3. Heart Block

   Heart block refers to a problem of electrical conduction within the heart. There are three levels or degrees of abnormality. First-degree heart block can only be detected by use of the ECG. A P-R interval in excess of 0.20 second is indicative of this condition. The electrical impulse is being conducted from atria to ventricles; it is too slow however. The ECG record will also disclose second- and third-degree heart blocks.

   If second-degree block exists, the ECG will show more P waves than QRS complexes, but there will be a definite ratio between them, perhaps 2:1 or 3:1. That means that only some of the electrical impulses originating in the atrium are successfully being passed on to the ventricles. The atrial rate will therefore be faster than the ventricular rate. The P-R intervals will be consistent, and not necessarily too long.

   In third-degree block, there is absolutely no communication between atria and ventricles. Both the atria and the ventricles contract at their inherent rates. Therefore, the atrial rate will be faster and there are more P waves than QRS complexes. Also, there is no discernible or consistent ratio between atrial and ventricular activity and the P-R intervals are widely variable.

4. Bundle Branch Block

   Figure 10 below shows the effect of asynchronous ventricular contraction due to a defect in conduction through one or the other of the bundle branches and its overall effect on the QRS complex. The duration of the QRS complex is abnormally prolonged (0.12 sec of more). The reason for the prolonged complex is the failure of the two ventricles to beat simultaneously. The delay of the impulse in the blocked bundle branch causes the contraction of the ventricle served by that branch to lag behind the contraction of the ventricle with the intact bundle branch, thus prolonging the QRS complex. This also accounts for the fact that the QRS in bundle branch block is frequently notched (see Figure 2B below). Very often the S-T segment slants in the direction opposite to the main QRS deflection. By the use of chest (precordial) leads, it is possible to determine whether the block is in the left or right branch.

Figure 10: Bundle Branch Block

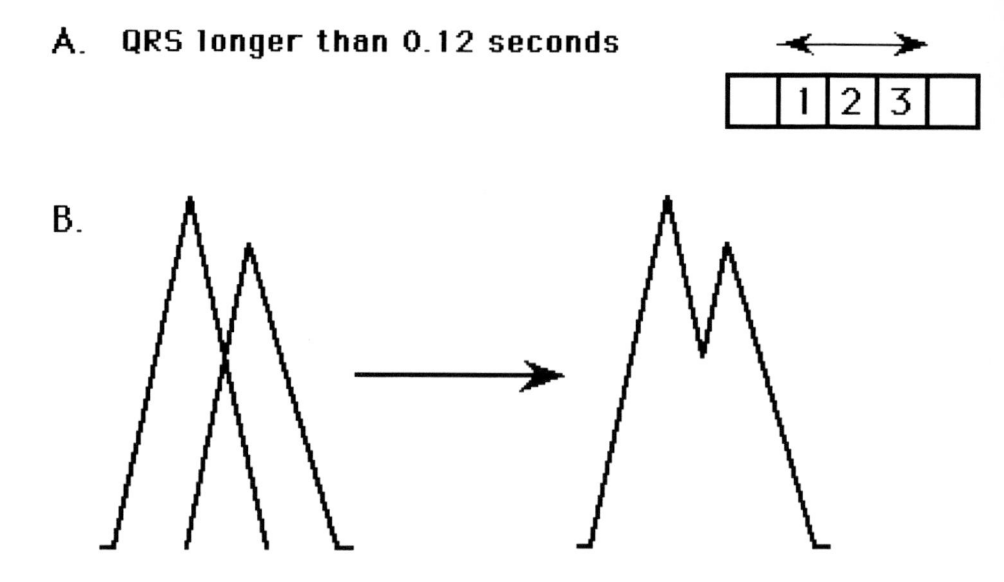

A. QRS longer than 0.12 seconds

5. Myocardial Infarction
   Cardiac muscle <u>requires</u> oxygen in order to metabolize fuel. It does not tolerate oxygen stress the way skeletal muscle does. An infarct is a region of dead tissue resulting from the interruption of blood flow and a lack of oxygen to the tissues. Such an area of infarction in the heart cannot undergo depolarization and repolarization, and therefore is often represented by an abnormality or predictable change in the ECG (Figure 11). The two most important findings are:
   a) elevation of the S-T segment; and
   b) inversion of the T wave.

Figure 11: Changes Seen in Myocardial Infarction

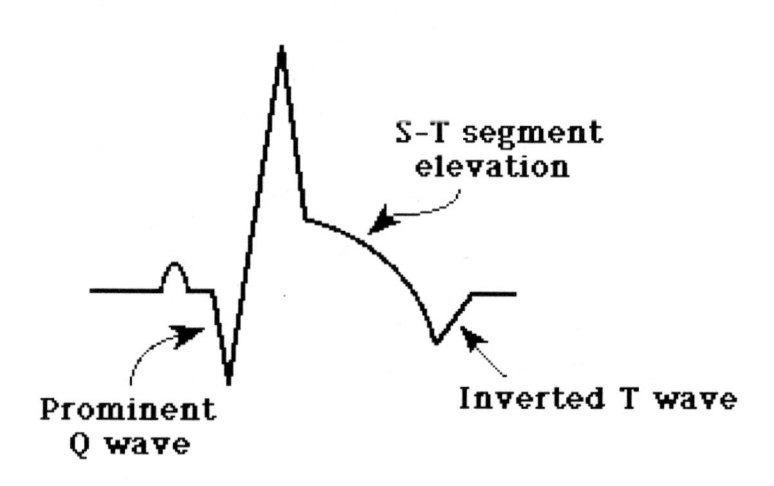

In addition, if a preinfarction ECG is available, comparison generally shows more prominent Q waves following an infarct.

Analysis and Application: ECG/EKG Interpretation   Name _____

1. What abnormality of EKG would indicate a 1st degree heart block?

2. What abnormality of EKG would indicate a bundle branch block?

3. What abnormality of EKG would indicate an ectopic <u>atrial</u> pacemaker is present?

4. An abnormal T wave may indicate damage to what area of the heart?

5. How would a premature beat originating in the SA node differ from one which originates in the ventricles?

6. Can tachycardia be determined from an EKG? Yes / No   If yes, how?

7. Examine any sample EKG tracings provided by your instructor. Examine each tracing for the presence and shape of P waves, the duration and amplitude of the QRS complex, P-R and Q-T interval durations, and the nature of the T waves and S-T segments. Also consider the regularity and rate of ventricular activity. Notice any significant differences from the typical tracing.

Part 2: The Electroencephalogram (EEG)

Background

Unlike the heart which provides a relatively simple repetitive electrical sequence that follows a well established conduction path, the gray matter of the cerebral cortex contains countless numbers of synapses which engage in an equally unfathomable numbers of synaptic events every second. With each neurotransmission event the post synaptic membranes on the receptor sides of these synapses undergo slight depolarizing or hyperpolarizing changes. These graded potentials create electrical variations in the extracellular fluid around the cortex. The EEG records these variations as a summation of these tiny voltages based on the net changes between the recording electrodes. When synaptic activity is relatively slow a synchronous relatively low frequency high amplitude wave pattern emerges. However high levels of synaptic activity over a wide range of cortical regions produce asynchronous relatively high frequency low amplitude waves.

EEG tracings from a normal, awake individual generally exhibit two basic wave types.

Alpha waves:
Alpha waves are indicative of relaxed wakefulness. These are generally obtained with a subject resting quietly with eyes closed. Alpha waves (Figure 12) are characterized by larger amplitudes and slower frequencies (8-12 cps).

Figure 12: Alpha Waves

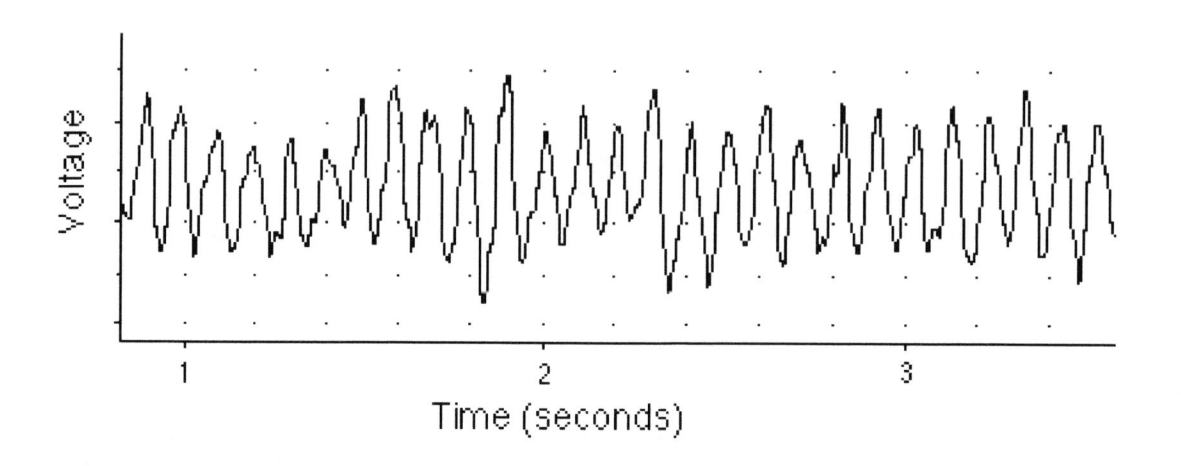

Beta waves:
Beta activity (Figure 13) indicates a brain that is active or stimulated. The amplitude of beta waves is smaller and the frequency faster (13-25 cps).

Figure 13: Beta Waves

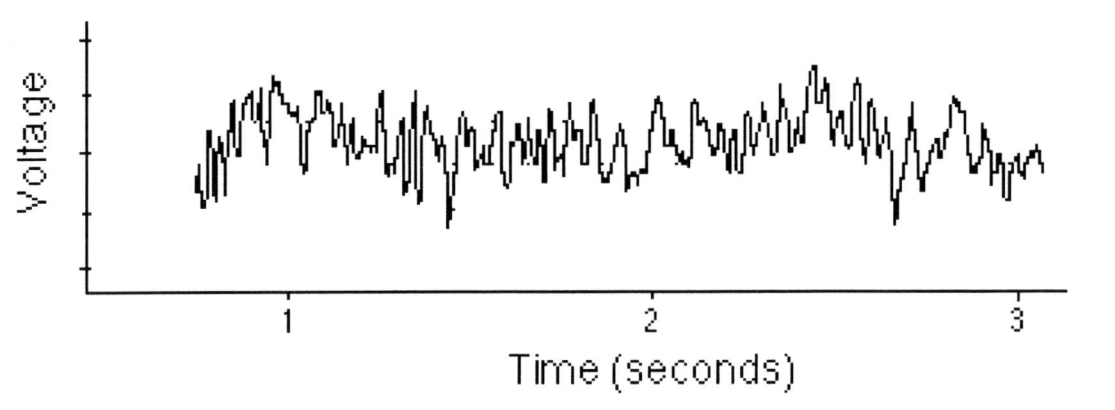

The abrupt cessation of alpha rhythm and its replacement by beta activity is referred to as alpha block (Figure 10).

Figure 14: Alpha Block

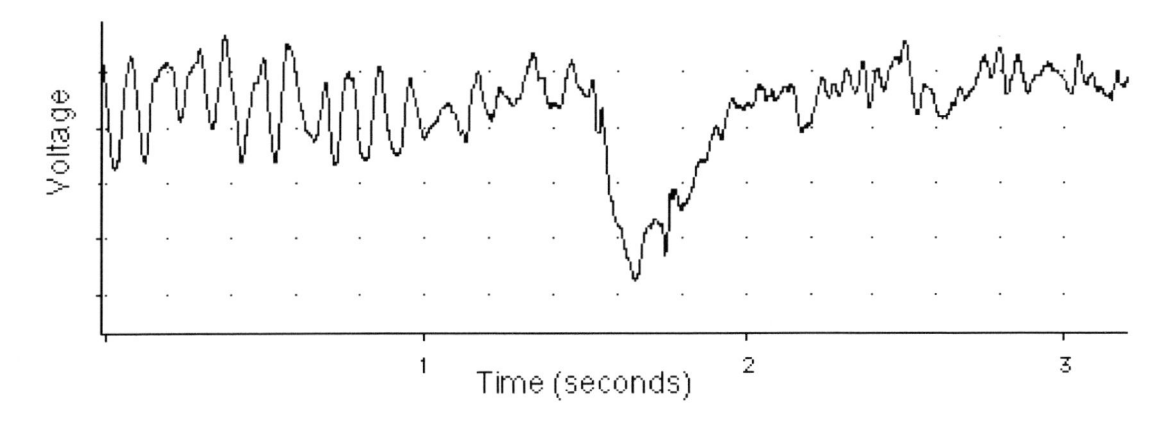

Analysis
Using the 6 inch tracing recorded and printed by your group, determine the following information. Record this information in the Results section of your lab report.
- Be able identify alpha rhythm from an EEG tracing and describe the level of brain activity that causes it.
- Be able identify beta rhythm from an EEG tracing and describe the level of brain activity that causes it.
- Be able to recognize an instance of alpha block on an EEG tracing and explain what has happened.

Be prepared to demonstrate these waves and events to your instructor.

Results:
Analyze the tracing obtained to complete the following.

	Alpha Rhythm	Beta Rhythm
Frequency (cps)	_____	_____
Amplitude (mm)	_____	_____

Analysis and Application:
You are responsible for:
- The physiological basis of biopotentials;
- The relative magnitudes of different biopotentials;
- The general procedures for recording biopotentials.

Be generally familiar with EEG recording (equipment used, calibration, subject hook-up).

Be able to compare and contrast the characteristics of the various EEG wave patterns on the basis of frequency, amplitude, and significance.

Exercise P-5

Physiology of Systemic Circulation:
Capillary Microcirculation & Cardiac Physiology

Part 1: Capillary Microcirculation

The arterial and venous divisions of the circulatory system are united by an intricate network of capillaries. Capillaries are short, thin-walled vessels, approximately 9 micrometers in diameter. They are so numerous that all living body cells are no more than two to three cells removed from one of these vessels. The vast number of capillaries makes their combined diameter so great that blood flows most slowly through them. This slow flow of blood is of great importance because it allows sufficient time for exchange of materials between the blood and tissues. Since there is insufficient blood to fill all capillaries simultaneously, blood is passed through particular capillaries according to the needs of surrounding tissues. Whether or not blood enters a capillary is determined by the size of its preceding arteriole and the action of precapillary sphincter muscles.

Both the arterioles and their precapillary sphincters are under autonomic control via the vasomotor center in the medulla. The vasomotor center is influenced by many factors. Local conditions also influence the status of arterioles and precapillary sphincters and therefore the volume of blood flowing through the capillaries. The oxygen and/or carbon dioxide concentration in tissues, blood levels of epinephrine and norepinephrine, histamine, and serotonin all have vasomotor effects which influence capillary blood volume.

In this exercise we will use a video titled "Frog Microcirculation" (produced by S. Drogo and R. Jubenville) to study some of the factors that influence capillary circulation. The video is contained at the end of "Endocrine Anatomy & Histology" video which is on open reserve in the Library. Your instructor will run this videotape of an actual demonstration of microcirculation and vascular physiology using a live frog. Students will make and record their observations as described below while the video runs.

Expected Observations

When viewing the video, attempt to make the following observations. Record your observations on the Results sheet which follows.

- Locate an arteriole, a venule and a capillary.

- Describe the relative rates of blood flow in each of these three types of vessels.

- Locate vascular bifurcations (places where vessels divide into two or where two vessels merge to form one vessel). Draw the bifurcations characteristic of arterioles and of venules. Clearly indicate the direction of blood flow in relation to each type of bifurcation.

- Attempt to locate a precapillary sphincter and the junction of a capillary and an arteriole.

- Categorize the blood flow between an arteriole and capillary as compared to the blood flow within an arteriole or capillary.

- Observe a capillary closely. How do blood cells move through a capillary?

- Observe any changes in blood flow that accompany application of histamine (1:10,000) solution.

- Observe any changes in blood flow that accompany application of epinephrine (1:1000) solution.

Results: (Frog Microcirculation)   **Name** _____

1. Describe the relative rates of blood flow in:

    Arterioles   _____

    Capillaries   _____

    Venules   _____

2. Draw an arteriolar bifurcation. Use arrows to indicate the direction of blood flow.

    Arteriolar

3. Draw a venous bifurcation. Use arrows to indicate the direction of blood flow.

    Venous

4. Distinguish between the blood flow in an arteriole and a capillary.

    _____

    _____

5. Describe the blood flow within capillaries. _____

    _____

6. Describe the observed effects of histamine. _____

    _____

    _____

7. Describe the observed effects of epinephrine. _____

    _____

    _____

Analysis and Application: (Frog Microcirculation) Name _____

1. Define arteries and veins on the basis of blood flow relative to a capillary plexus.

2. Explain, on the basis of physical principles, the different blood flow rates in arterioles, capillaries and venules.

3. Can you distinguish arteries and veins on the basis of blood flow at a bifurcation? Explain in words or with a drawing.

4. How does the diameter of a capillary compare with that of a RBC?

5. Histamine is released as part of the inflammatory response. What is its observed vasomotor effect and how is it beneficial in the event of infection or injury?

6. How might an adrenergic agent like dopamine or epinephrine be useful in the treatment of circulatory shock?

7. Draw and label a simple diagram which illustrates the principal routes of microcirculation.

Part 2: Cardiac Physiology

Having studied the electrical events which comprise the cardiac cycle and which contribute to an electrocardiogram tracing, you are now prepared to observe some of the various factors which can influence the strength and rate of cardiac contraction. The turtle is an excellent study specimen to illustrate some of these effects. A demonstration of selected aspects of cardiac physiology using a prepared turtle heart has been videorecorded and will be shown. Students are expected to answer the questions included below.

This video, titled "Turtle Heart Physiology" by S. Drogo and R. Jubenville can also be found at the end of the "Endocrine System Anatomy and Histology" video which is on open reserve in the Library.

Analysis and Application: (Cardiac Physiology)   Name _____

1. What is the expected effect of epinephrine administration on cardiac activity?

   _____

   _____

2. Describe the effect of acetylcholine administration on the rate and strength of cardiac contraction.
   Rate: _____

   Strength: _____

3. Various procedures performed in the hospital setting (eg. suctioning mucous from the lungs) may result in mechanical stimulation of a branch of the vagus nerve. With this in mind, what possible adverse effects might a clinician anticipate during such a procedure?

   _____

   _____

4. When sympathetic impulses predominate over those of the parasympathetic division, what change in cardiac activity would you anticipate?

   _____

5. How would severing the vagus nerve affect the strength and rate of cardiac contraction?
   Rate: _____

   Strength: _____

6. How will the heart respond if stimulated during its refractory period?

   _____

   _____

Exercise P-6

Respiratory Physiology-1:
Spirometry

Part 1: Spirometry: Pulmonary Volumes and Capacities

Several rather important features concerning respiration may be discerned by observation of one's own quiet breathing. A fairly constant volume of air is exchanged during each respiratory cycle but, as quiet respiration continues over a period of time, there is an occasional sigh. It is therefore apparent that we are capable of inhaling more air than is contained in a normal inspiration. We also observe that more air can be exhaled after the completion of a normal quiet expiration. The simple experiment of thumping on the chest after a maximal expiration produces a sound which indicates that even though as much air as possible has been exhaled, there still remains a definite volume of air within the thoracic cavity. And certainly we have all "had the wind knocked out of us" when our chest is unexpectedly compressed as a result of a fall.

These simple observations allow us to divide the total amount of air one's lungs can possibly contain into four definite and mutually exclusive functional volumes. Note: By "functional" volumes we mean that there does not exist a distinct anatomical structure that contains just that specific amount of air. Rather it indicates a specific amount of air that can be measured during various breathing maneuvers.

These volumes are defined as follows:

1. Tidal volume (TV or V_T) - the amount of air inspired or expired during a normal quiet respiratory cycle.

2. Inspiratory reserve volume (IRV) - the amount of air which can be inspired above and beyond that which is inspired during a normal quiet inspiration (the maximum volume that can be inhaled from the normal end-inspiratory point).

3. Expiratory reserve volume (ERV) - the maximal amount of air which may be expired following a normal quiet expiration (the maximum volume that can be exhaled from the normal end-expiratory point).

4. Residual volume (RV) - the amount of air remaining in the lungs after a maximal expiratory effort.

In addition to these four volumes which <u>do not overlap</u>, there are four (functional) capacities, each of which is made up of two or more of these volumes. They are:

1. Total lung capacity (TLC) - the amount of air contained in the lungs at the end of a maximal inspiration (TLC = IRV + TV + ERV + RV).

2. Vital capacity (VC) - the maximal amount of air which can be exhaled after a maximal inspiration (VC = IRV + TV + ERV).

3. Functional residual capacity (FRC) - the amount of air remaining in the lungs after a normal expiration (FRC = ERV + RV).

4. Inspiratory capacity (IC) - the maximal amount of air which can be inspired after a normal expiration (IC = IRV + TV).

All of these volumes and capacities are depicted in figure 1 below.

Figure 1: Lung Compartments

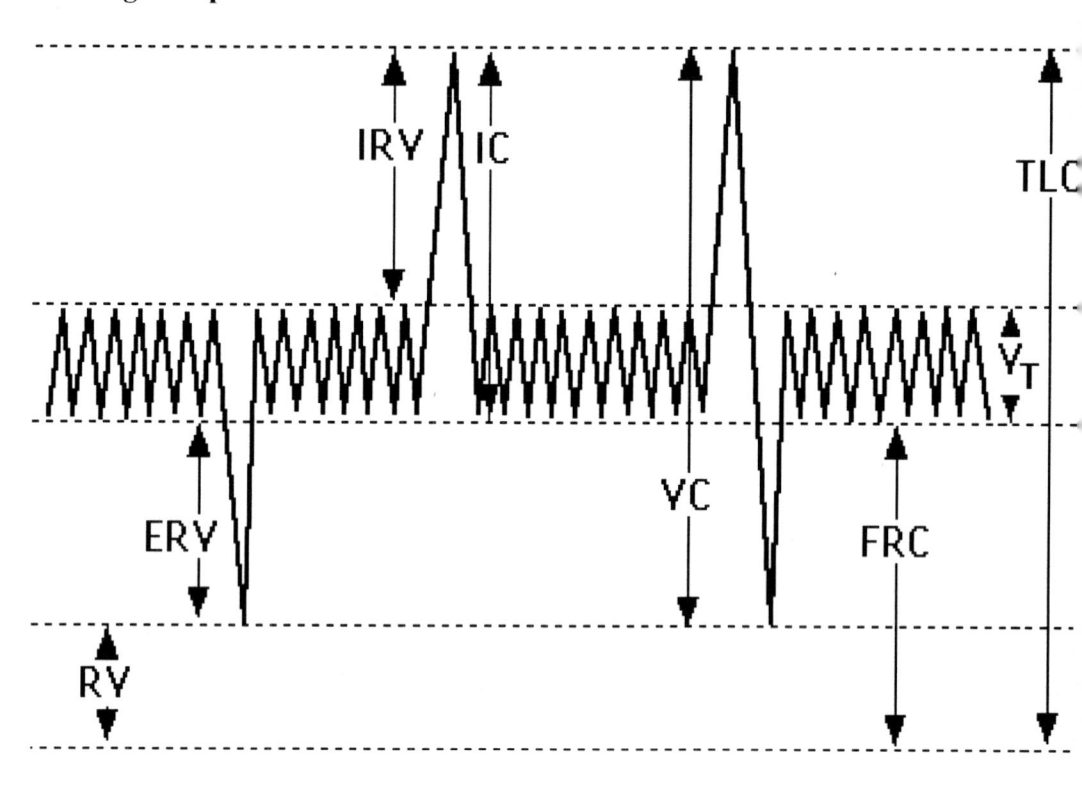

Several disease states will alter these volumes and capacities. However, the usual variation from one individual to another makes small deviations from the normal of little significance. The principal value of these pulmonary measurements lies in following changes caused either by disease or by therapy in an individual over time.

The purpose of the following experimental procedures is to demonstrate the measurement of those pulmonary volumes and capacities which may be obtained by direct spirometry, to demonstrate the variation in these volumes in a normal group of individuals, and further, to demonstrate the effect of different postures on pulmonary volumes.

A. Apparatus:
For this demonstration, we can utilize either an older Collins water-sealed spirometer or a newer pneumotachometer which is part of a computerized system.

1. Water-Sealed Spirometer
   The water-sealed spirometer is a relatively simple apparatus. A very lightweight bell floats in a drum filled with water. A large bore tube connects the air space beneath the bell with a mouthpiece. The bell is calibrated so that gas volume changes during inspiration and expiration are measured by the vertical distance the bell moves. The bell is counterweighted to avoid compression of the gas and to reduce the respiratory effort of the subject breathing into the spirometer. An internal blower also greatly reduces the effort required of the subject and insures a one-way gas flow pattern during use. This reduces the likelihood that exhaled air will be rebreathed and makes breathing through this system essentially effortless and surprisingly comfortable. An internal cannister filled with absorbent barium carbonate granules scrubs the carbon dioxide from the system during use and allows a subject to remain attached for several minutes with no discomfort or artificial change in breathing pattern due to CO_2 stimulation.

   The spirometer has two recording pens and a rotating drum with chart paper calibrated in 50 or 100 milliliter increments (depending on the size of the bell used). The respirometer pen deflects upward with each inspiration and downward with each expiration. A second ventilograph pen only moves upward in discrete steps with each inspiration. The excursion of this pen is 1/25th that of the respiration pen and provides an easy means for summing the total volumes inhaled over time (ie. per minute).

   Tidal volume, inspiratory reserve volume, expiratory reserve volume, inspiratory capacity and vital capacity can be determined by conventional spirometry and will be determined in today's exercise. Since residual volume represents air which cannot be exhaled, it must be determined indirectly by methods beyond the scope of this exercise.

2. Pneumotachometer
   A pneumotachometer is an electronic device that directly measures air flowrates. Such devices can electronically derive volumes from this input. The flow sensor is a simple looking, hand-held device. It is essentially a tube with a fine mesh screen in the middle. When air moves through the tube, there is a pressure differential created that is analyzed to yield the flowrate of the gas moving through the device. When this data is input to the computer, volumes are determined. It is an extremely convenient means to determine simple exhaled volumes, such as tidal volume, vital capacity, inspiratory reserve volume, and expiratory reserve volume.

Because the data which is obtained is analyzed by computer, the potential for very precise measurement of pulmonary parameters is much greater than is the case with the older water-sealed device. Assuming the pneumotach is accurately calibrated, accurate volumes with precise time references, accumulated inhaled and exhaled volumes (ie. minute volumes), and instantaneous flowrates are easily obtainable. Pneumotachs can also be adapted for use during exercise by addition of a heater that reduces or eliminates any condensation on the screen and maintains the accuracy of the measurements.

B. Demonstration:

Because oxygen utilization data is needed for the estimation of metabolic rate later in the exercise, the water-sealed device will be used first to obtain a tracing of 4-5 minutes of quiet breathing. Toward the end of the trial, a slow vital capacity maneuver will be performed. For comparison purposes and for separate analysis, a forced (fast) vital capacity maneuver will also be performed. Later in the session, the pneumotach will be used to determine both slow and forced vital capacities and peak inspiratory and expiratory flowrates.

1. Water-Sealed Spirometer Demonstration

A student volunteer serves as the subject. A cleaned and disinfected rubber mouthpiece is connected to the free-breathing valve which is in the off position (marker dots are aligned vertically). The subject is first seated and then connected to the apparatus. He/she is instructed to bite firmly on the internal block of the mouthpiece and to keep his/her lips sealed tightly throughout the entire exercise. A nose clamp is applied such that the subject is unable to inhale at all through the nose.

The kymograph (recording drum) motor is turned on with the speed selector in the slow position (one full minute for the pen to cross two consecutive vertical time lines on the recording paper). The free-breathing valve is opened so that the subject can breathe through the bell system. A normal recording of quiet respiration is made for approximately 5 minutes or until an adequate reference baseline of normal respiration is obtained. Both the bell pen and the ventilograph pen should be recording.

After obtaining a record of normal quiet respiration, the subject is instructed to inhale as deeply as possible, and immediately exhale as completely as possible (slow vital capacity), extending the exhalation to expel every bit of air possible. Both the inhalation and exhalation should be slow, steady and maximal efforts. These maneuvers should not be done quickly. The subject is then directed to resume normal quiet breathing. The slow vital capacity maneuver (SVC or VC) may be repeated once or twice.

From the resulting spirograms, tidal volume, expiratory reserve volume, inspiratory capacity, and vital capacity are determined. Using the stairstep ventilograph tracing, it is also possible to calculate minute ventilation. Dividing this value by breathing rate will yield average tidal volume. Examples of spirograms/ventilograms obtained from actual subjects using this water-sealed apparatus are included following these directions (figures 2, 3 & 4).

To illustrate the influence of posture on lung compartments, the slow vital capacity maneuver can be repeated with the subject first in the standing position, then while sitting, and lastly in the recumbent (supine) position.

Because volumes of gases are affected by temperature, pressure and the presence of water vapor, volumes of gases in the lungs must be corrected to reflect these influences. Lung volumes are reported at body temperature and pressure, saturated (BTPS). A list of BTPS conversion factors is included below (Table 1). Values obtained in this way can then be compared to expected normal values for individuals of the same age, sex and height. Selected nomograms and tables for this purpose are available in the lab. Percent predicted values are then computed by dividing the actual measurement by the predicted value. In general, lung volumes that are at least 70% of predicted are considered clinically acceptable.

Table 1: Gas Volume Conversion Factors (ATPS to BTPS)

BTPS Factor	Gas Temp (°C)	Water Vapor Pressure (mm Hg)
1.102	20	17.5
1.096	21	18.7
1.091	22	19.8
1.085	23	21.1
1.080	24	22.4
1.075	25	23.8
1.068	26	25.2
1.063	27	26.7
1.057	28	28.3
1.051	29	30.0

Note: ATPS means ambient temperature and pressure, saturated with water vapor.

BTPS means body temperature and pressure, saturated with water vapor.

Figure 2: Spirogram-1

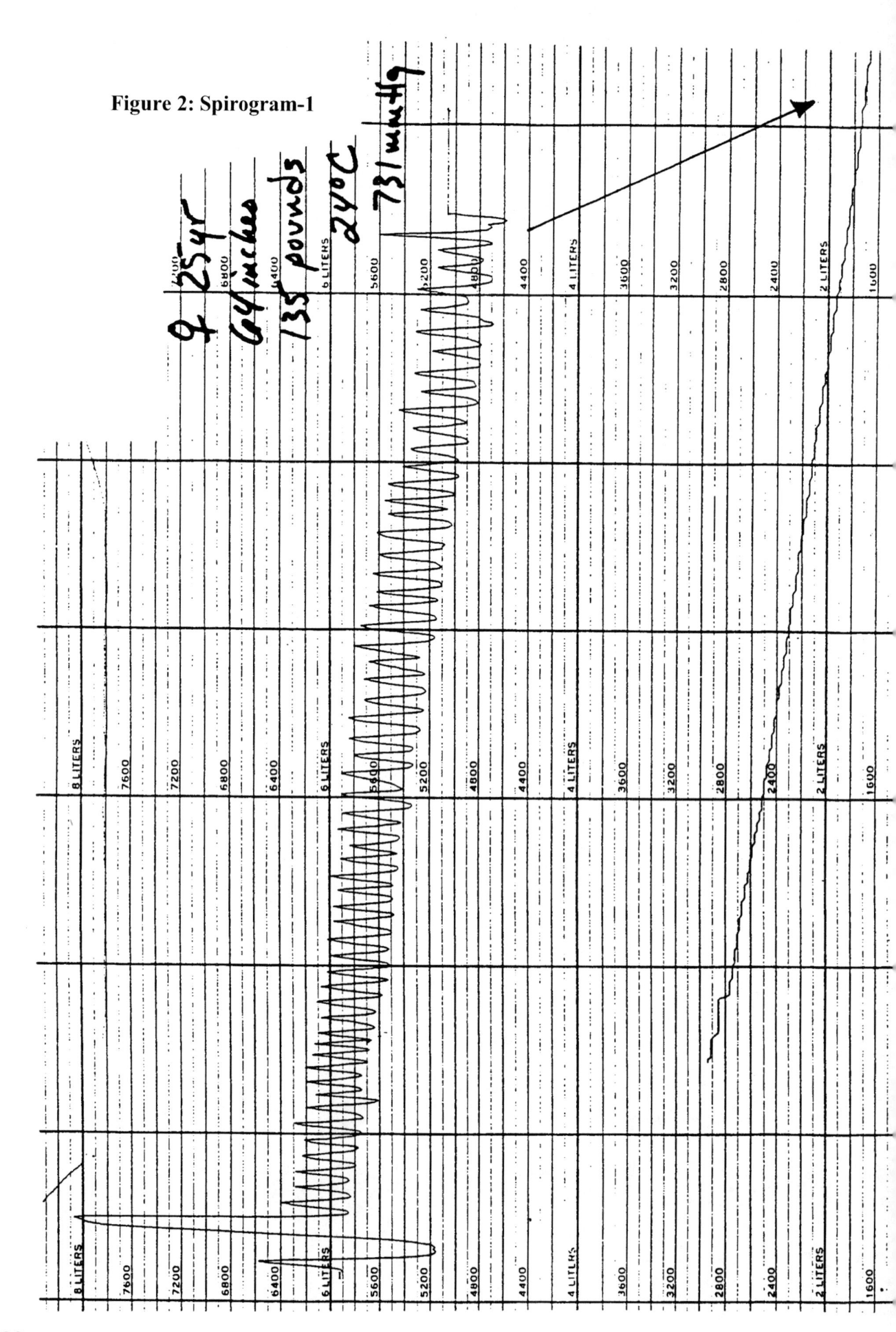

Figure 3: Spirogram-2

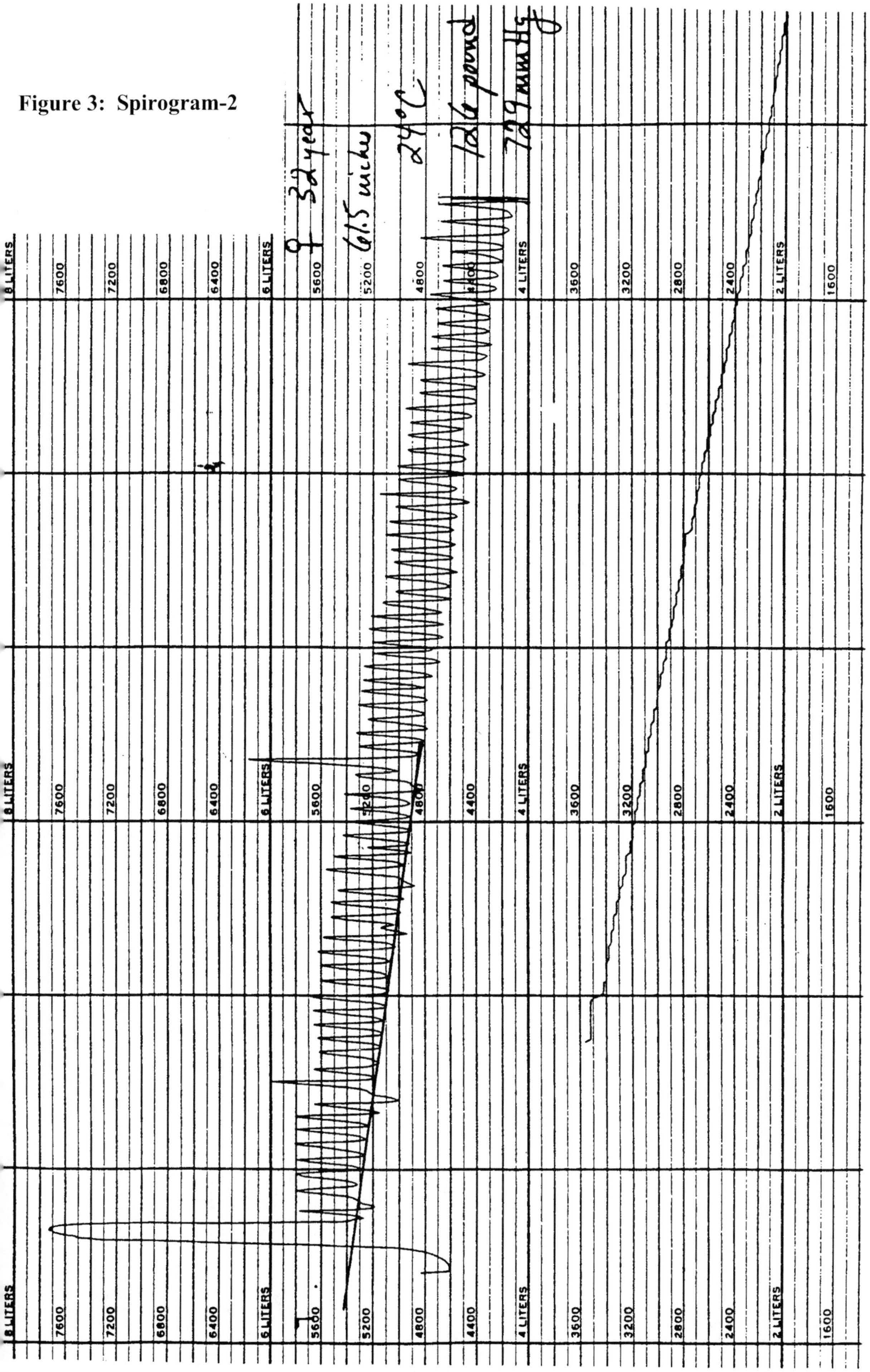

Figure 4: Spirogram-3

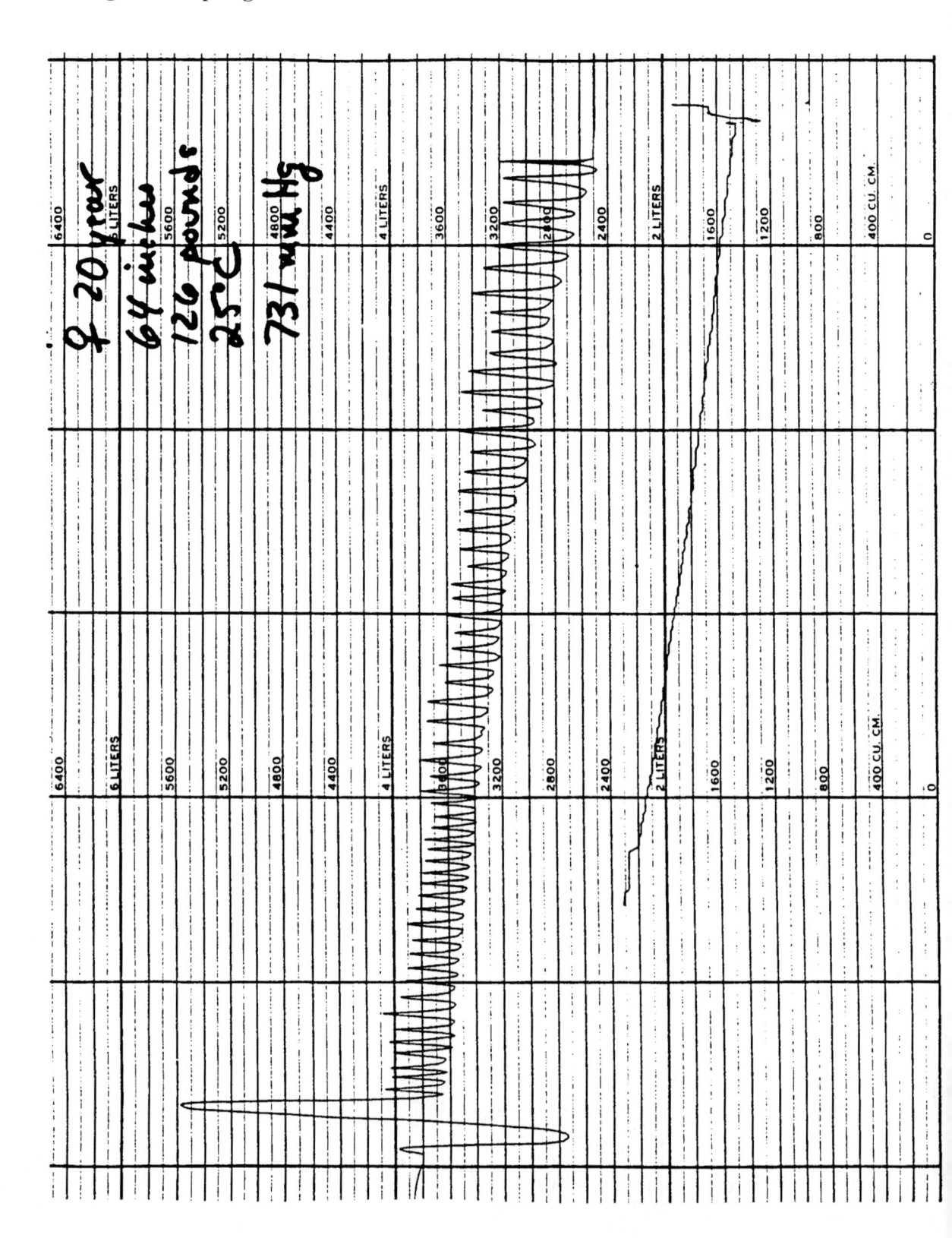

Results: (Spirometry)   Name _____
(expressed in liters)

	Predicted Value	Actual Value (Standing)	Actual Value (Seated)	Actual Value (Recumbent)
Minute Volume	_____	########	_____	########
Breathing Rate (bpm)	_____	########	_____	########
Average Tidal Volume	_____	########	_____	########
Inspiratory Reserve	_____	_____	_____	_____
Expiratory Reserve	_____	_____	_____	_____
Inspiratory Capacity	_____	_____	_____	_____
Vital Capacity	_____	_____	_____	_____

Analysis and Application: (Spirometry)

1. How does the data recorded compare with normal values?

   _____
   _____
   _____
   _____

2. Did postural alterations change the vital capacity obtained? Yes / No
   If yes, how so? Please explain why.
   _____
   _____
   _____

3. What is the function of the FRC? _____
   _____
   _____

Part 2: The Forced Vital Capacity Maneuver (Optional: May be assigned or demonstrated by individual instructors)

Clinical evaluation of respiratory function generally includes an evaluation of a forced, maximal expiratory maneuver (forced vital capacity). Many individuals with varying degrees of respiratory impairment will be able to move relatively normal volumes of air during breathing if given enough time to do so. A forced maneuver creates very significant and abrupt thoracic and airway pressure changes which accentuate the natural tendency of airways to narrow during exhalation. Flow restrictions not apparent during quiet breathing can be identified during forceful exhalation. Increased airway narrowing and/or collapse will be indicated by lower total exhaled volumes (FVC) and a lower exhaled volume in the first second of exhalation (FEV1). The FEV1 can then be compared to the FVC and the volume of the full exhalation that was able to be exhaled in the first second can be expressed as a percentage (FEV1/FVC%). Generally individuals with clinically normal lung function can exhale better than 70% of their FVC in the first second of a forced, maximal maneuver. The subject's cooperation and full effort are essential components of the test.

1. FVC Procedure with Water-Sealed Spirometer
   For this test the soda lime cannister for absorbing CO_2 is removed, a simple tubular cardboard mouthpiece replaces the rubber device used earlier and there is no need to prefill the system with oxygen. Before the test, the bell system is flushed with room air by gently moving the bell up and down several times with the free breathing valve in the "on" position. A true maximal effort is most likely with the subject standing. With a noseclip in place, the subject is instructed to take one or two normal breaths before a maximal inhalation which is held just long enough for the operator to switch the recording drum speed to fast (1 second between consecutive time lines). Once switched, the subject exhales as fast and strongly as possible and continues to push out every bit of air that he/she can. The forced exhalation should last at least 5-6 seconds with the operator actively encouraging the subject throughout the maneuver. Representative FVC tracings are shown in figures 5 and 6. The start and the 1-second point in each forced exhalation is indicated. Your instructor will instruct you in their analysis.

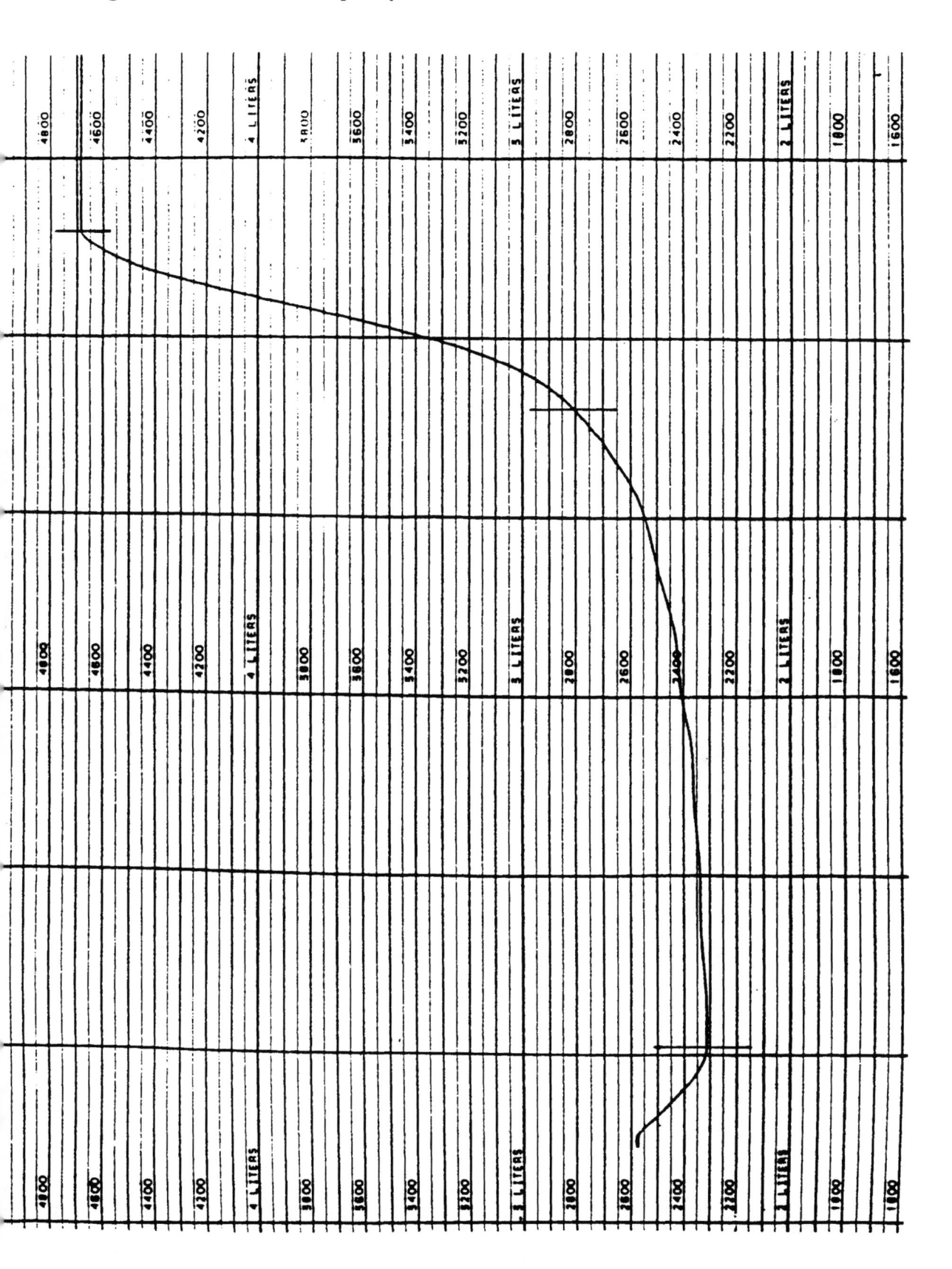

Figure 5: Forced Vital Capacity-1

Figure 6: Forced Vital Capacity-2

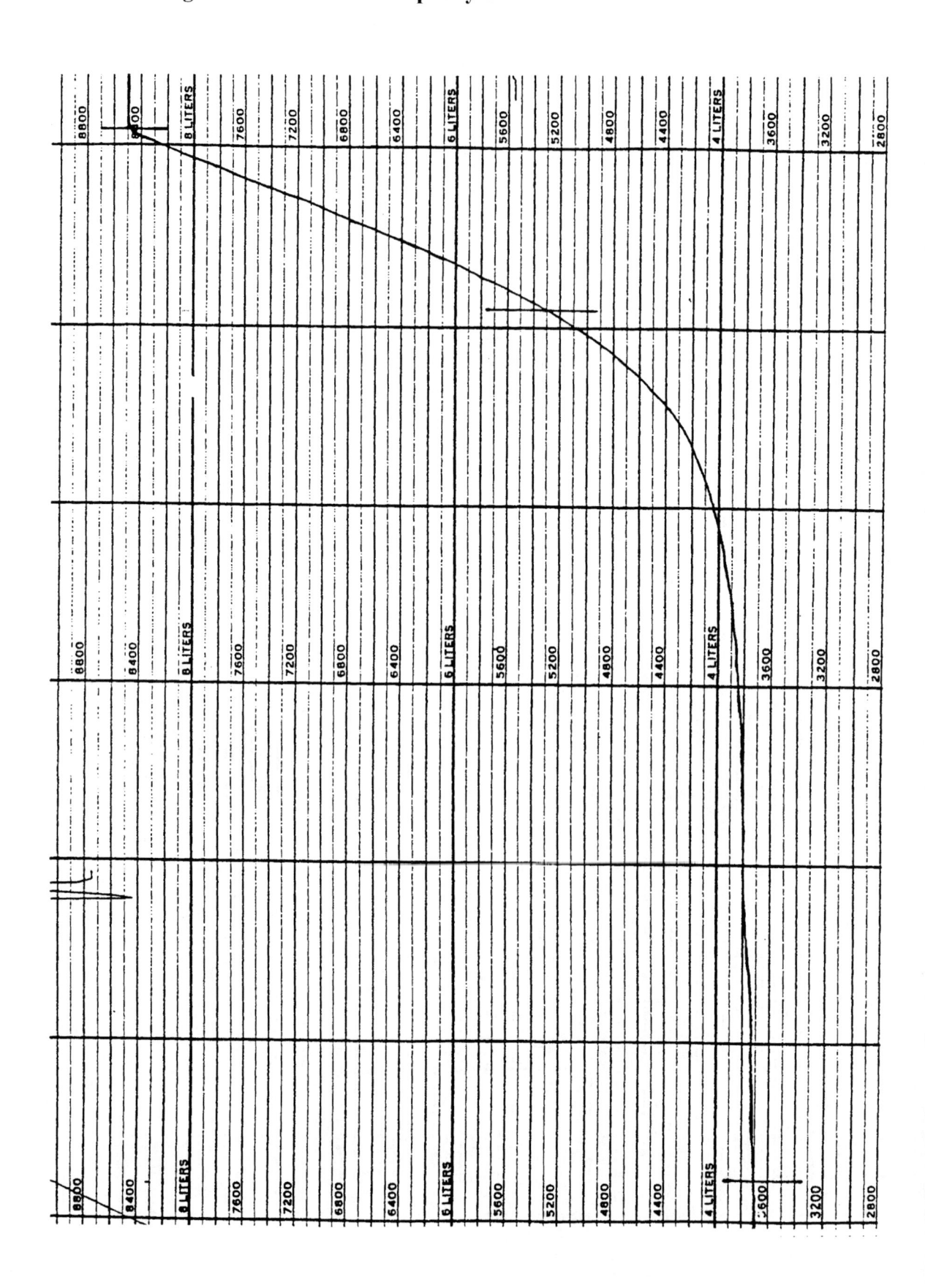

2. FVC Procedure with Pneumotachometer

The FVC maneuver with the pneumotach is actually a rapid maximal inspiration followed quickly by a forced maximal exhalation. Again the subject has a noseclip in place and stands when performing the test. The subject fits the cardboard mouthpiece tightly in his/her mouth and, when told by the instructor, inhales and exhales quickly and maximally as previously described. At the same time, the operator activates the computer and the subject's effort is recorded. Just as with the water-sealed spirometer, the operator encourages the subject to squeeze out every last bit of air. In this instance a flow-volume loop is obtained from which FVC, FEV_1, peak inspiratory and peak expiratory flowrates are readily determined. Sample tracings are shown in figure 7 following.

Figure 7: Flow and Volume Curves

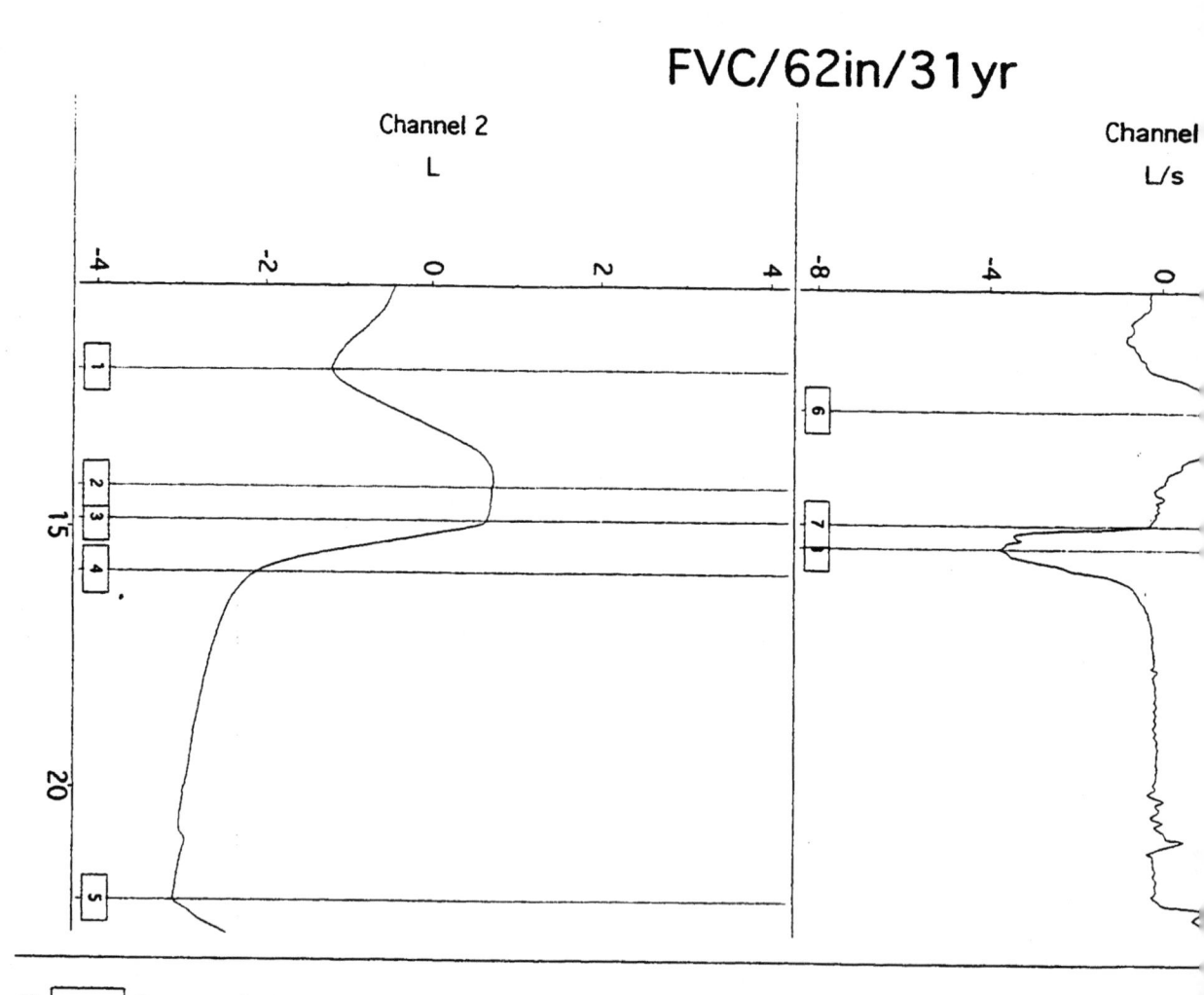

2	1	Start of deep inspiration
1	6	Peak Inspiratory flow (1.36 L/sec)
2	2	Peak inflation
2	3	Start of forced exhalation
1	7	Start of forced exhalation
1	8	Peak expiratory flow (3.71 L/sec) at .5 seconds
2	4	FEV1 (2.75 liters)
2	5	End of FVC maneuver (3.73 liters)

Exercise P-7

Respiratory Physiology-2:
Respirometry

Measuring Metabolic Rates

The energy which the body derives from food and utilizes for its life processes eventually becomes heat. Thus, if a measure of the heat liberated by the body can be made, the energy obtained from foodstuffs may be determined. The result of such a measurement is called the metabolic rate and is expressed as Calories (kilocalories or 1000 calories).

Any factor which alters the rate of energy production by metabolic processes also alters the rate of heat output by the body. The normal daily activities are reflected by alterations in the rate of metabolism. Increased adrenaline in the circulating blood from increased sympathetic nervous system activity will cause the metabolism of most tissues of the body to increase. Changes in environmental and body temperature alter metabolic rate. Even the process of digesting food itself, in particular the digestion of proteins, increases the rate of metabolism.

Perhaps the most common disease associated with increased metabolic rates is hyperthyroidism. Thyroid hormone increases the rate of metabolism of all cells of the body. If very excessive amounts of thyroid hormone are present, the metabolic rate may increase by as much as 200%.

In view of the many things which can affect metabolic rate, measurement of metabolism will be of little value unless it is done under extremely well-controlled conditions, such as are required for determining the basal metabolic rate (BMR). These conditions require that the subject:

1) shall not have performed any strenuous exercise within the past 8 to 12 hours;

2) has been resting quietly in a reclining position for the previous 30 minutes to 1 hour;

3) is at complete mental rest;

4) is in surroundings that are quiet and at a comfortable ambient temperature;

5) has not eaten any food within the past 12 hours; and

6) has a normal body temperature.

Total body calorimeters which directly measure the caloric output of the body are rather expensive and complicated instruments. Therefore, the BMR is usually measured by indirect means. The final products of metabolism of all nutrient inputs of the body (carbohydrate, fat, and protein) result in the production of heat, water, and carbon dioxide. Oxygen is required for the combustion of these nutrient sources of energy. The metabolizing cells remove from the available oxygen supply in the blood and tissue fluids only that amount of oxygen required by their existing rates of metabolism. Furthermore, the lungs remove only that amount of oxygen from the inspired air which is necessary to resaturate the hemoglobin of arterial blood. Thus, the amount of oxygen consumed (the difference in oxygen content of the inspired and expired air) is directly related to the rate at which nutrient substances are being converted into heat.

The relationship between the heat liberated and the amount of oxygen utilized during the complete conversion of carbohydrate into water and carbon dioxide (the Caloric rate for carbohydrate) is 5.05 Calories per liter of oxygen. The Caloric rate for proteins is 4.6 Calories per liter of oxygen, and that for fat is 4.70 Calories per liter of oxygen consumed. The Caloric rate for an average mixed or balanced diet is 4.825 Calories per liter of oxygen consumed. Thus, the metabolic rate may be calculated (estimated) from a measurement of oxygen consumption.

Since individuals vary greatly in body size and mass and therefore have varying abilities to produce and liberate heat, some type of adjustment or normalization must be made if comparisons of metabolic rates amount different persons are to be made. It has been found that basal metabolic rate is closely related to the body surface area. Therefore, the BMR is expressed as Calories per square meter of body surface area per hour ($C/m^2/hr$). Body surface area is determined by height and weight and may be obtained from the DuBois nomogram which is available in the lab.

The basal metabolic rate is usually reported as a positive or a negative percent deviation from normal for a member of a particular sex and age group. Percent deviation from normal is calculated using the formula on the following page.

$$BMR(+/-\%) = \frac{\text{measured value - predicted normal}}{\text{predicted normal}} \times 100$$

If the measured value is less than the normal value, the BMR is expressed with a minus sign. If the measured value exceeds the normal value, the BMR is expressed with a plus sign. For example, a hypothyroid individual may have a BMR of -15%, while a hyperthyroid individual may have a BMR that equals +50% or more.

1. BMR Procedure with the water-sealed respirometer:
   The subject should meet the criteria listed for establishing a basal metabolic state. During the final 5 minutes of recumbent rest prior to recording the test, a cleaned and disinfected rubber mouthpiece is connected to the free-breathing valve which is in the off position. The subject is then connected to the apparatus. He/she is instructed to bite firmly on the internal block of the mouthpiece and to keep his/her lips sealed tightly throughout the entire exercise. A nose clamp is applied and tightened such that the subject is unable to inhale at all through the nose. Any

detected leaks are corrected. While the subject is resting, the instrument is prepared for recording. (Usually, since the was able to breathe comfortably for at least 5 minutes during the earlier exercise, the tracing which was obtained is used to determine basal metabolic rate.)

Allow the subject to breathe atmospheric air for approximately 5 minutes (valve in the off position), then start the kymograph motor at slow speed. Turn the free-breathing valve to connect the subject to the respirometer system and record the subject's breathing activity for approximately 5 minutes. Observe the subject's breathing and the excursions of the respirometer recording pen. It will be noted that the recording pen rises and falls during inspiration and expiration respectively and that as oxygen is utilized, there is a continuous rise in the tidal volume, end-expiratory base line. The bottoms of the recorded excursions (end-expiratory points) tend to be more constant in their placement along a slope line than the tops of the individual tidal air excursions. During the first minutes of the test, the rate of oxygen consumption will generally not be that of basal conditions, as the subject is adjusting himself both to the apparatus and to breathing pure oxygen rather than air. However, after 2 to 4 minutes, the bottoms of the tidal air excursions should assume a more constant upward slope. If this does not occur, there may be leaks in the system. The system should be checked and any leaks present corrected before proceeding further.

After a steady-state rate of oxygen consumption has been reached, a 4-minute record is obtained. The free breathing valve is again turned to the bypass position and the subject is disconnected from the respirometer. The instrument may then be readied for another test.

Included after this section are typical respirometer recordings from which the BMR can be computed (figures 8 and 9). A slope line (of best fit) is drawn along the bottom of the tidal air excursions. This line is extended over at least a 4-minute time period as indicated by the vertical time lines. The starting volume (the intersection of this slope line with the time line denoting the start of the 4-minute period) is read on the horizontal scale. The final volume is found in a similar fashion. The difference between these two volumes is the oxygen consumed over the 4-minute period. This value, multiplied by 15, yields oxygen consumption per hour.

Since both the temperature of a gas and the pressure to which it is exposed can affect the volume of a gas, both of these variables are monitored. The temperature of the gases in the bell system is read from the respirometer thermometer, and the barometric pressure is read from the laboratory barometer. Also since the exhaled gases are saturated with water vapor, the volume must also be corrected for water vapor pressure. The volume of oxygen consumed per hour is corrected to standard conditions (STPD) according to the formula shown on the data sheets. The corrected value is then multiplied by the factor indicating the Calorie production per liter of oxygen (4.825) to obtain Calories produced per hour. This figure, divided by the subject's surface area (meters^2), yields the BMR expressed as C/m^2/hr. Nomograms are available in lab to allow determination of heat production and the subject's metabolic rate as a percent deviation from predicted BMR.

The data grid shown below is arranged to facilitate the step by step calculation of BMR. The calculations have been written into a spreadsheet which the instructor will project onto a screen for all to see. The calculations therefore need not be done by hand.

Oxygen Consumption / Metabolic Rate Determination

Subject		Units	Explanation
Height		centimeters	
Weight		kilograms	
Age		years	
Sex		male or female	
Spirometer Volume @ time 4		liters	From tracing - exhalation baseline
Spirometer Volume @ time 0		liters	From tracing - exhalation baseline
O$_2$ used per 4 min		liters/4 min	(O$_2$ used @ t$_4$) - (O$_2$ used @ t$_0$)
O$_2$ used per hour		liters/hour	(O$_2$ used per 4 min) X 15
Pressure (mm Hg)		mm Hg	Lab barometer
Temperature (°C)		° Celsius	From spirometer thermometer
H$_2$O vapor pressure (mm Hg)		mm Hg	From lab or reference
O$_2$ used @ STPD		liters/hour	Gas law conversion to STPD
Heat Production/Hour		Cal/hour	4.826 Cal/liter O$_2$ (mixed diet)
Body Surface Area		square meters	From Dubois nomogram
Actual Metabolic Rate		Cal/msq/hour	Cal/hour adjusted to BSA
Predicted Metabolic Rate		Cal/msq/hour	From nomogram (Consolazio)
BMR (% variation)		percent	Actual MR/Predicted BMR -100

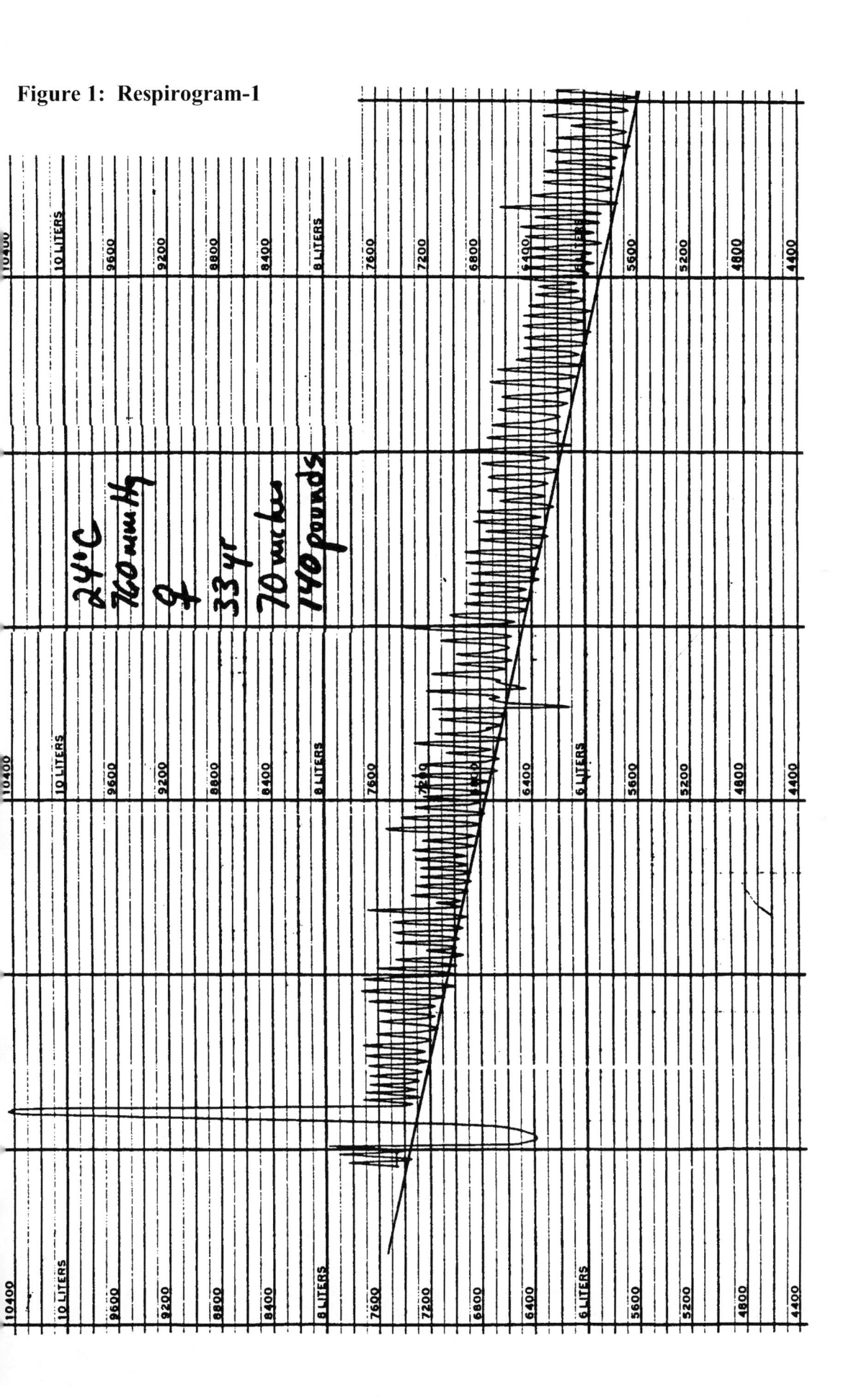

Figure 1: Respirogram-1

Figure 2: Respirogram-2

Analysis and Application: (Respirometry)   Name _____

1. How does the rate of heat loss change if body surface area increases?

   _____

   How does this affect metabolic rate? _____

2. What is the effect of recent exercise on the metabolic rate?

   _____

3. List at least five possible sources of error in the indirect method used in lab to determine basal metabolic rate.

   _____

   _____

   _____

   _____

4. Why should the subject be in a post-digestive state before a BMR is measured?

   _____

   _____

5. List two diseases in which abnormal BMR values would be expected. Indicate how each affects BMR.

   _____

   _____

   _____

   _____

Exercise P-8

Physiology of Systemic Circulation: Part 3
Measurement of Blood Pressure, Heart Rate and (Breathing Rate)

Part 3: Blood Pressure, Heart Rate and (Breathing Rate)

Each time the heart beats, it forces a volume of blood into the aorta. This <u>periodic</u> entry of blood into the arterial system causes the pressure within the arteries to rise and fall. The peak pressure obtained during each cardiac cycle is the systolic pressure (occurring when the ventricles contract), while the lowest pressure reached just before the next heartbeat is the diastolic pressure (occurring when the ventricles are filling). These pulsations are transmitted throughout the arterial vascular system.

Occasionally, however, if the heart beats too soon after the preceding heartbeat, the volume of blood ejected into the aorta is not sufficient to produce a detectable pulse in the radial artery in the wrist. Such pulse deficits cause a difference between determinations of heart rate by electrocardiography or listening to the heart sounds and the pulse rate palpated at a peripheral vessel site.

The strength of the arterial pulse transmitted to the peripheral arteries depends upon both the amount of blood ejected into the aorta by a heartbeat and the distensibility of the arterial vascular system. Thus, if the arteries are dilated and allow a fast runoff of the blood, diastolic pressure may be low, while systolic pressure remains relatively unchanged. This produces a wide pulse pressure (difference between systolic and diastolic pressures). When palpated at the radial artery, this wide pulse pressure yields a very strong pulsation, described as bounding. On the other hand, if the arteries are tightly constricted, the systolic pressure may rise higher than normal; but diastolic pressure will also remain higher than normal, and the pulse pressure may be narrowed. The pulse in this instance yields a sensation that is short and sudden, often described as thready.

Arterial pressure depends upon the amount of blood forced into the aorta by the heart (cardiac output) and the resistance to flow offered by the peripheral vessels (total peripheral resistance). Cardiac output (liters/minute) is the product of the amount of blood pumped with each beat of the heart (stroke volume) and the number of beats per minute (heart rate). Stroke volume depends, to a large extent, upon the amount of blood available to fill the ventricles during diastole (venous return).

Methods and Observations:
The <u>direct</u> measurement of blood pressure is an invasive technique which involves sensors which are positioned within a blood vessel. Obviously this is impractical for routine measurements. For this reason, an indirect method which is based on the amount of pressure required to close off the flow of blood through the brachial artery is most commonly used. The brachial artery, located in the upper arm, lies close to the ventral surface of the humerus. The instrument used for the measurement of blood pressure by auscultation (using a stethoscope) is a sphygmomanometer.

A sphygmomanometer consists of:
1) a compression bag surrounded by an unyielding cuff for application of extra-arterial pressure;
2) a mercury manometer or pressure gauge by which the applied pressure is read (in mm Hg);
(3) a bulb for inflation of the cuff in order to create pressure in the system;
(4) a valve to release the air from the cuff; and
(5) tubing attachments for connecting the cuff to the manometer and the bulb.

1. To practice blood pressure, heart rate and breathing rate determinations, students should work in groups of three.

2. The subject should be seated, relaxed for a brief time, with his/her arm on a flat surface.

3. To determine the blood pressure by auscultation, wrap the cuff around the subject's arm, approximately one inch above the antecubital space (anterior elbow) with the arrow on the cuff positioned over the brachial artery which runs just medial to the midline. The cuff should fit snugly but not too tightly.

4. Palpate the brachial artery and place the stethoscope over the site where the brachial pulse is felt, just below the cuff. Neither the tubing nor the head of the stethoscope should touch the cuff since this will create sound artifact and make auscultation difficult. The stethoscope head should be applied to the arm firmly throughout the experiment but not so tightly that it compresses the brachial artery. No sound should be heard in the artery at this time. Verify this.

5. Pump air into the cuff until the mercury column or pressure reading on the gauge is 180-200 mm Hg. If the pressure is high enough, the brachial artery is compressed, and no sound should be heard through the stethoscope.

6. While listening through the stethoscope, release the pressure slowly by means of the valve on the bulb. The pressure should fall 2-3 mm per heartbeat. At some point as the pressure is being released, thumping sounds begin to be heard. These are known as Korotkoff sounds. These sounds are heard with each beat of the heart and indicate that blood is again flowing through the artery. The pressure at which these sounds are first heard is considered the systolic pressure. The height of the column of mercury or the pressure indicated on the gauge should be read <u>at this point</u>.

7. Continue reducing the pressure slowly and carefully. The sound first becomes louder, then dull and muffled, and finally ceases. The point of <u>complete cessation</u> of sound is taken as the diastolic pressure. If no cessation of sound occurs, the point of first muffling should be taken as the diastolic pressure. It should then be

recorded as the point of muffled sounds. (As a general rule, the muffling of sounds occurs 5 to 10 mm Hg above the point of sound cessation.

8. Rapidly release the pressure once the diastolic pressure is determined.

9. With blood pressure readings taken in this manner, a mean error of +/- 8 mm Hg may be expected in individual readings of systolic and diastolic pressure (the systolic pressure tends to be too low and the diastolic too high). A release of pressure that is too rapid makes it difficult to identify the systolic and diastolic pressures accurately. Variations in auditory acuity are also important causes of error. Errors are also likely to be obtained in subjects with unusually large or unusually small arms. In some such instances, the error may exceed 30 mm Hg.

10. Determine systolic and diastolic pressures two additional times. Allow two minutes between readings since, due to relaxation of arterial tone, the last readings may be lower than the previous ones. Record the values you obtain for systolic and diastolic pressures in the spaces below. Average them.

    Systolic   _____   _____   _____   _____ Avg

    Diastolic   _____   _____   _____   _____ Avg

11. Subtract the average diastolic pressure from the average systolic pressure to obtain pulse pressure and record it as well.

    Pulse pressure _____ mm Hg

12. Add 2 times the average diastolic pressure to the average systolic pressure and divide the sum by 3 to obtain the mean arterial pressure. Record it as well.

    Mean pressure _____ mm Hg

13. For determining pulse rate, the student should count beats at the radial artery for 15 seconds and multiply by 4. Record the reading below.

    Pulse Rate _____ bpm

14. For determining breathing rate, the student should count breaths for a full minute. Because breathing rate often changes when the subject is aware that breathing is being assessed, most clinicians palpate the wrist (as if taking a pulse) when counting breaths. Record your finding below.

    Breathing Rate _____ bpm

Compare the values you obtained with the standard textbook normal values shown below.

Normal Cardiovascular Values	
Pulse Rate	60-80 bpm
Blood Pressure	120/80 mm Hg
Pulse Pressure	40 mm Hg
Mean Arterial Pressure	93 mm Hg
(Breathing Rate)	~12-15 bpm

Note: There is considerable variation in heart rates in normal individuals, particularly in those is good cardiovascular health as a result of regular and vigorous aerobic exercise. In such individuals, heart rates well below the traditional low end of the normal range are common.

Exercise P-9
Physiology of Systemic Circulation: Part 4
Finger Plethysmography: Pulse Pressure Monitoring

Introduction
Measuring changes in the size of a body part as blood flow changes to that body part is called plethysmography. Finger plethysmography provides a convenient, non-invasive way of indirectly measuring blood flow to the periphery. A number of factors can influence peripheral circulation. This exercise investigates the effects of the following three factors on blood flow to the periphery:
1. Hand position relative to the heart and its impact on venous pressure
2. Body position and the movement of blood relative to capacitance vessels
3. The application of cold
4. Vessel occlusion via external pressure
5. Activity of respiratory muscles and increased thoracic pressure

Equipment
The equipment required for this exercise includes the following: the PowerLab 410 physiological data recording system, an infrared (IR) finger plethysmography transducer, an eMac with PowerLab software installed, and a USB cable connecting the eMac with the PowerLab unit.

Equipment Set-up
Use the USB cable to connect the PowerLab unit to one of the USB connections provided on the eMac.

Secure the infrared sensor to the middle or ring finger of the student volunteer. If the transducer is secured by a Velcro strap, position the transducer on the middle portion of the finger. If the transducer uses a spring clip, position the transducer over the tip of the finger. Plug the lead from the finger plethysmograph into recording Channel 2 of the PowerLab unit. There are two input sockets for recording Channel 2. Use the socket which corresponds to the plug on the plethysmograph and be sure to line up the plug correctly.

Recording
Now, turn on the PowerLab unit and start up the eMac. Once the eMac starts up and the desktop is established, move the mouse cursor to the left side of the screen and find the icon for the Chart software. This software controls the PowerLab. Double-click on the Chart software icon. The Chart software will start up and begin to communicate with the PowerLab unit. After a short time, you will be brought to a screen labeled "Experiments Gallery", Figure 1.

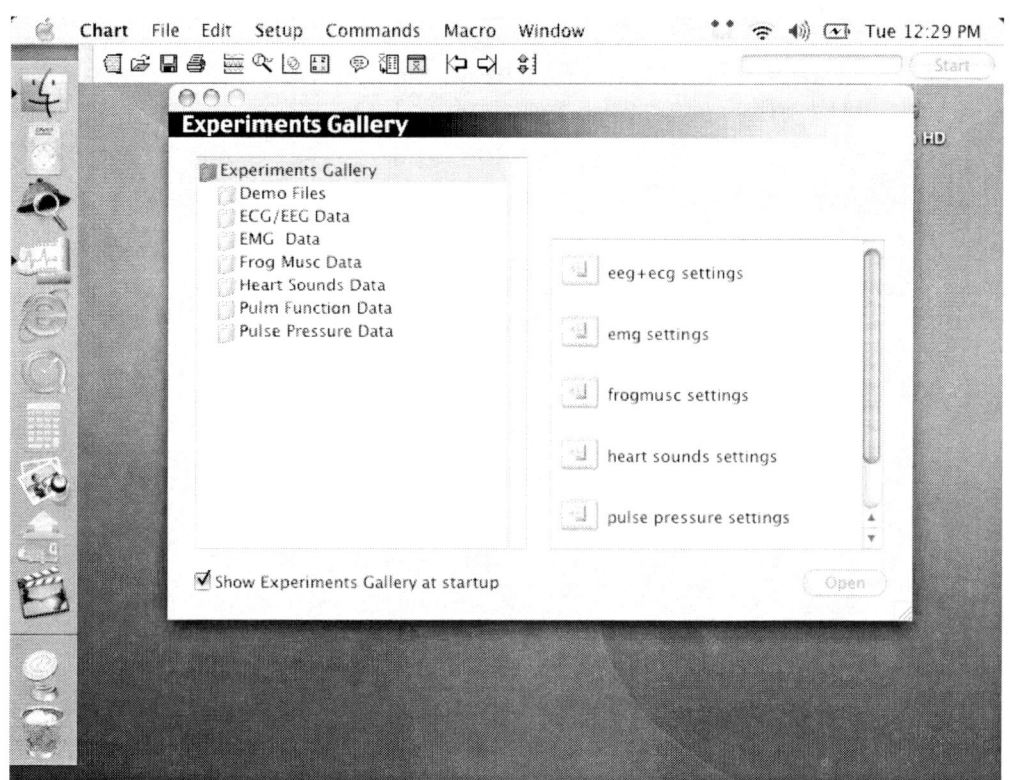

Figure 1

In this window, select the "pulse pressure settings" file. You will find this file along with a number of other settings files on the right side of the window in a small scrolling window. Double-click on this "pulse pressure settings" file. This will open an untitled settings window,

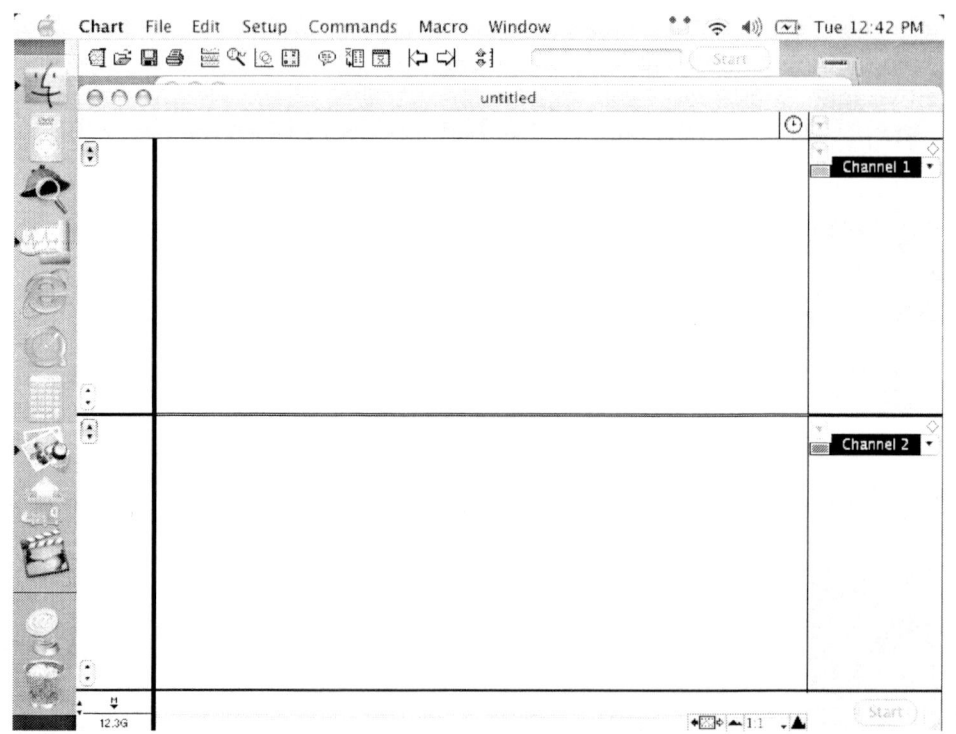

Figure 2.

At this point, it is a good idea to convert the settings file to a data file, Figure 3. Do this by going to the File menu choice at the top menu bar and selecting Save. The file name needs to be entered since the default file name is "untitled". Name your file "pulse" followed by the subject's name. Don't bother with quotation marks, commas, or spaces. Now save this file. It should be saved into the Documents folder of the home directory. To reopen this file at some future time to review today's results, you can access the home directory from the desktop by selecting the Go menu choice in the top menu bar.

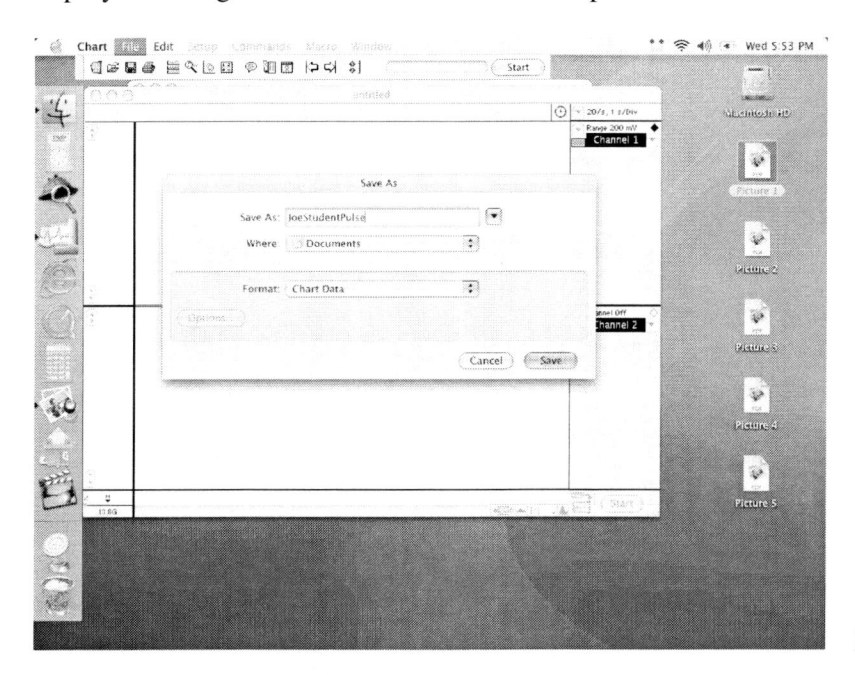

Figure 3

Once the file is saved, the recording window provided by the Chart software is renamed to match the file name, Figure 4.

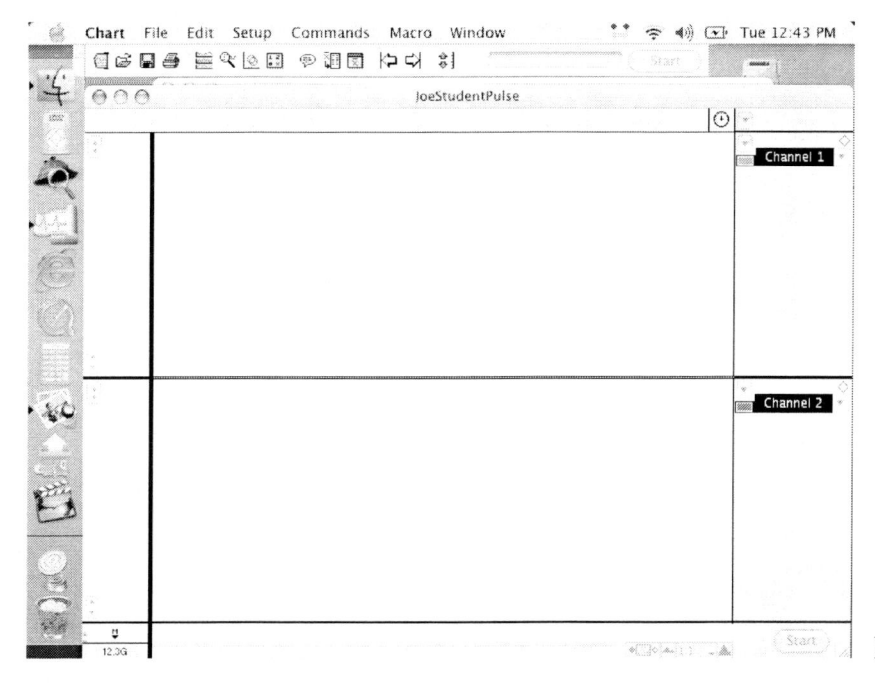

Figure 4

403

Have the subject sit comfortably and position the hand with the plethysmograph sensor at approximately the level of the heart. Click the Start button in the recording window. Record for eight to ten seconds and then click stop. If the subject is connected correctly, your tracing should look like this, Figure 5.

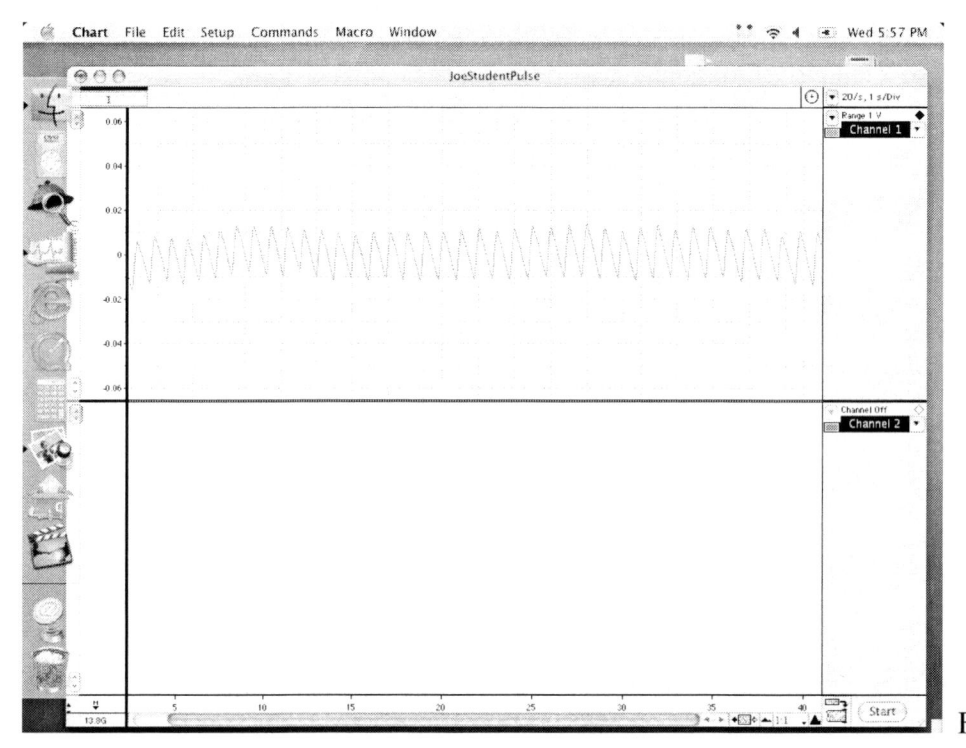

Figure 5

Although two channels are displayed, we are recording only on the top channel. If you don't get a tracing like Figure 5, check your connections. If your connections seem secure, check with your instructor.

Adding Comments
It is possible to add comments to a Chart window. This may be done as the tracing is being recorded or after the tracing has been recorded. To add a comment while recording, position the cursor over the channel where you wish to add the comment. Click and hit the return key. The comment will be added at the time of the return entry. To add a comment to an existing record, position the cursor at the point you wish to enter the comment, click and choose "Add Comment" from the Command menu in the Chart software. To add text into a comment or to edit a comment, use the Window menu in the Chart software and open the "Comments and Exclusions" window.

eMAC Printing
The eMac is set up to print to the HP printer in the A&P lab. In Chart, simply select the records you wish to print and select "Zoom Window" from the Window menu. The print commands are under the File menu. Select "Print Zoom" from the File menu to print the selected records. If you wish to print comments, open the "Comments and Exclusions" window under the Window menu and select "Print Comment"s from the File menu.

Saving Your Work
It is a good idea to save your work often. To save your Chart data, select "Save" from the File menu.

The Lab Exercise
In order to interpret the data which we collect during the various activities and maneuvers which are part of this exercise, we need to understand what the tracing provided through the finger plethysmograph is actually revealing. As you are well aware, the heart cycle consists of two phases: the systolic (heart contraction) portion and the diastolic (heart relaxation) portion. As a result, there is a pulsating quality to blood flow. We would expect that blood flow and finger volume would be greatest during systole and lowest during diastole. The wave-like nature of the tracing we have recorded is consistent with these expectations. Each wave peak corresponds to finger volume during systole and the trough of each wave corresponds to finger volume during diastole. Treatments or maneuvers we perform that change the amplitude (height) of the wave pattern need to be interpreted based on changes in finger volume related to this blood flow pattern. For example, restricting the blood supply to the finger should decrease the amplitude of the plethysmograph waveform. A similar result would be obtained if blood draining away from the finger were restricted and flow through capillary beds of the finger dropped. Restricting blood flow draining from the finger would cause blood to accumulate within that distal structure. As a result, the difference between systolic volume and diastolic finger volume would diminish.

Since each wave form present on the plethysmograph tracing corresponds to one heart cycle, the record obtained gives us a convenient way to measure heart rate as well. Therefore, it is also possible to determine the impact on heart rate of any of the maneuvers performed during this exercise. When our waves get closer together, it indicates that heart rate is increasing. Likewise, if waves get farther apart, it indicates a decrease in heart rate.

Figure 6 on the following page depicts a representative pulse plethysmograph tracing.

- A baseline tracing is first established.
- The subject then performs a maneuver anticipated to affect pulse pressure.
- A comment is inserted just before the subjects performs the maneuver. You can see that upon initiation of the maneuver, some movement-related artifact is introduced into the tracing.
- Following the maneuver, a regular tracing is reestablished that shows the effect of the treatment. In this case it is decreased pulse pressure with no change in rate.

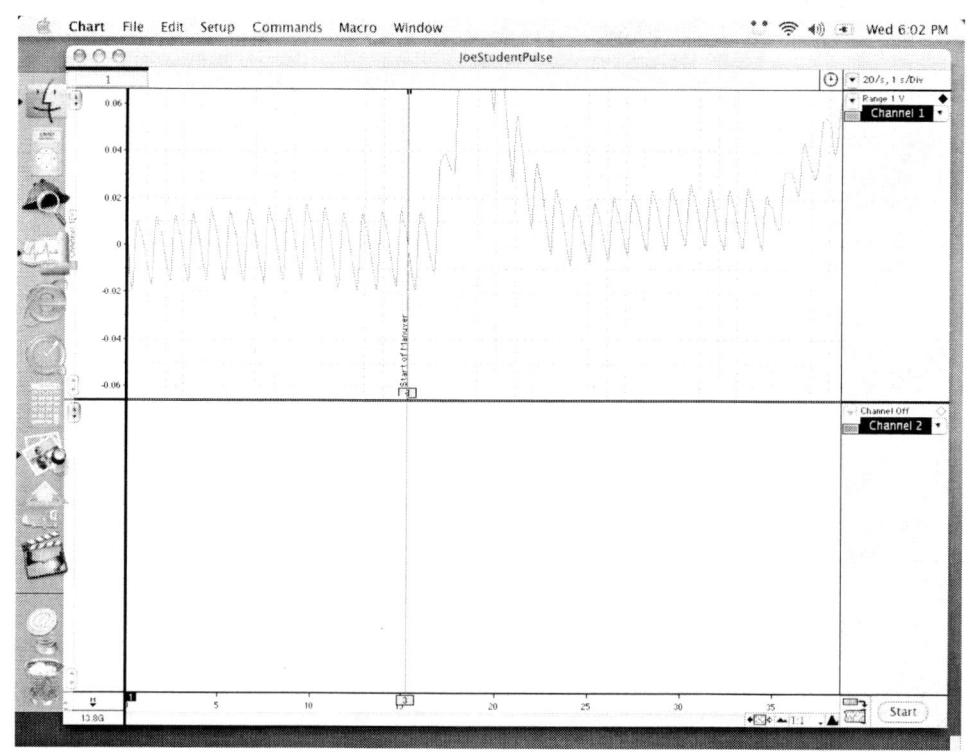

Figure 6

For this lab exercise, students will work in groups of three or four. One student will serve as the volunteer subject. Another student will be in charge of controlling the recording through the use of the Chart software. It is important that the group rehearse the maneuver a number of times before actually generating the tracing. One student should tend the lead attached to the finger plethysmograph transducer. For any activity that involves hand movement or changing body position this student should gently guide the movement of the lead to follow the movement of the hand. This should prevent any stress on the transducer and prevent the transducer from changing position on the finger. Remember, before doing each maneuver and based on discussion within the group, predict the expected results of the maneuver on wave amplitude and heart rate. Once the group has come to a consensus and recorded the prediction, perform the maneuver and compare the actual results with the predicted results.

Activities 1 and 2
Hand Below Heart to Hand Above Heart followed by
Hand Above Heart to Hand Below Heart

With the subject comfortably seated and the pulse pressure transducer on the middle or ring finger, the subject is instructed to hold the limb with the transducer at the side with the palm directed medially. The arm should be extended downward at 180 degrees without hyperextension at the elbow. The hand should be positioned below the waist in a relaxed fashion with the fingers relaxed and directed towards the floor. Begin recording and allow 10 or 15 seconds for the recording to stabilize. Once stable, obtain a baseline tracing. Without changing body position, the subject slowly raises his/her hand by flexing at the shoulder. The palm should be maintained in a medial orientation. Note: During this maneuver, another member of the group will tend the transducer wire to insure that it does not bend or cause any shift in the transducer's position on the subject's finger. Hold the hand steady half way between the level of the head and the 180 degree vertical (hand straight up) position. Once the record stabilizes, obtain a 3 or 4 second tracing. **Don't stop recording.** Insert a comment to mark the next activity. Leave the hand above the heart for three or four more seconds. Now slowly return the hand to its original position below the waist. Maintain the hand in the relaxed state with the fingers pointed towards the floor. Wait 10 or 15 seconds for the recording to stabilize and then stop recording.

1. Hand Below Heart to Hand Above Heart

Prediction:

Amplitude:	Increase	Decrease	Remain the Same
Heart rate	Increase	Decrease	Remain the Same

Results:

Amplitude:	Increase	Decrease	Remain the Same
Heart rate:	Increase	Decrease	Remain the Same

2. Hand Above Heart to Hand Below Heart

Prediction:

Amplitude:	Increase	Decrease	Remain the Same
Heart rate	Increase	Decrease	Remain the Same

Results:

Amplitude:	Increase	Decrease	Remain the Same
Heart rate:	Increase	Decrease	Remain the Same

Activity 3
Supine with Legs Elevated to Standing
Cover the table top with a 4 foot length of bubble wrap. The subject should position himself or herself supine on the bubble wrap with legs elevated. Secure the pulse transducer to either the middle or ring finger. Instruct the subject to hold the transducer hand against the chest at the level of the heart. Begin recording and establish a baseline tracing. Without changing the position of the hand relative to the heart, ask the subject to stand. Another team member should assist the subject to the standing position and should be prepared to assist if he/she has any difficulty with the maneuver. The subject should then remain standing quietly for approximately 5 seconds. After five seconds, examine the tracing for the effect of this position change on wave amplitude and heart rate.

Prediction:
Amplitude:	Increase	Decrease	Remain the Same
Heart rate	Increase	Decrease	Remain the Same

Results:
Amplitude:	Increase	Decrease	Remain the Same
Heart rate:	Increase	Decrease	Remain the Same

****

Activity 4
Application of Cold
Before this activity insure that the subject's hand on which the transducer will be placed is thoroughly warmed by running warm water over it. Dry the hand before securing the transducer. With the subject comfortably seated and the pulse pressure transducer on the middle or ring finger of the warmed hand, instruct the subject to place the forearm of the hand with the transducer on the lab table in the supine position. Begin recording and allow 10 or 15 seconds for the recording to stabilize. Once stable, obtain a baseline tracing. Then carefully place a cold pack on the wrist, heel and/or palm of the monitored hand. Ignore any artifact that may result from the act of placing the cold pack on the hand and wait for a response to occur. This may take 20 or 30 seconds.

Prediction:
Amplitude:	Increase	Decrease	Remain the Same
Heart rate	Increase	Decrease	Remain the Same

Results:
Amplitude:	Increase	Decrease	Remain the Same
Heart rate:	Increase	Decrease	Remain the Same

Activity 5
Venous Occlusion

Before this activity, position a blood pressure cuff securely on the brachium of the limb on which the transducer is placed. Place the cuff in the same fashion as required for taking a blood pressure. Don't inflate it at this time. Now, with the subject comfortably seated and the pulse pressure transducer on the middle or ring finger, instruct the subject to position the forearm and monitored hand palm up (supine) on the lab table. Inflate the cuff to 50 mmHg pressure and begin recording. Allow 20 or 40 seconds for the recording to stabilize. Once stable, obtain a baseline tracing. Carefully deflate the cuff. Ignore any artifact from releasing the pressure. Once the recording stabilizes, note the effect and stop recording.

Prediction:
Amplitude:	Increase	Decrease	Remain the Same
Heart rate	Increase	Decrease	Remain the Same

Results:
Amplitude:	Increase	Decrease	Remain the Same
Heart rate:	Increase	Decrease	Remain the Same

****

Activity 6
Arterial Occlusion

Before this activity the subject should have a blood pressure cuff positioned securely on the brachium of the monitored limb. Position the cuff in the same fashion as required for taking a blood pressure. Don't inflate the cuff at this time. With the subject comfortably seated and the pulse pressure transducer on the middle or ring finger, instruct the subject to position the forearm of the monitored hand palm up (supine) on the lab table. Begin recording and obtain a stable tracing. Once a stable tracing is achieved, inflate the cuff to 150 mmHg pressure. Ignore any artifact from the inflation. Once the recording stabilizes note the effect and stop recording. Deflate the cuff. **Note: In no case should you leave the cuff inflated for more then 15 seconds.**

Prediction:
Amplitude:	Increase	Decrease	Remain the Same
Heart rate	Increase	Decrease	Remain the Same

Results:
Amplitude:	Increase	Decrease	Remain the Same
Heart rate:	Increase	Decrease	Remain the Same

Activity 7
Valsalva Maneuver

The final maneuver we perform is called the Valsalva maneuver. The subject should be seated with the hand positioned at the level of the heart. Begin recording and establish a baseline tracing. Then instruct the volunteer to exhale strongly against a closed glottis for approximately 10 seconds after which he/she should resume normal breathing. Once a tracing is obtained, cease recording and analyze the effect of the Valsalva maneuver on wave amplitude and heart rate.

Cautionary Note: Do not perform this maneuver unless you are in good cardiovascular and respiratory health.

Prediction:
Amplitude:	Increase	Decrease	Remain the Same
Heart rate	Increase	Decrease	Remain the Same

Results:
Amplitude:	Increase	Decrease	Remain the Same
Heart rate:	Increase	Decrease	Remain the Same

Analysis and Application

1. Describe a mechanism which explains the observed change in pulse pressure following talking.

_____

_____

_____

_____

_____

2. Based on your observations, in what part(s) of the body is tissue edema most likely in an individual in the standing position?

_____

How might this change in an individual who is bedridden?

_____

_____

3. Describe the change in pulse pressure observed following the change from the standing position to sitting with legs elevated. Try to explain or describe the mechanism operating here.

_____

_____

_____

_____

4. Sometimes elderly (or not so elderly) individuals experience episodes of syncope (fainting) during a difficult bowel movement. Can this involve the cardiovascular system? If so, how?

_____

_____

_____

5. How does blood flow across a capillary bed in the hand change when the arm is raised? Please explain your logic.

6. What happens to venous return when one changes position from sitting/legs elevated to standing? Explain briefly the reason for this.

   How does this affect cardiac output (or does it) and why?

7. Describe and explain the likely effect of venous occlusion on pulse pressure and blood flow across a capillary bed.

Exercise P-10
Graded Aerobic Exercise

During physical activity of a <u>prolonged</u> nature, the ATP needed to power the muscles being used is generated <u>aerobically</u> by the oxidation of carbohydrate, lipid and/or protein substrates. In order for such an increased level of activity to be sustained, the delivery of increased amounts of oxygen- and nutrient-laden blood to the active muscles must be insured. These muscles must then be able to extract the greater amounts of oxygen needed to continue the oxidation processes which are required of a higher cellular metabolic rate.

The body copes with the stress of increased muscular activity in a number of ways reflected in predictable changes in various body functions. Increased capabilities to deliver blood to active muscles are largely reflected in vital sign changes. Enhanced extraction processes at the muscle capillary level are assessed by a comparison of the oxygen levels of arterial and venous blood. The collection of some of these data requires the use of invasive procedures (ie. blood sampling) which are obviously beyond the scope of this course. However, a number of noninvasive techniques (some very basic and manual, others technological and quite sophisticated) can be utilized in our lab to obtain a variety of measurements of real physiological significance.

Using a programmable treadmill, we are able to increase a subject's level of physical activity in a controlled, safe, and progressive way. During this activity, teams of students monitor a number of physiologic parameters and collect a variety of data at regular intervals. These data can then be analyzed to provide insights into the mechanisms operating in the body to ensure a continued and adequate energy supply to skeletal muscles during periods of increased metabolic activity.

A. Materials (some of which may not be utilized in a given exercise session):
  1. Programmable treadmill with variable speed and incline controls.
  2. Low resistance, one-way valve/mouthpiece system, complete with head mount, large bore tubing, and nose clip or similar low resistance valve with mask system;
  3. PowerLab 410 equipped with pulse pressure transducer module;
  4. Cardiotachometer or other heart rate monitor;
  5. Douglas air collection bag or weather balloon;
  6. Pneumotachometer, hand-held Wright's-type respirometer, or other tidal volume/minute volume monitor;
  7. Digital oxygen monitor;
  8. Pulse oximeter with finger probe;
  9. Carbon dioxide analyzer (if available);
  10. Remote electrocardiogram unit (optional, if available);
  11. Sphygmomanometers and stethoscopes;
  12. Stopwatches;
  13. Assorted adapters and tape; and
  14. Alcohol wipes and tissue.

B. Subject Selection Guidelines
The subject should be a physically active, aerobically fit, non-smoker who is not more than 50 years of age. He/she should engage in aerobic physical activity 3 or more times per week with reasonable regularity. Any subject for this activity will be required to sign a release form attesting to the fact that he/she engages in regular aerobic activity, is in good general and cardiovascular health as described below, and is serving as a subject for this activity on a purely voluntary basis.

1. Resting pulse < 80 bpm;
2. Resting blood pressure within normal limits (<140 systolic at rest);
3. Body weight within 20% of ideal body weight;
4. No history of diagnosed chronic disease; and
5. Free from any upper or lower respiratory infection.

C. Procedure:
1. The instructor will assign student helpers (individually, in pairs, or in larger groups depending on the task) to collect and record physiologic data throughout the session. To reduce unnecessary error, once begun, the same student should perform the same task for the duration of the test. One student (or the instructor) will act as timer, announcing times throughout the test to cue those students who are recording data. Most data collection will occur during the final 30-60 seconds of each three minute interval. Each student involved in the measurement of physiologic data will report his/her findings to the student who has been selected to act as data recorder.

2. While seated and before being connected to the breathing system, the subject's resting pulse and blood pressure are measured. While still seated, the subject is connected to the experimental system (breathing unit, finger pulse pressure monitor, oxygen analyzer, CO_2 analyzer, sphygmomanometer, respiration monitor, heart rate monitor). After being allowed to acclimate to the system, a complete set of baseline, resting measurements are collected. These are recorded in the data grid on the Results page and on the computer spreadsheet in lab . Note: If the pulse and BP obtained at this time are elevated when compared to the initial assessment, the initial values should be considered a more accurate reflection of true resting values.

3. Once the resting baseline data have been recorded, the subject is positioned on the treadmill (set to zero incline). The test is begun with the treadmill belt speed set at a comfortable walking pace (3-4 miles per hour depending on the subject). Throughout the session, the belt speed remains at its original setting. At 3-minute intervals, the incline of the belt is increased in 3° increments up to a maximum slope of 15°. This is done automatically by the treadmill program. Each increase in grade is signaled

by a beeping sound to alert all to the end of one interval and the start of the next.

3. During the test, students will perform the following physiologic assessments using the following guidelines:

   a. Heart rate – To obtain the heart rate as it is continuously monitored continuously via finger probe sensor the student should read and record the digitally displayed rate at 5-second intervals for the last 15 seconds of every 3-minute interval. These three values should be averaged to yield the heart rate that is reported to the data collector. In addition, as a backup, one student may manually assess the radial pulse during the final 30 seconds of each 3-minute interval or a heartr rate sensor on one ear lobe may be utilized. Note: If a radial pulse is to be obtained, it must be done on the arm not being used for blood pressure determination. Both rates are reported to the data recorder who will enter them separately.

   b. Blood pressure - During the final 30 seconds of each 3-minute interval, a pair of students will obtain a blood pressure. Note: This is difficult to accomplish with accuracy on a moving individual, especially given that there is a lot of activity in the room and also constant background noise from the treadmill. It is easier for a taller student to obtain a BP under these conditions. Care must be exercised so that neither the subject's arm nor the arm or body of the recorder touch the treadmill rail because the hum of the device will drown out or make it difficult to hear the Korotkoff sounds. Be sure to pump up the cuff to a high enough pressure to start so that a second determination will not be necessary. If a diastolic reading cannot be heard, record only the systolic reading and immediately inform the instructor (who may quickly repeat the assessment). Once the assessment is done, deflate the cuff completely. The cuff can be left in place throughout the entire trial but <u>it must remain completely depressurized</u> during the interval. Report your values to the data collector.

   c. Pulse pressure – When blood pressure data is entered into the spreadsheet on the computer, pulse pressure (the difference between systolic and diastolic pressures) is automatically computed.

   d. Mean arterial pressure – This is a weighted average of systolic and diastolic pressures, favoring diastolic pressure. It is calculated by adding 2 times the diastolic pressure to the systolic pressure and dividing the sum by three.

   $$MAP = (2sBP + dBP) / 3 \quad \text{or} \quad MAP = dBP + 1/3(sBP - dBP)$$

Mean pressure is also computed automatically in the spreadsheet.

e. Breathing rate – During the final 30 or 60 seconds of each 3-minute interval, one student will count breaths by carefully observing the movements of the <u>exhalation</u> one-way valve which is visible in the valve housing at the subject's mouth. The determination of breaths per time must occur precisely during the same time interval during which exhaled air is being collected. If a 30 second interval is used, before reporting this value to the data recorder, the collector must be sure to multiply by 2 to get a rate in breaths per minute (bpm).

f. Minute volume - For the last 30 or 60 seconds of the third minute of each interval, a group of 3-4 students will collect exhaled air in a Douglas-type bag or weather balloon. Before doing this, the group will practice using the bag and associated valve system so that there will be no errors during the actual exercise session. Note: Be sure that all air has been squeezed out of the bag prior to connection to the subject's exhalation tubing. Any air remaining in the bag prior to collection of the subject's exhalation will erroneously increase the volume of exhaled air that is collected during that interval.

One member will act as the timer for the group. His/her job is simply to <u>clearly and loudly</u> signal the beginning and end of a 30-second interval. Sometimes this timing function is performed by the instructor. Just prior to the start of the collection period, the bag/valve system is connected to the subject's exhalation line. When the signal is given, one student opens the valve and the bag will begin to fill with each exhalation. At the end of the interval (on the signal of the timer), the valve is quickly closed and removed from the breathing circuit. The bag, now partially filled with the subject's exhaled air, is then connected to either a pneumotachometer or to a Wright's-type respirometer. If the pneumotachometer/PowerLab system is used, the instructor will demonstrate the technique for the team. With the device being used already zeroed and turned on, one student opens the valve and another gradually squeezes the bag until there is no more air left. Before releasing the bag and disconnecting the bag/valve, the valve is closed. The system is now ready for the next collection interval. Remember that if a 30 second interval is used the value for exhaled volume must first be multiplied by 2 before it can be recorded as an exhaled <u>minute</u> volume.

An alternative approach is to attach the Wright's-type respirometer directly to the end of the exhalation line and measure the volume exhaled for 30 or 60 seconds. If 30 seconds is used, this value is multiplied by 2 to obtain a minute volume. Dividing this minute volume by the breathing rate for the same interval will yield the average tidal volume.

A third alternative is to incorporate a high flow pneumotach into the beginning of the exhalation line and leave it in place throughout the entire session. Because of the problems that condensation can cause, a pneumotachometer used in this manner must be heated. This approach can yield continuous readings of every tidal excursion and exhaled minute volume.

g. Average tidal volume – Dividing the minute volume in liters by the breathing rate will yield the average tidal volume, also in liters. When the breathing rate and minute volume values are entered into the spreadsheet, the tidal volume is automatically calculated. The spreadsheet we use for these data expresses tidal volume in deciliters (rather than in more traditional liters or milliliters). Although somewhat unusual, the use of deciliters (dL) allows tidal volume, minute volume (expressed in liters), and breathing rate (expressed in bpm) to be plotted together on the same pair of axes.

h. Exhaled oxygen concentration – The oxygen analyzer is incorporated into the Douglas bag set-up. Therefore, when the bag is being emptied during measurement of exhaled volume, the analyzer will indicate an accurate and stable <u>average</u> exhaled oxygen percentage. Note: Before incorporating the analyzer sensor into the Douglas bag system, it must first be calibrated to room air (20.9% oxygen).

Note: If the instructor decides to incorporate the oxygen sensor into the exhalation line rather than into the Douglas bag system, there will be noticeable fluctuation in oxygen percent during and between each breath. In this instance, the O_2 % should be read and recorded at 5-second intervals for the last 15 seconds of every 3-minute interval. These three values should be averaged to yield the number that is reported to the data collector.

i. Oxyhemoglobin saturation – SaO_2 is monitored continuously by oximeter using a finger probe sensor. Since its accuracy is adversely affected by poor blood flow, it should be positioned on the side <u>not</u> being used for blood pressure assessment. Also, the subject should be instructed not to hold the handrail with the hand on which the probe is positioned. If there is noticeable fluctuation, this value should be read and recorded at 5-second intervals for the last 15 seconds of every 3-minute interval. These three values should be averaged to yield the number that is reported to the data collector.

j. Exhaled carbon dioxide concentration (if available) – This may be monitored continuously or connected to the Douglas bag apparatus and analyzed during the measurement of exhaled volume. Because in the case of the Douglas bag a true average CO_2 percentage is obtained, the value should be stable and easily recognized and reported to the data collector. However, if the CO_2 % is being monitored continuously in the exhalation circuit, there will be noticeable fluctuation during each breath. In this instance, the percent should be read and recorded at 5-second intervals for the last 15 seconds of every 3-minute interval. These three values should be averaged to yield the number that is reported to the data collector.

6. At the conclusion of the final segment of the test (at 18 minutes), the speed of the treadmill is abruptly decreased to nearly zero and the incline returns to zero. Once the treadmill has been turned off, other students can assist the subject to a chair. The subject remains seated, still connected to all monitoring devices. Recovery measurements are taken every three minutes for at least 15 minutes or until heart rate and blood pressure and breathing rate approximate pretest levels. The first recovery data set is obtained 3-minutes after the end of the final exercise interval.

Note: If at any point in the session the subject's heartrate exceeds the recommended maximum based on the following formula…
  Maximum recommended heart rate = .8 (220 - age in years)
or systolic blood pressure exceeds **170 mm Hg**, the exercise portion of the session will be immediately terminated and the recovery phase of the activity will begin.

7. All data that has been collected and entered into the computer is then printed and distributed to all students. Some graphs of these same data are included with the spreadsheet. Students should carefully review this information and try to reconcile the data obtained to presentations about cardiovascular, nervous, and respiratory physiology already completed in lecture. This information will serve as the basis for further analysis and discussion that will take place during a subsequent lab session.

The data grid shown on the following page should be used by individual students or teams for data recording as the exercise session progresses.

Table 1: Aerobic Exercise Data

Graded Aerobic Exercise: Interval Effects from Activity to Recovery														
Parameter	Units	At rest	3 min	6 min	9 min	12 min	15 min	18 min	3 recov	6 recov	9 recov	12 recov	15 recov
Heart Rate	bpm												
Pulse	bpm												
Systolic Pressure	mm Hg												
Diastolic Pressure	mm Hg												
Pulse Pressure	mm Hg												
Mean Pressure	mm Hg												
Breathing Rate	bpm												
Minute Volume	liters												
Tidal Volume	deci-liters												
Exhaled Oxygen	%												
Exhaled CO_2	%												
Oxy-Hgb Saturation													

Analysis and Application:

1. Based on the interval data, which parameter changes at the fastest rate?

2. Discuss a mechanism for the observed changes seen in each of the following parameters during exercise. Note: A statement such as "the body/muscles needed more oxygen" is a teleological, not mechanistic explanation.
   a. Heart rate:

   b. Systolic blood pressure:

   c. Diastolic blood pressure:

   d. Breathing rate:

3. Describe the changes observed in exhaled oxygen concentration. Does this indicate a change in the oxygen level of systemic venous blood? Yes / No Please explain.

4. Why don't vital signs immediately return to normal following exercise?

5. One measure of aerobic capacity is recovery time. Who would have the shorter recovery time?

   ___ well-conditioned athlete ___ average indiviual

   Why? Indicate any anatomic changes which might help to explain this?

Exercise P-11

A Study of Blood
Modified from Marieb, 2000
Human Anatomy and Physiology Laboratory Manual, Main Version

Introduction
In this exercise you will first study plasma and the formed elements of blood and then conduct various hematological tests. These tests are extremely useful diagnostic tools because blood composition (number and types of blood cells, and chemical composition) reflects the status of many body functions.

Your major reference for understanding and appreciating blood as a tissue is <u>Cells and Tissues</u>. Other histological reference materials include the Histology Atlas found in this manual and a selection of histological reference materials available in lab. Another important aid in your study is chapter 18 (Blood) in your textbook. It will be helpful to bring your textbook to lab and refer to it during your study of blood.

Finally, there are a number of resources on reserve in the Library designed to aid you in your laboratory study of blood. These resources include a selection of CD's which demonstrate the various formed elements of blood, a projector with a set of 2" x 2" Kodachrome slides for in-library use, and two microscopes with accompanying slides. For the most part, the slides contained in the Kodachrome collection correspond quite nicely to the black and white photomicrographs which are described in <u>Cells and Tissues</u>. Use these resources to your advantage but realize that they cannot replace the microscope work that is a centerpiece of actual laboratory experience and the guidance that is provided by your laboratory instructor.

Please note: The decision to use animal blood for testing or to have students test their own blood will be made by the instructor in accordance with the educational goals of the student groups. For students in the nursing or laboratory technician curricula, learning how to safely handle human blood or other body fluids is essential. All work with human or animal blood will be performed in accordance with the "Universal Precautions" set forth by the Centers for Disease Control. This document is reproduced at the conclusion of this exercise. If blood samples are utilized, gloves **<u>must</u>** be worn at all times. If human blood is being tested (whether yours or that obtained from a clinical agency), proper precautions related to the disposal of human body fluids **<u>must be observed.</u>** All soiled glassware must be immersed in household bleach solution immediately after use. Used lancets must be placed in the "sharps" container specifically intended for that purpose. Other disposable items (cotton balls, alcohol swabs, soiled paper toweling, etc.) must be placed in a disposable autoclave bag so that they can be sterilized before disposal. Students may be required to wear safety glasses during portions of the laboratory session.

Composition of Blood
The circulatory system of the average adult contains about 5.5 liters of blood. Blood is classified as a type of connective tissue because it consists of a nonliving fluid matrix (plasma) in which living cells (formed elements) are suspended. The fibers typical of a connective tissue matrix become visible in blood only when clotting occurs. They then appear as fibrin threads, which form the structural basis for clot formation. The dominant component of plasma is water (over 90%). More than 100 different substances are dissolved or suspended in it. These include nutrients, gases, hormones, various wastes and metabolites, many types of proteins, and mineral salts. The composition of plasma varies continuously as cells remove or add substances to the blood.

Activity I - Formed Elements
There are three types of formed elements in blood. The most numerous are the erythrocytes (red blood cells or RBCs) which are literally membranous sacs of hemoglobin that transport the bulk of the oxygen carried in the blood (and some carbon dioxide and nitric oxide). Leukocytes (white blood cells or WBCs) are part of the body's nonspecific defenses and the immune system. Platelets function in hemostasis (blood clot formation). Formed elements normally constitute 45% of whole blood; plasma accounts for the remaining 55%.

In this section, you will conduct your observations of blood cells on an already prepared (purchased) blood slide or on a slide prepared from your own blood or blood provided by your instructor. Those using a prepared blood slide should begin their observations at step 6. Those working with blood provided by a biological supply source or an animal hospital should obtain a tube of the supplied blood, disposable gloves, and the other necessary supplies. After donning gloves, those students will jump to step 3b to begin their observations. If you are examining your own blood, you will perform all the steps described below **except** step 3b. If you are examining a prepared blood slide, go to step 5.

1. Obtain glass slides, a dropper bottle of Wright's stain and distilled water, two or three lancets, cotton balls, and alcohol swabs. Bring these materials to your workstation. Clean the slides thoroughly and dry them.

2. Open the alcohol swab packet and scrub your third or fourth finger with the swab. Sometimes it is helpful to run warm water over your hand for a minute beforehand to increase the circulation to your fingers. Because the pricked finger may be a little sore later, it is better to prepare a finger on your non-dominant hand. Load the lancet into the "Autoject" device, cock the device, and remove the protective cover from the lancet point. Press the prepared finger into the guide and trigger the "Autoject" mechanism to produce a free flow of blood. Do **not** squeeze or "milk" the finger to increase the flow of blood because this forces out tissue fluid as well as blood. If the blood is not flowing freely, another puncture should be made.

You must abide by the following rules:
> ***Under no circumstances is a lancet to be used***
> ***for more than one puncture.***
>
> ***Absolutely, under no circumstances is the same lancet***
> ***to be used for more than one student!!!.***

3a. With a cotton ball, wipe away the first drop of blood; then allow another large drop of blood to form. Touch the blood to one of the cleaned slides approximately 1/2 inch from the end. Then quickly (to prevent clotting) use the second slide to form a blood smear as demonstrated by your instructor. When properly prepared, the blood smear is uniformly thin. If the blood smear appears streaked, the blood probably began to clot or coagulate before the smear was made, and another slide should be prepared. Continue at step 4.

3b. If using blood that is supplied by your instructor, use a disposable pipette to transfer a generous drop of blood to the end of a cleaned microscope slide. For the time being, lay the pipette on a paper towel on the counter. Then, as described above, use the second slide to make your blood smear.

4. Allow the slide to dry. When it is completely dry, the smear will look dull. Place it on the staining rack and apply the Wright's stain. Follow the directions that are included on the cards at each staining station.

5. Once the slide is dry, scan it under low power to find the area where the blood smear is the **thinnest**. This is important. You should examine blood cells in an area of the slide where the red cells are separated from each other rather than in an area where the RBCs are clumped together in chains or stacks. After scanning the slide in low power to find the areas with the largest numbers of nucleated WBCs, read the following descriptions of cell types, and find each one. Then switch to the oil immersion lens and observe the slide carefully to identify each cell type.

Erythrocytes
Erythrocytes (red blood cells) average 7.5 micrometers in diameter. They vary in color from a salmon red color to pale pink depending on the effectiveness of the stain. They have a distinctive biconcave disk shape and appear paler in the center than at the edge. As you observe the slide, notice that the red blood cells are by far the most numerous blood cells seen in the field. Their number averages 4.5 million to 5.0 million cells per cubic millimeter of blood (for women and men, respectively). Red blood cells differ from the other blood cells in that they are anucleate when mature and circulating in the blood. As a result, they are unable to reproduce and have a limited life span of 100 to 120 days. After that they begin to fragment and are destroyed in the spleen and other reticuloendothelial tissues of the body.

Leukocytes

Leukocytes (white blood cells) are nucleated cells that are formed in the bone marrow from the same stem cells (hemocytoblast) as red blood cells. They are much less numerous than the red cells, averaging from 4000 to 11,000 cells per cubic millimeter. Basically, white blood cells are protective, pathogen destroying cells that are transported to all parts of the body in the blood or lymph. Important to their protective function is their ability to move in and out of blood vessels, a process called diapedesis. They then can wander through body tissues by amoeboid motion to reach sites of inflammation or tissue damage. They are classified into two major groups, depending on whether or not they contain conspicuous granules in their cytoplasm.

Granulocytes make up the first group. The granules in their cytoplasm stain differentially with Wright's stain, and they have peculiarly lobed nuclei which often consist of expanded nuclear regions connected by thin strands of nucleoplasm. There are three types of granulocytes:

> Neutrophils: The most abundant of the white blood cells (40% to 70% of the leukocyte population); nucleus consists of 3 to 7 lobes; the pale lilac cytoplasm contains fine cytoplasmic granules which are generally indistinguishable and take up both the acidic (red) and basic (blue) dyes (*neutrophil* = neutral loving). Neutrophils function as active phagocytes and their number increases exponentially during acute bacterial infections.
>
> Eosinophils: Represent 1% to 4% of the leukocyte population; nucleus is generally bilobed or figure 8 in shape; contain large, concentrated cytoplasmic granules (elaborate lysosomes) that stain red-orange with the acid dyes in Wright's stain. They increase in number in allergic conditions and parasitic infections and may selectively phagocytize antigen-antibody complexes.
>
> Basophils: Least abundant leukocyte type representing less than 1% of the population; large U- or S-shaped nucleus with two or more indentations. Cytoplasm contains coarse, less concentrated granules that are stained deep purple by the basic dyes in Wright's stain. The granules contain several chemicals which are discharged on exposure to antigens and help mediate the inflammatory response. Prominent among these is histamine, a vasodilator.

The second group of white cells, agranulocytes, or agranular leukocytes, contains no observable cytoplasmic granules. Although found in the bloodstream, they are much more abundant in lymphoid tissues. Their nuclei tend to be closer to the norm for a generalized cell, that is, spherical, oval, or kidney-shaped. Specific characteristics of the two types of agranulocytes are listed below.

> Lymphocytes: The smallest of the leukocytes, only slightly larger in size than red blood cells. Represent 20% to 45% of the WBC population. The nucleus stains dark blue to purple, is generally spherical or slightly indented, and accounts for most of the cell mass. Sparse cytoplasm appears as a thin crescent or a thin blue

rim around the nucleus. Lymphocytes are generally concerned with immunologic responses in body. One population, the B-lymphocytes, oversees the production of antibodies that are released into the blood. The second population, T lymphocytes, plays a regulatory role and destroys grafts, tumors, and virus-infected cells.

Monocytes: The largest of the leukocytes; approximately twice the size of red blood cells. Represent 4% to 8% of the leukocyte population. Blue nucleus is large, thick, and generally kidney-shaped; abundant cytoplasm stains gray-blue. Function as active phagocytes (the "long-term cleanup team"), increasing dramatically in number during chronic infections such as tuberculosis.

Students are often asked to list the leukocytes in order from the most abundant to the least abundant. The following silly phrase may help you with this task: **N**ever **L**et **M**onkeys **E**at **B**ananas (neutrophils, lymphocytes, monocytes, eosinophils, basophils).

Platelets

Platelets are cell fragments of larger multinucleate cells (megakaryocytes) which are formed in the bone marrow. They are much smaller than RBCs and appear as darkly staining, irregularly shaped bodies interspersed among the blood cells. The normal platelet count in blood ranges from 250,000 to 500,000 per cubic millimeter. Platelets are instrumental in initiating the clotting process that occurs in plasma when blood vessels are ruptured.

After you have identified these cell types on your slide, dispose of your slide in a bleach solution.

Activity 2 - Hematologic Tests

Materials such as cotton balls, lancets, and alcohol swabs are used in nearly all of the following diagnostic tests. Used or soiled items should be properly disposed of (into the "sharps" container or into the disposable biohazard bag) as previously described. Capillary tubes should be placed in the "sharps" container after use. All of these tests require a finger stab if you plan to use our own blood.

An alternative to using blood obtained from a finger stab is using heparinized blood samples supplied by your instructor. The purpose of using heparinized tubes is to prevent the blood from clotting. Thus blood collected and stored in such tubes will be suitable for all these tests.

Hematocrit

The hematocrit or packed cell volume (PCV) is routinely done as part of any basic hematologic assessment and certainly whenever anemia is suspected. Centrifuging whole blood in a tube causes the components of blood to separate out according to their respective densities (RBCs most dense, WBCs and platelets next, plasma the least). Once the capillary tube has been spun, the RBC and plasma layers are easily seen. Careful examination will show a very thin off-white (buff colored) band between the two. This layer is composed of WBCs and platelets and is referred to as the buffy coat. Since the blood cell population is primarily composed of RBCs, the PCV is generally considered equivalent to the RBC volume, and this is the only value reported. However, the relative percentage of WBCs can be differentiated, and both WBC and plasma volume will be reported here. Normal hematocrit values for the male and female, respectively, are 47.0 ± 7 and 42.0 ± 5.

The hematocrit is determined by the micromethod using a short glass capillary tube, so only a drop of blood is needed. If possible (and the centrifuge allows), all members of the class should prepare their capillary tubes at the same time so the centrifuge can be properly balanced and run only once.

1. Obtain two heparinized capillary tubes, end plugs or Seal-ease, an Autoject with lancet, alcohol swabs, and cotton balls.

2. If you are using your own blood, warm your hand before disinfecting with alcohol. Use the Autoject device to perform the finger stick. Allow the blood to flow freely. Wipe away the first drop and, holding the red-line-marked end of the capillary tube to the blood drop, allow the tube to fill at least three-fourths by capillary action. If the blood is not flowing freely, the end of the capillary tube may not be completely submerged in the blood during filling, and air may enter, requiring you to prepare another sample. Do not hesitate to seek assistance from your instructor if you are unsure about how to proceed.

    If you are using instructor-provided blood, simply immerse the red-marked end of the capillary tube in the blood sample and fill it three-quarters full as just described.

3. Plug the blood-containing end using the plastic plugs or by pressing it into the Seal-ease.

4. Place the prepared tubes opposite one another in the radial grooves of the microhematocrit centrifuge with the **sealed ends abutting the rubber gasket at the centrifuge periphery** (that is, toward the outside). This loading procedure balances the centrifuge and prevents blood from spraying everywhere by centrifugal force. Make a note of the number of the groove your tubes is in. When all the tubes have been loaded, make sure the centrifuge is properly balanced, and secure the centrifuge cover. Turn the centrifuge on, and set the timer for 4 minutes.

5. Determine the percentage of RBCs, WBCs, and plasma by using the microhematocrit reader. The RBCs are the bottom layer, the plasma is the top layer, and the WBCs are the buff-colored layer between the tow. If a reader is not available, use a millimeter ruler to measure the length of the filled capillary tube

occupied by the formed elements, and compute the percentage by using the following formula:

$$\frac{\text{Height of the column composed of the formed elements (mm)}}{\text{Height of the original column of whole blood (mm)}} \times 100$$

Record your results/calculations below.

% formed elements (essentially RBCs) _____

% plasma _____

How do your blood values compare to the normal percentages for RBCs and plasma?

_____

As a rule, a hematocrit is considered a more accurate test for determining the RBC composition of the blood than the total RBC count. A hematocrit within the normal range generally indicates a normal RBC number (assuming normal red blood cell size), whereas an abnormally high or low hematocrit may be cause for concern.

Hematocrit can be altered by factors other than the production and destruction of red blood cells. One such factor is an individual's hydration status. For instance, consider dehydration. How do you think hematocrit percentage would change in this case?
___ increase   ___ decrease   ___ would not change

Likewise, how would fluid overload affect hematocrit?
___ increase   ___ decrease   ___ would not change

Hemoglobin Concentration

As noted earlier, a person can be anemic even with a normal RBC count. Since hemoglobin is the RBC protein responsible for oxygen transport, the most accurate way of measuring the oxygen-carrying capacity of the blood is to determine its hemoglobin content. Oxygen combines reversibly with the heme (iron-containing portion) group of the hemoglobin molecule. It is picked up by the blood cells in the lungs and unloaded in the tissues. Thus, the more hemoglobin molecules the RBCs contain, the more oxygen they will be able to transport. Normal blood contains 12 to 16 g hemoglobin per 100 ml blood (grams %). Hemoglobin content in men is slightly higher (13 to 18 gram %) than in women (12 to 16 gram %). You will not directly measure hemoglobin level today. However, you will estimate the hemoglobin level from the hematocrit using the following information. Red blood cells are typically 1/3 hemoglobin by volume. Given this simple fact, determine how to use this information to estimate hemoglobin.

_____

What is the major shortcoming of this method? _____

Blood Typing
Blood typing is a system of blood classification based on the presence of specific glycoproteins on the outer surface of the RBC plasma membrane. Such membrane proteins are called antigens, or agglutinogens. They are accompanied by plasma proteins called antibodies or agglutinins which react with any RBCs bearing different antigens, causing them to be clumped, agglutinated, and eventually hemolyzed. It is because of this phenomenon that a person's blood must be carefully typed before a whole blood or packed cell transfusion.

Several blood typing systems exist, based on the various possible antigens, but the factors routinely typed are antigens of the ABO and Rh blood groups which are most commonly involved in transfusion reactions. Other blood factors, such as Kell, Lewis, M, and N, are not routinely typed for unless the individual will require multiple transfusions. The essentials of the ABO and Rh typing systems are shown below

Blood Type (ABO & Rh)	Agglutinogens (RBC membrane)	Agglutinins (plasma)
A	A	B
B	B	A
AB	A&B	none
O	none	A&B
Rh$^-$	none	***
Rh$^+$	Rh	none

*** Individuals whose red blood cells carry the Rh antigen are Rh positive (approximately 85% of the U.S. population); those lacking the antigen are Rh negative. Unlike ABO blood groups, neither the blood of the Rh-positive (Rh$^+$) nor Rh-negative (Rh$^-$) individuals carries preformed anti-Rh antibodies. This is understandable in the case of the Rh-positive individual. However, Rh-negative persons who receive transfusions of Rh-positive blood become sensitized by the Rh antigens of the donor RBCs. Their systems then begin to produce anti-Rh antibodies. On subsequent exposures to Rh-positive blood, typical transfusion reactions occur, resulting in the clumping and hemolysis of the donor blood cells.

Note: Although the blood of dogs and other mammals does react with some of the human agglutinins present in the antisera, the reaction is not as pronounced and varies with the animal blood used. Hence, the most accurate and predictable blood typing results are obtained with human blood.

1. Obtain a clean microscope slide, a wax marking pencil, anti-A, anti-B, and anti-Rh typing sera, toothpicks, Autojects and lancets, alcohol swabs, and cotton balls.

2. Divide the slide into thirds with the wax marking pencil. Label the sections "A" for anti-A, "B" for anti-B.,, and "Rh" for anti-Rh.

3. Place one drop of anti-A serum on the "A" section. Place one drop of anti-B serum on the "B" section. Place one drop of anti-Rh serum in the "Rh" section.

4. If you are using your own blood, warm your finger, and then disinfect it with an alcohol swab. Perform the finger stick and wipe away the first drop of blood. Obtain 3 drops of freely flowing blood, placing one drop in each section on your slide.

    If using instructor-provided animal blood or EDTA-treated red cells, use a medicine dropper to place one drop of blood in each section of your slide.

5. Quickly mix each blood/antiserum sample with a **fresh** toothpick. Then dispose of the soiled/used materials as previously described.

6. Place your slide on the illuminated typing box and rock it gently back and forth. (This is especially helpful for determining Rh type since a slightly higher temperature is required for precise Rh typing than for ABO typing.)

7. After 2 minutes, observe all three blood samples for evidence of clumping. The agglutination that occurs in the positive test for the Rh factor is very fine and difficult to perceive. If there is any question, observe the slide under the microscope. Record your observations in the chart below.

8. Interpret **your** ABO results and Rh results.

	Anti-A	Anti-B	Anti-Rh
Agglutination	yes/no	yes/no	yes/no

    Based on the above, your blood type is: _____

9. Share your results with your instructor.

10. Put the used slides in the bleach-containing bucket at the general supply area. Dispose of all used materials as already described. Clean your work area thoroughly using the ethanol spray solution.

**Centers for Disease Control
(CDC)
Universal Precautions for
Handling Blood and Other Body Fluids**

1. All health-care workers should routinely use appropriate barrier precautions to prevent skin and mucous-membrane exposure when contact with blood or other body fluids of any patient is anticipated. Gloves should be work for touching blood and body fluids, mucous membranes, or non-intact skin of all patients, for handling items or surfaces soiled with blood or body fluids, and for performing venipuncture and other vascular access procedures. Gloves should be changed after contact with each patient. Masks and protective eyewear or face shields should be worn during procedures that are likely to generate droplets of blood or other body fluids to prevent exposure of mucous membranes of the mouth, nose, and eyes. Gowns or aprons should be worn during procedures that are likely to generate splashes of blood or other body fluids.

2. Hands and other skin surfaces should be washed immediately and thoroughly if contaminated with blood or other body fluids. Hands should be washed immediately after gloves are removed.

3. All health-care workers should take precautions to prevent injuries caused by needles, scalpels, and other sharp instruments or devices during procedures; when cleaning used instruments; during disposal of used needles; and when handling sharp instruments after procedures. To prevent needlestick injuries, needles should not be recapped, purposely bent or broken by hand, removed from disposable syringes, or otherwise manipulated by hand. After they are used, disposable syringes and needles, scalpel blades, and other sharp items should be placed in puncture-resistant containers for disposal; the puncture-resistant containers should be located as close as practical to the use area. Large-bore reusable needles should be placed in puncture-resistant containers for transport to the reprocessing area.

4. Although saliva has not been implicated in HIV transmission, to minimize the need for emergency mouth-to-mouth resuscitation, mouthpieces, resuscitation bags, or other ventilation devices should be available for use in areas in which the need for resuscitation is predictable.

5. All blood and body fluid specimens should be placed in a sturdy, leak-proof container (such as a ziplock bag) for transport to the laboratory. The lab requisition should be placed outside the container to avoid contamination.

6. Health-care workers who have exudative lesions or weeping dermatitis should refrain from all direct patient care and from handling patient-care equipment until the condition resolves.

Appendix A: Exploring A&P C D

The content of this CD has been bundled free with your A&P Lab Book. It contains digital versions of all the histology exercises contained in *Exploring A&P in the Laboratory*. It contains the prelab quizzes for each histology exercise and two *QuickTime* videos. One video introduces the cadaver experience. The other covers the basic set-up for the EMG, a muscle physiology lab exercise in A&P I.

The CD is a Windows version. It has been tested under *Windows XP* and runs under *Internet Explorer 2004*. Test it with your system to ensure compatibility. You will need to set the security options of *Explorer* to **allow active content from a CD**. If *QuickTime* is not installed on your system, you will need to get a free download and perform the installation. If you prefer a Mac version, you may trade the Windows version for a Mac version. The content of this CD is also installed on the computers in the A&P Lab. You may work with this material on those computers during open lab times.

To use this CD, simply start up the Exploring A&P browser file with *Internet Explorer*. The videos take a long time to load from CD (about 3 minutes for the Cadavers video). You may copy the content of the CD to your computer. However, keep the Exploring A&P file and the A&P Lab Resources folders together. This material is for your use only in studying A&P and completing course assignments. It may not be distributed or copied for any other purpose. We hope you find this CD useful.

This CD was made possible through the support of the MVCC Staff Development Committee and the considerable efforts of Aaron Glass and Dr. Robert Jubenville.

Professors Drogo and Perrotti